A HISTORY OF AGRICULTURAL SCIENCE
IN GREAT BRITAIN

BY SIR E. JOHN RUSSELL

The Land Called Me
World Population and World Food Supplies

1. *Sir E. John Russell*

SIR E. JOHN RUSSELL
D.Sc., F.R.S.
former Director of Rothamsted Experimental Station

A HISTORY OF
AGRICULTURAL
SCIENCE
IN
GREAT BRITAIN
1620 – 1954

Foreword by
SIR BERNARD KEEN
D.Sc., F.R.S.

London
GEORGE ALLEN & UNWIN LTD
RUSKIN HOUSE   MUSEUM STREET

PRINTED IN GREAT BRITAIN
in 11 point Bell type
BY UNWIN BROTHERS LTD
WOKING AND LONDON

FOREWORD

BY

SIR BERNARD KEEN

D.Sc, F.R.S.

S IR JOHN RUSSELL's name will always be closely associated with the Rothamsted Experimental Station, and rightly so. He worked there for 36 years, and was Director for over 30 years until his retirement at the age of 70, in 1943, the Centenary of Rothamsted. It is given to few to be leaders for so long in the striking advances that came from the application of modern scientific disciplines to agriculture. It is given to fewer still—20 years after retirement, and at a great age—to complete a comprehensive account of that period and to set it in historical perspective. This, indomitably, Russell did. In his 91st year he wrote to me in his characteristic script, tiny, rather shaky, but very legible: 'The book goes slowly, but it goes: I don't write as quickly as I used to, but I write. It is now a Race against Time, with the odds in favour of Time, but I stick to it.' He just won the race: the book was completed a few weeks before his death on July 12, 1965.

Because the book covers three centuries of the development of agricultural science in Great Britain, ending with the mid nineteen-fifties, the account of his own researches, and the rehabilitation of Rothamsted, begun by Hall and carried on by Russell have, necessarily, been somewhat compressed. His best-known research, done in the early years at Rothamsted, was on the partial sterilization of soil. The discovery that soil after being heated to 100°C showed a great increase in its micro-bacterial activity, presumably because predators were destroyed, offered promise of an exciting break-through in the intricate subject of soil fertility, and the problem was vigorously attacked. So, also, was the suggested explanation, notably by those who claimed that steam, and mild chemical sterilizing agents, had marked effects on the soil organic matter, destroying toxic substances, and breaking down humus to more available forms.

A long controversy followed; it was not entirely resolved, mainly because increasing knowledge showed the subject was too complex to admit any simple solution. Russell and his team took little part in attacking the rival views; their policy was to persevere with the research, so that the results might decide the issue, one way or the other. It was a policy to which Russell always adhered, sometimes against considerable opposition. Agricultural research must be done under the most rigorous conditions permitted by the nature of the experimental material. The results would then have the maximum possible reliability. Even if they seemed unimportant they might well prove to be indispensable later for the solution of some new problem. And indeed, the partial sterilization work, conducted in that spirit, brought substantial dividends, to mention only three: soil microbiology was opened up as a large new research field of great promise; the work was so germane to the 'sick' soil problems of glass-house crops that the growers quickly provided money to establish in their area a sub-station (later independent) of Rothamsted; the puzzling experiences of legume failures, and the erratic responses to inoculation of soil or seed, were solved by studying the life history of the organisms in both the soil and the plant, and reliable inoculation techniques, with simple procedures, were evolved.

Concurrently with, and following on, this work, Russell was adding to the Rothamsted staff. Government grants, donations from industry and private individuals, were becoming available in increasing, but still modest, amounts. He had to cover the scientific disciplines needed for the sector of agricultural science traditionally associated with Rothamsted and formally allotted to it under the scheme for national Research Institutes that was slowly taking shape. Rothamsted's field was (and still is) adequately described by the title *Soil Conditions and Plant Growth* chosen by Russell for his best-known book, which grew through successive editions from the 150 page monograph of 1912 to the comprehensive 600 page text-book of today. His most valuable recruit was unquestionably R. A. Fisher, appointed to find out whether the extensive Rothamsted records would yield further valuable information when subjected to expert mathematical attack. The development of this work into the new statistical procedures that revolutionized the design of experiments in agriculture and in much of biology is now common knowledge. But Russell's flair for spotting a man with the right outlook is well shown by his reaction to the opinion of the Cambridge tutor of Fisher that he could have become a first-class mathematician had he 'stuck to the ropes', but he would not: 'That looked like the type of man we wanted, so I invited him to join us.'

The steady growth of Rothamsted brought with it the problem of planning its over-all programme. Russell had no doubts about the right course, and the outcome of the partial sterilization work was there to confirm his views. He believed that once Rothamsted had grown beyond a modest size, any close personal control of the researches was neither desirable nor, in fact, feasible, and he gave Heads of Departments a wide responsibility for their specialized programmes. But he was always available for consultations, and at other times often passed on suggestions and ideas that came from his wider experience. He held regular meetings of the whole staff, when some Department would describe its current research, followed by discussion. This largely avoided the danger of water-tight sub-programmes, and led directly to much joint work.

Over the period of Russell's directorship, the scientific staff increased from six to about 70, housed in new laboratories. The farm and the farm buildings were reorganized and extended to meet the heavy demands of the laboratories for field experiments essential to their investigations. Rothamsted was thriving, and the future seemed reasonably secure, when a grave crisis suddenly arose. The Trustee of the Rothamsted Estate had, reluctantly, to put it on the market. Although the Station was offered the first refusal, the price would be governed by the residential and not the agricultural value of the area. The farm was held on a short lease; the laboratory site and the famous classical fields were held on a peppercorn rent. It would have been impossible to maintain these fields when they became surrounded by roads and houses; in effect, the Rothamsted Experimental Station was threatened with extinction. The government offered no help, so Russell launched a public appeal for the money; the large sum needed was over-subscribed in a few weeks. It was his crowning achievement in the difficult task of raising funds.

As already mentioned, the account of Rothamsted does not overshadow the central theme of the overall expansion of agricultural research, advisory and education services. The greater part of the book deals with the many institutions and organisations—some old, others new—that were re-moulded or developed during the past half-century. Russell's memory for events and people, and his ability in extracting the actual guiding principle (or, failing that, a plausible one) from a seemingly intricate set of happenings, gives life to the story of these fifty years. He recounts instances of local indifference, and sometimes of opposition, overcome only because some land owner, county official, progressive farmer or the like, had the vision and enthusiasm needed to bring the scheme to fruition. Hall, who was the inspiration and driving force behind these developments, must have felt discouraged at times because, as quoted by Russell, of a 'sneaking fear that human affairs do not move on planned lines but by irrational and unconscious growth'. Be that as it may, the plan did achieve its intentions, and Russell lived long enough to put it all on record.

It is fitting to end this Foreword with an extract from another letter he sent me after the Diamond Anniversary of his marriage. It is a short passage but reveals much of the man. Dealing with this, his final book, he expressed his intention 'to record the good work of the pioneers in agricultural science, who did faithful work and mostly ill requited. I want at least to ensure that their names are remembered. And of course it is interesting to go over the old ground and the old battles once more. We had a great time.'

PREFACE

I HAVE called this book a History of Agricultural Science and the title is fully appropriate for the greater part of the period involved. Right up to the early days of this century a single book of modest size, Warington's *Chemistry of the Farm*, in just over 240 pages covered the whole of it and presented it as a distinct though not particularly coherent subject which could quite rightly be called agricultural science, though in fact it was usually practised by chemists and therefore was called agricultural chemistry. But this was changed in 1912 when the Development Commission set up research stations each dealing with a separate branch and each established at the most appropriate University with no provision for inter-communication. Each subject began to develop independently and the agricultural science of 1900 became the group of dis-sociated agricultural sciences of the 1950's. I hope a way will still be found of securing closer connection. There is a further complication that with few exceptions each branch of the subject is closely if rather spasmodically linked up with agricultural practice, and it is impossible to make a sharp distinction between the history of agricultural science and that of agricultural practice. The subject has no tidy boundaries and I make no pretence of setting any up. What I have tried to do is to set out the course of its development and to give some indication of the sort of men who did the work.

I came into the subject at the beginning of 1901 and was for-tunate in getting to know the men who for the previous ten or more years had been striving to develop it. They were handi-capped by the circumstance that the various branches of chemis-try needed: organic, physical and biochemistry, were only in their early stages and not yet very helpful, still more by the lack of recognition by the higher authorities of those days that agricultural science was really necessary for the benefit of the community. Yet those early workers kept on with their labours, unrecognized and unrewarded in their lifetimes, and quickly forgotten after death. In writing this book I hope to have done

A*

something towards conserving their memory. There were no scientific giants among them, no Darwins or Rutherfords, but some outstanding men like Lawes and Gilbert, Anderson, Hall and Wood, leaders in their day, who set the direction of the research work which was followed long after they were gone. The main foundation work was done by men keenly interested in it, anxious to do what they could towards building it up into a useful science, and I have tried to set out the results of their labours.

As this is not a text-book I have made no attempt to include all the research work done in Great Britain, but only such as shows how knowledge of agricultural science has expanded. Limitations of space have compelled omission of much that I should like to have included, especially of the Scottish work that found fruition later than my end date. Inclusion would have involved entry into a new period not yet ready to be treated as history. I have not usually gone beyond 1955 because I wanted to keep to finished work that has passed into the general body of accepted science. Unfinished work has been excluded and also various isolated studies the bearing of which was not clear, though this may appear later. There is no sharp boundary between agricultural science and agricultural practice nor between agricultural science and its closely related subjects, plant and animal physiology. No Agricultural Science Society was ever formed that could have set up conventional boundaries. I have kept within my boundaries whatever seemed essential for the development of a clear and coherent subject.

A vast amount of search through journals, reports and books has been necessary in preparing this book, and fortunately I have been helped by some of my younger friends to whom I wish to express my sincerest thanks. My son, Rev. J. L. Russell, S.J. has read through the various drafts of all the chapters in search of faults which he has helped to correct, and my Rothamsted colleague of long standing, H. V. Garner, has searched through piles of journals and numbers of old books from Rothamsted's rich store to obtain or confirm details necessary for the proper presentation of the subject. The librarians of the Oxford Department of Agriculture, Mr R. T. Shepherd; of the Cambridge School of Agriculture, Mr F. A. Buttress; of Rothamsted, Mr T. Cawley have, as always, been most helpful, as has Mr I. Kaye, librarian of the Royal Society, and the staff of the British Museum Library, the final Court of Appeal on doubtful matters within their purview. Also I wish to thank Mr Colin Clark of the Agricultural Economics Research Institute, Oxford and members of his staff for much help willingly given on various economic matters, and finally my wife for enduring hours of dictation as long as she was able, and Miss S. M. Fry for so kindly converting much of my difficult script into easily usable form. I owe a great debt of gratitude to Mr C. A. Browne for his *Source Book of Agricultural Chemistry* (Chronica Botanica, 1942), which helped me considerably in preparing the first two chapters, and to the Directors and senior staffs of the various Research Stations for much help in supplying information not otherwise easily obtainable.

CONTENTS

ILLUSTRATIONS

CHAPTER I

SEEKING A ROAD

1620 – 1750

EVER since scientific studies began some of them have been devoted to agriculture. For many years the science most actively concerned was not botany, as might have been expected, but chemistry, and throughout the nineteenth century the name agricultural chemistry was widely used to cover these studies. In more recent years, however, other sciences have been increasingly drawn in, and the more comprehensive name, agricultural science, has come into common use. There is a general understanding as to what the name actually connotes, but no strict definition has been agreed upon, and until the subject is more mature its boundaries are likely to be somewhat ragged. In this book it will be treated as the study on broad lines of the relations between the growing plant and its environmental factors, including also methods by which the plant may be changed to make it conform better to some desired standard; farm animals and their products so far as they are an integral part of the farm economy now form part of the subject.

Agriculture has been practised in Great Britain for some 4,000 years, and it reached a good standard during the Roman occupation when it not only supported a population estimated by Mortimer Wheeler to have numbered about 1½ millions, but in a good year had a surplus of food to export. No records of the methods exist; Britain was not important enough to attract the attention of the Roman writers on Agriculture at the time: Columella, Palladius and others.

The Greeks and afterwards the Arabs, however, had early thought about the growth of plants and what they fed upon—the beginning of agricultural science. But development came much later. The earliest chemists, the alchemists, were searching always for the philosopher's stone which was to change base materials into gold, or for the elixir of life which was to prolong active life indefinitely. Their method was to collect a few supposed facts, generally by searching through older writings, and then by much use of logical processes of reasoning (the ratiocination of the logicians) they arrived at a conclusion presumed to be true. There was much mysticism and secrecy about all they did. They contributed little to agricultural science.

A more promising method was started early in the sixteenth century by a brilliant but drunken Swiss reprobate, Philippus Theophrastus Paracelsus (1493–1541), who put forward the view that the proper function of chemistry was not to chase phantoms like the making of gold, but to make medicines and substances useful to the arts—as some of the Greek philosophers had already attempted. This was the period of iatro-chemistry—medical chemistry—but as organic chemistry was not yet born little development was possible: the search was usually backwards to recover some of the wisdom of the ancients. The botanists, however, began to be active; they collected, described and illustrated plants in the herbals which now began to appear, some of them, notably William Turner's *New Herbal* (1551)[1] and John Gerard's *Herbal* (1597) are of great interest.

Meanwhile a new intellectual movement was spreading throughout Western and Central Europe. Hitherto scholastic tradition had been all sufficient; it had been linked with superstition and mysticism and was completely dominated by the theologians of the day. The new learning was completely different from the old. It was based on direct objective studies of the thing itself: no opinion from any source whatsoever was allowed any weight. The three steps were usually observation: experiment: inference: often the inference would need checking by further experiment, and this by further observation and inference and so on *ad infinitum*—a recognition of the boundless range of science.

It was at this stage that the application of science to agriculture began. The first British scientist to concern himself with agriculture was the great Francis Bacon (1561–1626), the most versatile and highly cultured man of his age, and one of the most

---

[1] Turner is regarded as the father of English Botany.

heavily engaged, who carried out his agricultural studies at his palatial residence at Verulam, near St Albans. He began by explaining and justifying the new procedure. 'Man who is the servant and interpreter of Nature', he wrote, 'can act and understand no further than he has observed, either in operation or in contemplation of the method and order of Nature.' From a number of observations he may deduce a new conclusion, but that is only part of his task: he must prove the discovery, and that usually requires experiments. Bacon elaborated this thesis and much more in his *Novum Organum* (1620) written to show how best to increase knowledge of Nature: it is a remarkable system and a great philosophical classic, but it proved too complex for use.

He began his experimental studies by making simple observations of the effects of various agents on the germination and growth of wheat: a sufficient number of these, he argued, should lead to discovery. Seeds were soaked in water suspensions of the dung of cows, horses and pigeons, also of chalk and of human urine and 'claret wine', and the stimulation of germination and of growth was compared with that of 'wheat simple', i.e. untreated.[1] He also studied the various materials used to increase the productiveness of the soil: 'helps', he called them. 'Stercoration' was 'the first and most ordinary'; the order of effectiveness of the various dungs was that of sheep, cattle, horses, but for a garden pigeons' dung 'excelleth'. A second group of 'helpers' included the earths: marl, chalk, sea sand, pond earth and others. The third group included substances different from either dung or earth, but which nevertheless 'have a Vertue to make Ground Fertile': ashes, soot, salt, (though it is too costly). The fourth was 'the suffering of Vegetables to die into the ground so as to fatten it', e.g. 'stubbles of Corn and Pease'. He knew that saltpetre (crude potassium and sodium nitrate) was a good fertilizer—'the life of vegetables' he called it—and also that it was produced naturally in soil. 'Such Earth as hath 'Salt-Peter bred in it', he wrote, 'if you can preserve it without too much charge, doth excel. The way to hasten the breeding of Salt-Peter, is to forbid the sun, and the growth of Vegetables. And therefore, if you

[1] This and other experiments and observations are described in *Sylva Sylvarum* published in 1651, twenty five years after Bacon's death.

make a large Hovel, thatched over some quantity of Ground:
nay, if you do but plank the Ground over, it will breed Salt-
Peter.'

Other observations dealt with fruit. He noted without comment that the ripening of apples was hastened by storing them
with crab apples and onions. The explanation has been found
only recently. Ripe apples produce small quantities of ethylene
which stimulates ripening of unripe fruit. It is not known
whether onions also do this.[1]

In spite of his many observations, however, no discovery
ensued. Chemistry was not yet sufficiently advanced to throw
light on these and other observations that were accumulating.

The notion of chemical elements as we know them was not
yet born. A common view, inherited from Empedocles of Agri-
gentum (c. 495–435 BC) and adopted by Aristotle (384–322 BC)
was that all substances were made up of four elements: earth,
air, fire and water: later three 'principles' had been substituted
by the alchemists who took them from the Arabs: mercury,
sulphur and salt. These, however, were not the actual substances that we know, but a kind of ethereal substratum or
essence beyond the power of our senses to recognize.

Water was generally regarded as the element out of which
plants were made; it was supposed to have the power of trans-
muting itself into the various plant substances. Unlike many of
the old ideas this was based on experiment and seemed to be
beyond dispute. The experiment was made by a Belgian
chemist, Jan Baptiste van Helmont (1577–1644), but it played
so important a part in the development of British agricultural
science that it must be described here. It was one of the simplest
but most remarkable in the history of agricultural science.

'I took an earthen vessel in which I put 200 lb. of soil dried in
an oven, then I moistened it with rain water and pressed hard
into it a shoot of willow weighing 5 lb. After exactly five years
the tree that had grown up weighed 169 lb. and about 3 oz.
But the tree had never received anything but rain water or
distilled water to moisten the soil (when this was necessary)
and the vessel remained full of soil which was still tightly

[1] These problems were studied in the 1960's by Dr J. C. Fidler of the Ditton Lab-
tory of the Agricultural Research Council, Larkfield, Maidstone.

packed; lest any dust from outside should have got into the
soil it was covered with a sheet of iron coated with tin but
perforated with many holes. I did not take the weight of the
leaves that fell in the autumn. In the end I dried the soil once
more and got the same 200 lb. that I started with, less about
2 oz. Therefore the 164 lb. of wood, bark and root arose from
the water alone.'[1]

This was left in manuscript by van Helmont who himself
published nothing, but in 1652 his son Franz Mercurius van
Helmont collected his scripts and published them in Amsterdam
under the title *Ortus Medicinae*.

It is a model scientific communication: terse, clear, omitting
nothing essential. Life would be much easier for scientists and
their students if more were like it. Everything is right except
the conclusion, and that is wrong because van Helmont did not
know, and for more than a century nobody knew, that a gas
present in the air, carbon dioxide, took part in the process and
supplied the carbon which formed a large part of the growth
material. So long as it was held, however, the theory put soil
into the humble position of being merely a prop to hold up the
plant, a protection against too much heat or cold, and a storage
for the water out of which it would be formed.

About the middle of the seventeenth century British scientists
already caught up in the pursuit of the new learning began to
take more interest in agriculture than ever before, probably the
result of inspiration by Robert Boyle (1627–1692), one of the
most remarkable men of his age. He was the seventh son of
Richard Boyle, Earl of Cork, and was born at Linsmore Castle
in 1627, one year after Bacon's death. At the age of eight he was
sent to Eton where he remained for three years: then he spent
six years with a tutor on the Continent and returned to England
in 1644 resolved to dedicate his life to the pursuit of the new
learning.

Before long he met in London a group of young men with the
same purpose. About 1645 they had begun to meet weekly to
share and discuss their knowledge: absence unless fully justified

---

[1] This experiment had already been suggested by Nicolas of Cusa (1401–1464)
in his *De staticis Experimentis*.

was punished by fine. Boyle joined them. They called themselves 'The Philosophical College', but Boyle called them 'The Invisible College' and this is the name that has stuck. Hartlib and Evelyn (p. 21) also attended the meetings. In a letter to his old tutor in Geneva describing the group Boyle wrote: 'They value no knowledge but as it has a tendency to use.' He therefore counsels his friend to 'take the pains to inquire a little more thoroughly into the ways of husbandry, etc., practiced in your parts, and when you intend for England to bring along with you what good receipts of choice books of any of these subjects you can procure, which will make you extremely welcome to our Invisible College.'

Among Boyle's experiments was a repetition of van Helmont's; he obtained the same result and concluded as van Helmont had done that the water had been transmuted into plant substances. He even went further than van Helmont and argued that as worms and insects arise spontaneously from the decay of plants they also must be produced by the transmutation of water. The experiment also showed, he writes, that the salts in the soil are not essential to plant growth, though they are undoubtedly helpful. He insists on the need for studying the various 'saltnesses' that occur in soils and in knowing 'with what sort each plant or seed is most delighted'. Better crops can be obtained by sowing 'a proper variety of seed, agreeable to the nature of the particular salt, at present inherent in the earth'. And again: 'The fertility of manure, seems to depend on its salino-sulphureous parts; a practical enquiry into the differences and various operations of salts, may, probably, assist to discover various kinds of compost, with the proper manner, wherein to multiply, compound, and apply them'. 'Natural philosophy' (the name he gave to the subject) 'may also help in solving other problems of great importance to the husbandman: preserving cattle from diseases, and the fruits of the earth from putrefaction. He who can accelerate, and delay putrefaction in bodies, may show the husbandman how to prepare a variety of manures; to enrich the ground with the peculiar kind of salt it wants; and also, how to preserve several seeds, flowers, and fruits, beyond their natural duration.'

Many problems were studied after the air pump was invented, among them was one on 'hindering the Growth of Seed Corn in the Earth, by extracting the Air, and furthering their Growth by admitting it'. Another of special interest was 'to try how long a Man can live by expiring and inspiring again the same air; to try whether the Air so respired might not by several Means be purified or renew'd'. The range was very wide: one investigation was 'of a Spider's not being inchanted by a circle of Unicorn's Horn, or Irish Earth laid round about it'; and yet another 'of Flesh not breeding worms when secur'd from Flyblowing'.

Boyle's best known book, *The Sceptical Chymist* (1661) takes the form of a dialogue between two chemists, one a supporter of the old chemical views, the other setting out objections to them and putting forth his own ideas, which, as they developed, earned for him the title of Father of Chemistry. He exposed the fallacy of the current idea that the four 'elements', earth, air, fire and water, and the three 'principles': salt, sulphur and mercury were the basic components of all substances. His own idea was very much that of the Greek philosopher Democritus (460–360 BC) who supposed that all matter is built up of extremely minute indivisible atoms all composed of the same substance but differing in size, shape and weight: Boyle's view was that all matter is built up of water: it being 'an elementary body, and far more homogeneous than any other fluid', and 'by a different texture of its parts, it may be brought to constitute bodies of very different qualities.'

The year 1660 is one of the most momentous in the annals of British science. At a meeting of scientists and others on December 5th it was decided to form a Philosophers' Society, the members of which agreed to meet weekly 'to consult and debate concerning the promoting of experimentall learning.' Robert Boyle and John Evelyn were both invited to join but not Hartlib. In 1662 the Society received the Royal patronage and was renamed the Royal Society.[1]

From the outset the Society was interested in agriculture and when in March 1665 it set up eight committees to take charge of its various activities one of them, the Georgical Committee, was devoted to husbandry, as agriculture was then commonly called. It functioned so well that the early numbers of

---

[1] Sir Henry Lyons, *The Royal Society 1660–1940*, Cambridge University Press, 1944, where also the history of the Invisible College is recorded.

the Society's journal, The *Philosophical Transactions of the Royal Society*, contain numerous articles relating to agricultural science and practice, and when in 1681 under the vigorous Presidency of Christopher Wren the organization of the Society was overhauled the Georgical Committee was one of the two that survived, the other being the Anatomical Committee. One of its first acts had been to urge the Fellows to plant potatoes as a valuable food crop and to urge their friends to do the same.

The Georgical Committee early resolved that 'the best endeavours should be used to compose as perfect a History of Agriculture and Gardening as might be'. A questionnaire was drawn up out of Georgical Authors:[1] it was to be sent to experienced Husbandmen in all the Shires and Counties of England, Scotland and Ireland where the members had special interests, with a request for 'as full and as punctuall answers thereunto as they could': that thereby 'it might be knowne, what is knowne and done already, both to enrich every place with the aides, that are found in any place, and withall to consider, what further improvements may be made in all the practice of husbandry.' Various members of the Committee undertook enquiries in certain areas, and one was to collect 'out of Mr Hartlib's Legacie' such enquiries as should occur to him.

The questionnaire was printed for distribution and also in the fifth number of the *Philosophical Transactions*.[2] It is particularly interesting as showing the type of factual information which the Committee considered necessary for building up a picture of British Agriculture. It is as follows:

(1) The several kinds of the soyls of *England* being supposed to be, either Sandy, Gravelly, Stony, Clayie, Chalky, Light-mould, Heathy, Marish, Boggy, Fenny, or Cold weeping Ground; information is desired, what kind of soyls your Country doth most abound with, and how each of them is prepared for *Arable*.

(2) What *peculiar* preparations are made use of to these Soyls for each kind of Grain; with what kind of Manure

---

[1] John Houghton however, states that Boyle drew it up. He certainly was keen on linking science and agriculture.

[2] *Phil. Trans.*, Vol. 1, pp. 91–4, 1665. Mr Lennard (*vide infra* p. 24) has shown that there was an earlier and slightly different form.

they are prepared; when, how, and in what quantity the
Manure is laid on?

(3) At what seasons and how often they are ploughed, what
kinds of Ploughs are used for the several sorts of Ground?

(4) How long the several Grounds are let lie fallow?

(5) How, and for what productions, Heathy Grounds may be
improved? And who they are (if there be any in your
Country) that have reduced *Heaths* into profitable
Lands?

(6) What ground Marle hath over head? How deep generally
it lieth from the surface? What is the depth of the
Marle itself? What the colour of it? Upon what grounds
it is used? What time of the year it is to be laid on?
How many loads to an acre? What Grains *Marled* land
will bear, and how many years together?

(7) The kinds of Grain or Seed, usual in England, being
supposed to be either Wheat, Miscelane,[1] Rye, Barley,
Oats, Pease, Beans, Fitches, Buck-Wheat, Hemp, Flax,
Rape; We desire to know, what sorts of Grains are
Sown in your Country, and how each of these is prepared
for Sowing? Whether by *steeping*, and in what kind of
liquor? Or by mixing it, and with what?

Other questions related to the many sorts of wheat, oats and
barley in cultivation, the quantities of seed sown; the yields
expected in very good, less good and the worst years; The
common diseases being supposed to be 'Meldew, Blasting,
Smut; what are conceived to be the Causes thereof, and what
the Remedies?'

There were nineteen questions on arable land and crops and
six on meadows. These include:

(1) How the above-mentioned sorts of Soyle are prepared,
when they are used for Pasture or Meadow?

(4) What are the several kinds of Grass, and which are
counted the best?

(6) What kind of Grass is fittest to be preserved for Winter
feeding? And what Grass is best for Sheep, for Cows,
Oxen, Horses, Goats, etc.?

[1] Mixed grain, usually Rye and Wheat.

The Questionnaire ends with a warning 'that by reason of the present Contagion in London' (it was the time of the plague) there will be delays in printing, etc.

It is not known how many copies of the questionnaire were sent out or what kind of response was obtained: only eleven reports are now known. They came from Yorkshire, Kent, Dorset, Devon and Cornwall. It is possible that more came in and were lost: the Committee had scarcely begun its work when the terrible plague broke out, followed by the Great Fire of 1666, and life in London was severely disorganized. All the material available was carefully examined in 1932 by Reginald Lennard and much valuable information was extracted.[1]

The commonest manures were dung, marl and lime; in some places the dung was mixed with lime and left for three months before being put out on to the land. Around Ashford, Kent, usual dressings per statute acre were, in loads of 9 bushels: dung 100, marl 300 or 400, lime 160; chalk 80 to 100. In Gloucestershire on stone brash, gravel or marly land use was made of 'Shovellings of streets, courts, ponds, ditches or any other good earth with straw, weeds or muck rotting amongst it'. In Cornwall and West Devon sea-sand was carried on horseback in canvas sacks containing 18 gallons apiece; it cost 5s to 12s per 100 sacks at waterside and the dressing was 60 to 200 sacks per acre. Seaweed, however, was but little used, except very near the sea. Near Bristol, and 'very neare the Cyty' 'Coleashes,[2] soape-ashes and woolen raggs' were used. But manures were not always needed: a fallow every third year kept land in Kent in good heart for thirty or forty years and wanting 'noe improvement by dung or otherwise'. Paring and burning (Devonshire) were known, but not much practised.

'Mildew or blast' of cereals was wide-spread. It was encouraged by late sowing or over-manuring: the East Yorkshire Report states that 'our country being open and not over-manured hath little Mildew; that Mildew we have is always on our Manured Land'. Mists also were supposed to cause it in Yorkshire.

Wheat, oats and barley are mentioned in all Reports; rye, beans and peas in most of them, vetches in five—all in the South of England; hemp and flax only in the south-west and the

[1] 'Agriculture under Charles II', *Econ. Hist. Rev.*, 1932.   [2] Charcoal ashes

Holme Beacon district of Yorkshire, which was the only place where rape was reported; tares were reported only in Kent. Turnips are not mentioned. In connection with meadows and pastures a variety of plants are reported: 'white and red naturall Clover' in the Ashford district (Kent), wild trefoil in Gloucestershire—which springs up as 'a flourishing mat' after dressings of 'cole-ashes' or soot and which 'they account the best sort of grass'—'of farre longer continuance than the larger sort of Trefoile or Clovergrass which they use to sowe and which is a great impoverisher of land.' The correspondent for Devon and Cornwall reports that clover seed 'is commonlie sold in Exeter and other Easterne marketts for 3d or 2d per libram (lb.) and is sowne the last year of tillage with Oates'; its best crop is in the second year; by the fourth it is 'quite decay'd'. 'This Clover feedes well for the Grassier, but ill for the Butcher; for it will not Fallow.'

Numerous varieties of wheat, oats and peas are mentioned, and the advantage of using seed grown in a different district or on a different kind of soil was widely known. Wheat seed was commonly steeped in lime, brine or blood before sowing; instructions are given for liming it. A usual rate of sowing was: wheat 2 bushels per acre, barley 3 or 4 bushels, oats 4 to 6. In good seasons the yield of wheat might be 20 bushels per acre, in bad seasons only 10 bushels and an average yield would be 15 bushels: in 'marl country' the seeding rate would be about 1 bushel per acre, a good yield would be 12 bushels per acre and a poor one five. For barley the values were about 25 per cent less.

The replies suggest that convertible husbandry[1] was fairly widespread: it was common around Ashford, Kent, though not elsewhere in the county. The reports are not all quite clear, but there are indications that the much described three course system (two crops, then fallow) was frequently modified.

Bacon's precept had been obeyed: many observations had been made but no significant discoveries had resulted.

In one of Boyle's numerous books, *Some Considerations Touching the Usefulness of Experimental Natural Philosophy*, he makes a direct appeal to farmers to carry out experiments on their land.

[1] See footnote, p. 39.

It is in a second volume published in 1671 (the first having been issued in 1664) and it reads: 'Chymical experiments . . . may probably afford useful directions to the Husbandman towards the meliorations of his Land, both for Corn, Trees, Grass and consequently Cattel,' and he goes on to refer to Francis Bacon's view that nitre (crude potassium nitrate) is 'the life of vegetables',[1] that most fat earths (i.e. fertile soils) defended from the sun and rain, and left to themselves, will soon abound in nitrous salt'. In view of its importance he expresses the opinion that 'an inquiry into the nature of Salt Peter may be of great use in farming'.

Unfortunately there was no way of bringing scientists and farmers together, and this offer of collaboration was not accepted; indeed farmers may not have been aware that it had been made. In any case chemistry had not yet emerged as a science and it is by no means certain that even Boyle could have done much for farmers until it was more advanced.

In 1668 he left Oxford for London where he lived with his sister, Lady Ranelagh at her house in Pall Mall till his death in 1692. For some time he had been in ill health and although he continued his chemical experiments in a laboratory he had set up in Southampton Row he could do no more for the Royal Society. He had always been interested in religion and deplored the antagonism beginning to appear between some of the clergy and the scientists. His missionary zeal never flagged, and despite failing health he strove to increase the circulation of the Bible in other lands.

This brilliant outburst of activity was followed by a long period of groping for new ideas that always eluded capture. Various aspects and subjects were investigated, but there was no co-ordination of efforts, and much hampering caused by the inability to abandon old ideas even after they had been proved wrong.

---

[1] This idea had already been put forward by the German Chemist Johann Rudolph Glauber in 1648. Much nitre was required for making gunpowder in those days of frequent warfare: some was collected from stables and much was made from urine, etc., on nitre beds where all known conditions for active nitrification were provided. Glauber made the brilliant proposal during the Thirty Years' War (1618–1648) that its manufacture should be continued after the war was over to aid in the restarting of agriculture. But it was not done.

John Evelyn (1620–1706), the famous diarist, came into this period. He is of special interest because he also wrote the first English book on soil. He came of an old Shropshire family, but his father had migrated to Wotton, Surrey, in the reign of Queen Elizabeth, and it was there that he was born. In 1637 he went up to Balliol College, Oxford and three years later to the Middle Temple. The political situation was uncertain: his family tradition and upbringing made him a Royalist, and he deemed it expedient to go to the Continent where he spent much of the next seven years in Holland, France and Italy. He returned to England in 1647 and went to live at Sayes Court, near Deptford, Kent, which came to him through his newly married wife. He was obviously very astute, for he lost nothing in the Civil War and apparently managed to keep his friends on both sides.

His interests were very wide. He knew the best scientists of the time, and played an important part in the founding of the Royal Society in 1660. In 1661 he published an interesting pamphlet, *Fumifugium, or the inconvenience of the air, and smoake of London dissipated*; this was reissued in 1772, more than a century later, showing what a perennial problem it is.

His book on soil, *A philosophical discourse of earth, relating to the culture and improvement of it for vegetation*, was produced in response to a letter sent at the end of December 1674 by the President of the Royal Society, Viscount Brouncker, stating that the Council wished the Thursday meetings to be 'constantly provided with Entertainments suitable to the design of their Institution' and inviting his cooperation. He delivered a discourse in the following April which fortunately the Council ordered to be printed. The book was issued in 1676 and a second edition in 1678; it remained popular throughout the eighteenth century when the title was slightly modified by prefixing the word 'Terra', while the York quarto edition of 1786 was prefaced by a delightfully naive illustration of the 'Tartarian lamb', a plant shaped like a lamb, with a body standing on four stalks and a head apparently able to browse on plants growing around it. Unfortunately the editor, Alexander Hunter, gives no description. The book requires fuller treatment than usual because it gives the best available summary of soil science as it was understood in the seventeenth century, presented to the best scientists of the time by an author who was not only one of their number but was also very interested in forests, woods and gardens, and had much more than the ordinary gentleman's knowledge of them.

The lecture began with an invitation to the 'acute and learned judges' constituting his audience to descend from their 'more sublime and noble speculations' to consider the 'innocent and humble subject' he had to offer. Then followed the rather discouraging statement that the theorists of his day 'reckon up no fewer than one hundred seventy nine millions one thousand and sixty different sorts of Earths', though in fact he described only eight or nine and he discussed in detail even fewer.

The text is difficult to follow, with long involved unbroken passages. In reading it the underlying seventeenth century conceptions always have to be borne in mind: that all things are built up of water; that transmutation is a regular natural process, and the division into animal, vegetable and mineral substances had much less significance than now.

Evelyn explained that he should deal only with 'underturf Mould', the surface layer of about one foot depth. This owed its fertility to its constant enrichment by the 'Air, Dews, Showers, Salts and Celestial Influences' supplied continuously by the atmosphere. 'It is verily almost a miracle to see . . . that the bare raking and *combing* only of a Bed of Earth, now one way then another, as to the *Regions* of Heaven, and *Polar* Aspects, may diversify the annual *Production*, which is a *Secret* worthy to be considered.' Also the Sun's heat drew up fatness from below which the native 'grass and tender Verdure' did not dissipate.

He briefly described a few kinds of soils: the best was black mould, 'fat, yet porous, light and sufficiently tenacious, not easily crumbling to dust but without sand or gravel;' the poorer soils were sandy of different colours. '. . . there is a kind so obstinate and ill-natured as almost nothing will subdue it, and another so voracious and greedy, as nothing will satiate, without exceeding industry, because it ungratefully devours all that is applied to it, turning it into as arrant Clay, as itself'. The worst soil is Clay; 'cursed stepdame to almost all vegetation as having few or no meatus's (passages) for the percolation of alimental showers'. 'Laxatives' should be applied: sand, marl, chalk or sawdust, and constant 'vexing with the spade and plow'; he especially commends sea sand and the burning of clay. Loam, he wrote, is an excellent mean between extremes of looseness and adhesiveness.

He then examined methods of testing the productiveness of soils. He described Virgil's test: to dig a hole, put the soil back again and stamp it down; if it more than filled the hole it was good, if not it was poor.[1] As evidence he quoted two German writers: one describing a soil in Wittenburg that passed the test and was so good that rye grown on it changed to wheat in three seasons, and the other a soil in Thuringia that failed, on which in three seasons wheat had reverted to rye. Bacon's suggestion was less promising: it was that the end of the rainbow pointed to a 'more roscid and fertile mould'. Evelyn's objection to this was that the rainbow has two ends and they are opposite to each other. He suggested that a study of the native flora would indicate the crops for which the soil was most suited. Thyme and sorrel indicated woodland; camomile indicated wheat; and mallow indicated roots; gorse showed that the land was too cold for crops. He was naturally interested in the rapid reappearance of flints on the ploughed land of the higher South Downs after the surface had been cleared of them. His explanation was that they were simply petrified worm casts: also water could easily become solid and turn into stones. Rotting plants, trees etc, produced soil, and in places this had accumulated massively, 'I affirm it to grow and increase yearly in Depth from the Causes aforesaid, and in some Places to that 'Proportion, as to have raised no inconsiderable Hills'.

Much of the discourse consisted of disconnected observations which were not followed up at the time though some had great possibilities. He tried to discover the structure of soil. He collected a number of samples 'such as I could find about this Territory', washed them and examined them 'with an indifferent microscope and noted the presence of Chrystals' and other particles: they were dried and broken to see what sort of powder they yielded. He tried 'to incite the curious' to introduce exotic plants and 'as our soils might be unsuitable to make new

[1] *Georgics*, Bk. II, lines 226–237.

Confections of earths for the entertaining of the most generous
and profitable plants, as well as curious . . . especially if we could
skill to modify also the *Air* about them and make the Remedy as
well regional as topical'—an early foreshadowing of a modern
plant growth chamber.

He attached great importance to exposing the soil to air
as thoroughly as possible and described an experiment 'taught
by a learned Person of this illustrious Body' to demonstrate
the advantages thereof. Take the most barren soil you can find,
reduce it to a fine powder, let it be 'for a Time uncessantly
agitated, expos'd for a *Summer* and *Winter*, to the Vicissitudes
and Changes of the Seasons and Influences of Heaven': the soil
would then 'have obtain'd such a generous and masculine
Pregnancy . . . as to make good your highest Expectations'. It
was the 'Nitrous Spirit' and other bodies in the air that constituted the food of plants: all that the soil did was to bring it
down. 'If once the *Nitrous Spirit* be quite mortified the *Earth*
produces nothing till being long exposed, it have attracted a
fresh supply to give it Life. The *Earth* especially if fresh has a
special magnetism in it by which it attracts the *Salt*, Power, or
Virtue (call it either) which gives it Life'. The Earth also contributed something, an Efflorescence he called it, which associated with the aerial aids, promoted fermentation. 'These
Ferments of the *Earth*, by this Amity, and genial Intercourse
with the Air, are innumerable, to concoct, digest, accelerate,
and restore, equal to, yea, beyond any artificial Enforcements
of *Dumps* and *Composts* whatsoever'.

The soil could be fertilized from within as well as from
without and this was done by adding various substances to it
which, however, might require 'no ordinary Dexterity'. A
thin sprinkling of salt or of ashes might be very beneficial,
but too much would be harmful. He gave the usual list of
manures with some interesting comments. As usual at the time
he recommended treatment by contraries: lime, which is hot,
should go on cold wet lands. Blood was excellent for fruit on
almost any soil. He relates that after the Battle of Badnam
Fields, Devonshire, 'the blood of the slain did so fertilize the
Fields (when Corn had been sown a little before) that most of
the *Wheat stalks* bare *two, three, four*, yea to *seven* and some even
to *fourteen* Ears, a thing almost incredible'.

Hair, horn shavings, woollen rags, leather waste, and skins used down to our own time as useful sources of nitrogen, are commended as being 'full of volatile Salts', and blood and flesh of animals as being 'much more powerful for the enriching of Land than their *Dung* and Excrements':—one estimate was of twenty times more potent. He described the different dungs as having different values: sheep's dung is described as very effective for flowers and roots, and an instance is quoted of a 'Reddish-root' (radish) manured only with sheep's dung and grown 'as big as half a Man's Middle, which being hung up "for some time in a Butcher's Shop, People took for an Hog"'. Pond mud was good, so was '*Dust* of unstony *Highways*, where the drift of *Cattle*, and much Passage is': collected March to November it excelled all other composts.

The instructions for making composts are very elaborate. A large pit was to be made thirty or forty feet long, one side sloping to admit a cart; the sides and base were 'paved 'then successive layers of '*stable soil* with the *Litter*', fine mould, 'Garden offal', were to be thrown in, then 'a Couch of *Pigeons* and *Poultry-dung* with more *Horse dung Litter*', then a stratum of Sheep's dung; then another layer of earth, then neat's dung, lastly ashes, soot, bottom of wood stack, sawdust, dry scourings of ponds and ditches and other materials 'Upon all this cast plentiful water from time to time', preferably from a cattle pond. The material must then be left for two years, after which the heap could be broken up and different layers stored in separate small pits. Here they could be mixed with more soil, or with each other. The material must then be sieved, and whatever passed through was ready for use; the coarse material was put back with the new material for a second passage through the process.

This gave what he called the 'dry compost'.

The second type of compost, liquid compost, was made from different materials: '*acid* Plants, bitter and rank *Weeds* . . . such as *Esula*[1], *Hemlock*, *Docks*, *Thistles*, *Tobacco-stalks*, *Wormwood* Leaves, Trash and Offal such as cattle will not touch. Garbage', and a long list of other unsavoury things, kept moist till well decomposed. Various other recipes are given including one for making 'Muck water' which had been highly

[1] Euphorbia, spurge.

praised: To a thick mixture of the best marl and water were added the dung of fowls, conies, sheep, etc., horses, cows, also lees of wine, ale, beer, and other beverages, broths and kitchen waste, lime, blood, urine and water: the mixture was distributed by a 'great *Syringe* or watering Engine, such as are being used to extinguish *Fire*'. Another recipe was: '*Rain water* of the Equinox q.s. boil'd with store of *Neat's dung*, till it be very strong of it, dissolve one Pound of Saltpetre in every Pottle[1] of Water . . . water Fruit-trees with it, for prodigious Effects'. Quoting an Italian proverb that 'Every plant smacks of its roots' he gave a warning about dungs: 'some people not without good *Reason* prefer the *Corn* and *Grain* which is reaped from *Marl*, *Chalk*, *Lime* and other more natural Manure, before what is produc'd from a Crop which grows on a *Dunghill*'. He regarded human excrement as so offensive that he excluded it from his list: it 'perniciously contaminates the Odor of *Flowers*, and is so evident in the *vine*, as nothing can reconcile it'. Among all these recipes is one with a very modern touch. 'Dissolve 3 lb. of the best Indian nitre in 15 gallons of water.' This was to be used on bulbs. It is interesting to note that there was already in these early days an import of Indian nitre.

Other improvements are also discussed.

He commended burning of the soil provided it did not go beyond blackening; beyond that the Nitre was destroyed and the soil would produce nothing till long exposure to air had attracted a new supply. The burning of the vegetation did no harm: out of the ashes new plants of the same kind would arise: wheat ashes would produce wheat; ashes of fruits and berries 'bring forth the same'; no treatment of the *Seminal Rudiments* whatsoever, 'seems totally of Power to annihilate their virtue'. Burning thus increases the variety of vegetation, but it also increases the weight of the soil—the reason for this 'let the curious examine'.

Irrigation is highly praised: 'one of the richest improvements that ever was put in practice'. Many scraps of information of this kind are included. His account of salt is extremely interesting. First he sets out what it does. It enables the soil to maintain its 'wonderful prolific virtue' which otherwise

[1] Neat—any animal of the ox kind: Pottle—half a gallon: q.s. (quantum sufficit: as much as is necessary).

would be in danger of being lost. It entices roots to remain in the upper and saline layers of the soil upon which the nitrous Rains and Dews descend'. It 'gives Vigor to Places sprinkled with *Urine, Soot, Ashes, Bones, Hair, Feathers, Blood'*. It is not 'our common artificial salt, but a certain more *unctuous Spirit*, or *airy Nitre* pregnant with a *vital Balm'*, the first and last of *Elemental* Bodies, . . . the Original of all *Fecundity'*. These were translated into scientific terms, *Salts embryonata, Spermatic Vapours*, etc. but further discussion 'I leave to those who affect to wrap up *easy* Notions in *hard* and uncertain Terms'. Then descending to practical issues he added. 'I firmly believe that were *Saltpetre* (I mean factitious Nitre)[1] to be obtained in plenty we should need but little other *Composts* to meliorate our ground'.

For many years this was the only English book on soil: it had an exceptionally long life; the first issue was in 1676 and the last in 1788. Ernle records that it was well known to all well-read agriculturists.

The book was not without its critics. Jethro Tull writing more than fifty years later was perhaps the most severe. He could make nothing of Evelyn's account of the food of plants and quite characteristically does not hesitate to say so. 'And when a Man, no less sagacious than Mr Evelyn' he wrote, 'has trac'd it through all the *Mazes* of the *Occult Qualities* and even up to the Metaphysics, he declares he can not determine, whether the Thing he pursues be *Corporeal or* Spiritual'—here he gave it up.

Evelyn is better known for his book *Sylva, or a Discourse of Forest trees*, first published in 1664; it had run into five editions by 1729 and was reissued by Hunter at York in 1776 and 1786. He also wrote a companion volume *Pomona*, or an appendix concerning fruit trees in relation to cider, and he produced the first gardening Calendar, *Kalendarium Hortense* in 1664.

His studies of soil particles were carried a stage further by John Houghton who used a sedimentation method to separate the sand from the clay in soils. He pointed out that the irregular

---

[1] Artificial nitre (crude potassium nitrate) made in the Nitre Beds for the manufacture of gunpowder.

B

shapes of the larger particles left passages down which water could drain away.[1]

Later came Nehemiah Grew, (1641–1715), a Cambridge graduate who took his medical degree at Leyden in 1671 and set up in practice in London, but was able to make important studies of the growing plant: they are recorded in his book *The Anatomy of Vegetables*, published in 1675 and enlarged in 1682. He deals not only with the structure of plants but with their physiology also. The four external factors determining their growth are, he states, 'Earth, water, aer, and Sun', and he describes the various kinds of earth and water concerned. The 'Aer' may be 'impregnated with vegetable principles' and it may contain 'a true Aerial Salt . . . dissolved in the Aether as other Salts are in Water or in the Vaporous parts of the Aer'. This idea of nutritive salts in the air constantly recurs over a long period.

Grew was one of the first to study the ash constituents of plants. As there was no method of analysing them, however, he could do little beyond determining the total quantity in various plants.[2]

One of the tragedies of the seventeenth century agricultural science was the early death of John Mayow (1643–79) whose studies of nitre promised very important results, especially those indicating a common principle in air and in nitre that brings about combustion—the 'nitro-aerial or igneo-aerial spirit', he called it. He also confirmed earlier statements that soil from which the 'sal nitrum' has been washed out recovered it again on exposure to the air. Unfortunately no one continued his work.

An important advance was made when John Woodward (1665–1728) finally disposed of the idea that plants were composed simply of water, in spite of van Helmont's and Robert Boyle's apparently incontrovertible experimental results. He grew sprigs of mint in distilled water, in water from Hyde Park

[1] Recorded in one of his *Letters for the Improvement of Husbandry and Trade* which were issued weekly from 1681 to 1683, and again from 1692 to 1703, and which Lord Ernle described as "the first attempt to found a scientific agricultural paper". A fuller account is given in B. A. Keen's *The Physical Properties of the Soil*, pp. 8–16.

[2] It was the Swiss Chemist, Theodore de Saussure (1767–1845) who made the first detailed analysis of ash in plants. (1804.)

conduit, and in the Hyde Park water shaken up with earth. After 56 days the sprigs had made the following gains in weight in grains:

	Distilled water	Hyde Park conduit	Hyde Park conduit shaken with soil
Gain in weight	41	139	284
Weight of water transpired	8,803	13,140	14,956
Water transpired per unit of gain	214	94	52

The gain in weight was not proportional to the amount of water transpired as it should have been if the plant substances had been made up solely of congealed water, but to something in the water that had come from the soil: 'a certain peculiar terrestrial matter', Woodward called it.[1]

'It hath been shown that there is a considerable quantity of this matter contain'd both in rain, river, and spring water; that the much greatest part of the fluid mass that ascends up into the plants does not settle or abide there, but passes through the pores of them and exhales up into the Atmosphere; that a great part of the terrestrial matter, mixt with the water, passes up into the plant along with it; and that the plant is more or less augmented in proportion as the water contains a greater or smaller quantity of that matter. From all which we may reasonably infer, that Earth, and not Water, is the matter that constitutes vegetation.'

Woodward's life was too interesting to be passed by unnoticed. As a youth he was apprenticed to a linen draper in London, but disliked the work and devoted all his spare time to science. Fortunately he came to the notice of an eminent physician, Dr Peter Barwich, who educated him with his own family. He then studied philosophy, anatomy, and medicine, and was so successful that he was invited by Sir Ralph Dutton to his residence at Sherborne (Glos.) where he collected all the varieties of fossils and rocks he could find. Geology was in its infancy and he was one of its early students. Later (1692) he was appointed Professor of Physic at Gresham College and

[1] *Phil. Trans.*, Vol. 21. pp. 193–227, 1699.

in the following year became a Fellow of the Royal Society. His was one of the success stories in the history of the scientists; unfortunately he was very hot tempered and probably did not get as far as he might have done.[1]

New ground was broken in 1727 when Stephen Hales (1677–1760) published his *Vegetable Staticks, or an Account of some Statical Experiments on the Sap of Vegetables*, which for the first time dealt with the water and temperature conditions of soil. He measured the temperature of the soil at different depths, and showed that the day and night fluctuations lessened considerably as the depth increased. He was the first to measure the force with which roots of trees imbibe soil water, and its variation at different times of the day. He also studied leaf size and leaf transpiration. He felt certain that air played an important part in the nutrition of plants, and supposing it to be fixed in the plant, he tried to learn something about it by destructive distillation of numerous plant materials, wheat, peas, sugar etc. and collecting the gases evolved. He also obtained gases by heating sulphur, sal ammoniac and other substances and by the action of various acids on metals. He accepted the current views that all these 'airs' were identical, and also that plants were composed of sulphur, volatile salt, water, earth and a large portion of air; and also

'The opinion of Chymists, that there is but one volatile salt in nature, out of which all other kinds of salt are formed by very different combinations, all which nutritive principles do by various combinations with the cultivated earth, compose that nutritive ductile matter, out of which the parts of vegetables are formed, and without which the watry vehicle alone cannot render a barren soil fruitful.'

Among other useful inventions was a method of fumigation by brimstone for protecting grain from damage by weevils.

Unlike Woodward, Hales seems to have been rather a likeable person. He was born at Bekesbourne, Kent, in 1677 and trained for Holy Orders at Cambridge. In 1708 he was presented with the perpetual curacy of Teddington, Middlesex. Charles A.

[1] Lyons, *The Royal Society, 1660–1940*, pp. 99, 135.

Browne described him as a 'gentle, truth-loving curate'. He was, however, more than that, his scientific work showed him to be an able chemist, inventor and physiologist.

THE AGRICULTURAL IMPROVERS OF THE
SIXTEENTH CENTURY

During most of this period of scientific endeavour some of the farmers and landowners of England, while completely ignoring the work of the scientists, were trying to improve their practice. The story of these efforts belongs to the history of farming rather than to that of agricultural science, and it is fully recorded in Lord Ernle's *English Farming Past and Present*. But some account of them is necessary to show the kind of problems confronting the farmers of the sixteenth and seventeenth centuries, and the methods evolved empirically for dealing with some of them. The improvements were proceeding more rapidly than in earlier times because they were more easily effected on the individual farms of the enclosed land than on the open fields of the old communal systems; and enclosure began in Tudor times and proceeded at an increasing rate.

Some of the improvements came from Western Europe, parts of which were already far ahead of Britain in their farm practice, but as the British farmers rarely travelled most of them were unaware of the difference, or else they ignored it. The Royalist war of the 1640's, however, sent a number of English landowners overseas as refugees; among them was Sir Richard Weston who, while exiled in Flanders, learned from a Flemish merchant in 1644 why farmers on the poor soil between Ghent and Antwerp were so prosperous. They rotated their crops: first flax, then turnips, then oats undersown with clover. The turnips and clover provided large quantities of food for the livestock, enabling larger numbers to be kept; these provided greater amounts of manure which led to still larger crops. It was in fact an ascending spiral of productiveness such as Sir Richard had never seen in England, and it set him wistfully thinking 'what a huge *Improvement* I might make on my own estate . . . if God Almighty pleased to permit me quietly to enjoy it'. Unfortunately this was not to be: the Estate was sequestrated.[1] But when peace came others took up some of these better methods modified to suit the different conditions, and much improvement resulted.

Some of the agricultural books published during this period give interesting accounts of what farmers had done, and suggestion of more that they could do, to improve their farming. Many of these empirically ascertained facts proved helpful to the development of the science. The most useful is Walter Blith's *The English Improver Improved* (1652). It describes the practical farming operations and illustrates the difficulties awaiting solution. It was written in the time of the Commonwealth and, as not unusual in those days, it opens with an unctuous dedication to Cromwell and the Council of State: 'As a Man, or Christian; out of pure love to mankind, I chuse rather to cast myself at Your Lordships Feet, and come under Your greatest censure for this high Presumption, than to omit so necessary a Duty and Discovery, as the substance of this discourse Imports'—with more in the same strain, till he gets down to business. The methods of improvement recommended are (1) Irrigation, already described by Rowland Vaughan in his *Most approved and long experienced Water Workes* (1610), (2) drainage of bogs, fens etc. (3) enclosure, (4) tillage, much more thorough than usual. (5) manuring. This last sets out some constantly recurring problems, the most serious arising from the chronic shortage of farmyard manure. The cropping was mainly for the production of grain for human food; the animals had little beyond grazing of the commons and stubbles and such hay, straw and suitable wastes as were available. There was nothing like enough food to last all the animals all the winter and many had to be slaughtered before it set in.

> At hallontide, slawten time enterith in
> and then doth the husband mans feastinge begin.
> from thence unto shroftyde, kill now and than some:
> their offall for howsold, the better will come,

---

[1] Sir Richard in 1645 wrote an account of what he had seen under the title *A Discours of Husbandrie used in Brabant and Flanders* and left the manuscript as a legacy to his sons. They did not publish it, but it got into the hands of Samuel Hartlib who published it under his own name in 1650, though in the second edition (1652) he acknowledges that it was written by Sir Richard.

wrote Tusser in 1573, and the long survival of autumn fairs, feasts and wakes especially in the north of England testifies to the joyfulness of the time. The result was a very meagre production of dung during the winter months in the sheds where it could remain stored, and a scattered distribution of dung over commons and wastes during the summer, making collection difficult.

Blith gives a list of manures, and he describes a field trial comparing over a number of years the effects of marl, 'muck' (i.e. farmyard manure), manuring by folding and mud from an old clay pool; there was also an untreated plot.[1] Neither manures nor crops were weighed; the comparison was purely visual. He was working on the alternate cropped and wild grass system.[2] Marl had striking effects: 'this was Ryeland most naturally, but (after marling) it turned to Wheat, Barley and Pease, and as it is thus excellent for Corn, so it is also very fruitful and enriching to Grass-land'.[3] Other manures included sand carried by land floods, but best of all from the coast, especially of Devon and Cornwall, these being enriched by 'that fat or filth the Sea doth gather in by all Inland-floods and Streames that bring it from the Lands.' The modern explanation is that these sands contain quantities of minute shells composed mainly of calcium carbonate. Another manure was mud or 'sludg' from deep rivers 'full of Eyes and Wrinckles, and little shels: this was so rich that in some parts many men get gallant livings onely by taking it up out of the Rivers and selling it again by the Load'. One sort sold at 1s 2d and another at 2s per load at the river side: it was called *Snayl Cod*. Men would go 20 miles for it. The Thames from Oxford to Reading and beyond to 'Brainford' (i.e. Brentford) was a rich source: one load was as

---

[1] This is the earliest field trial of which I have been able to find any record.

[2] There were two systems of land use. In the older and more primitive an area of the wild grassland was ploughed up and cropped for a period of years; the manuring was, however, inadequate to keep it indefinitely in cultivation, and when the yields fell off too much the ground was left to cover itself again with wild grass, clovers, and weeds through which it would regain fertility. This was called 'Wild field grass husbandry' or 'convertible husbandry'. In the other system part of the area was permanently arable and the rest was permanently wild grass. This was the Open Field system: it was much more widely practised than the convertible system, especially in the drier eastern and midland regions.

[3] Rye will grow on the poorest land; wheat, etc. requires something much better. He instances among the virtues of Marl that it 'saddens land exceedingly' i.e. makes loose soil firmer or more compact. This was the original meaning of the word.

good as three of the best horse or cow dung. Chalk also was good, 'Chalk Earth and Manure, mixed together is a very excellent Unfallible Remedy against Barrenness, and raiseth Corn in abundance, and inricheth it also for Grazing when you lay it down (to grass)'.[1] Pigeons' dung is the richest of all, poultry dung is very good. Of the large animals sheep's dung is best, horses' dung good especially if much corn is fed, then cows' dung; whichever is used should be spread and ploughed in as quickly as possible. Hogs' dung is esteemed the poorest but wrongly so. Rags of all sorts are good, one load being equal to about half a dozen of the best cow dung. Marrow bones, fish bones, wool, horn shavings, malt dust, soot, ashes, especially wood ashes, all were good. Like others he includes oil but is doubtful if it will repay its cost.

Apart from oil the list still held good in the nineteenth century, and excepting rags (which were replaced by shoddy) it continued good up to our own time.

Grain was often lost through shrivelling or 'blasting' in the ear before it was ripe for harvest: Blith calls it 'one of the Kingdom's Curses', the cause is 'sinne' and the remedy must be sought in religious exercises. But there are 'naturall Helps', especially steeping the seed before sowing in 'thick fat water', lime water, urine or brine, also mixing lime or ashes with the moistened seed.

He then proceeds to deal with new crops, firstly with 'Trefoyle or Great Clover grass', the first seed of which came from Flanders, but seed grown here was better. Two cuts could be taken in the year and the aftermath grazed. St Foyne (Sainfoin) was also useful; the seed came from France: it would grow on the most barren soil, and it 'much fattens the land for corn'.[2] Another and even better crop in some people's estimation

---

[1] The mixing of earth and manure was a very ancient device. Walter of Henley (early thirteenth century) recommended it. 'Put your manure which has been mixed with earth on sandy ground if you have it. Why? I will tell you. The weather in summer is hot, and the sand hot, and the manure hot; and when these heats are united after St. John's Day (June 24th) the barley that grows in the sand is withered . . . In the evening the earth mixed with the manure cools the sand and keeps the dew and thereby is the corn much spared. If the manure was quite by itself it would last two or three years, according as the ground is cold or hot; manure mixed with earth will last twice as long, but it will not be so sharp'.

[2] An interesting account of the history of sainfoin is given by J.R. Thompson in *Jour. Min. Agric.* 45. 331–7, 1938.

is La-lucern (Lucerne) also from France; it was excellent fodder and did well on dry and barren lands.

The book ends with accounts of other crops which Blith thought might be useful: Welde (Dyer's Weed), Woad, Madder for Dyers, liquorice (said to be better than the Spanish sort) hops which were still spreading in spite of a petition to Parliament against them by the City of London on the score that they would spoil the taste of the beer. He ended by recommending turnips as a farm crop for the feeding of sheep and cattle, as Weston had already done—and for filling out the loaves of bread when the grain harvest was poor.

As might be expected there were books by inventors of new systems or appliances promising great wealth at small expenditure. One of the most pathetic was by an ingenious but luckless inventor, Gabriel Plattes (about 1600–1655), pompously styled 'A Discovery of infinite Treasure, hidden since the World's beginning, Whereunto all Men of what degree so ever, are friendly invited to be sharers with the Discoverer, G.P. 1639.' The 'Treasure' consisted in adventurous exploration to find new natural resources ('fat vaines of marle, chalke, limestone and other earth') at present undiscovered; when found to use them in conjunction with new methods of farming which he had devised—including sowing wheat etc. in rows, for which he had invented a drill. He appealed to all 'inventive brains to spend their studie and labour' with him for further developing his methods and he promised a hundredfold increase in crop over the seed sown in place of the usual six- or eight-fold. But it was in vain, and an undated letter published by Hartlib[1] tells the end of the story. After describing Plattes as 'a most faithfull seeker of his most ingratefull Countries good' he goes on:

'I never think of the great judgment, pure zeale, and faithfull intention of that man, and withall of his strange sufferings, and manner of death but I am struck with amazement that such a man should be suffered to fall down dead in the streets for want of food, whose studies tended to no less than the providing and preserving food for whole Nations, and that too as with much Skill and Industry, so without Pride or Arrogancie towards God or man.'

[1] His *Legacie* etc., 3rd Edn. 1655, p. 83.

B*

The most prolific and versatile agricultural writer of the time was Gervase Markham (1568–1637) who wrote so many books—or put his name to them—dealing with farm, orchard and garden management, animal diseases, etc., that he is said to have been required by his various publishers in 1617 to sign an undertaking to write no more books on diseases of any farm animal. He was an authority on horses and is said to have been the first to import an arab. The books, however, lack scientific interest.

Of all the agricultural writers of the period the most interesting from the scientific point of view was Jethro Tull, (1674–1744). He was born in 1674 at Basildon, Berkshire, the son of a local landowner. He had been intended for the Bar, and studied at St John's College, Oxford, and Gray's Inn; he was called to the Bar in 1699. But his health was poor, and in 1701 he returned to the country with his newly wedded wife and started farming at Howberry Farm, Crowmarsh, near Wallingford. He quickly realized the great losses of crop due to weeds and in his first year he invented a horse hoe to destroy them rapidly. Ten years later a serious breakdown in health compelled him to go abroad for three years. In the south of France he was so impressed by the beautifully cultivated vineyards that he started thinking out a comparable system for use at home. He returned to England in 1714, improved in health but impoverished in fortune, and settled down on Prosperous Farm, near Hungerford, Berkshire, where he spent the rest of his life devoting much time to inventing and experimenting and trying to give scientific reasons for his results. Ernle calls him the greatest individual improver that British Agriculture had ever known.

It was a time of considerable scientific activity. Robert Boyle, Stephen Hales, John Woodward and others were or had recently been active, and while at Oxford, Tull, young and active minded, might easily have heard about them and their work. He clearly regarded plant nutrition as the most important agricultural problem. 'The chief Art of a Husbandman is to feed Plants to the best advantage but how shall he do that unless he knows what is their Food? By Food is meant that Matter, which being added and united to the first Stamina of Plants, or Plantulae which were made in little at the Creation, and gives them, or rather is their increase'. He knew the various scientific hypotheses about the food of plants but rejected them. 'If Water or Air was the Food of Plants', he wrote, 'I cannot see what necessity there should be for Dung or Tillage'. The food of plants, he maintained, was earth, by which he meant soil, not the 'certain peculiar matter' of Woodward. The swelling of the roots as they grew forced the fine soil particles into their 'lacteal mouths'. All plants lived on these particles, i.e. on the same kind of food: it was incorrect to assume, as Woodward and others had done, that different kinds of plants feed as differently as horses and dogs, each taking its appropriate food and no other.[1]

The smaller the soil particles the easier it would be for plant roots to absorb them.[2] The necessary fine division was best attained by repeated hoeing. Dung by fermenting in the soil helps to break up the particles and nitre does the same; it was not a plant food as some of the older chemists had thought: 'it is useful to divide and prepare the Food and may be said to nourish vegetables in much the same manner as my knife nourishes me, by cutting and dividing my meat'. He did not, however, favour the use of dung; it spoiled the flavour of vegetables and encouraged worms that destroyed them. Hoeing was free from this disadvantage, and his horse hoe and horse-drawn seed drill enabled him to grow his crops in lines sufficiently spaced to allow of any desired amount of hoeing. The method was particularly successful with turnips and was an important factor in encouraging their spread, especially in the North of England and South Scotland where they grow well—and turnips brought in the four course rotation.

Tull shared a widespread view that plants resembled animals in their mode of nutrition. The soil was 'the Pasture of the Plant'. The roots were 'but guts inverted'; they imbibed the juices of the earth which thereupon became chyle; this passed to the leaves, 'the lungs and kidneys of the plant', 'the parts ordained for excretion'; it was there purified, became sap and descended to nourish the whole plant.

[1] This hypothesis was used to explain why a sequence of different crops was better than a succession of the same crop.
[2] B. A. Keen points out that Tull probably regarded the fine dust on the soil particle as the pabulum itself, and not the whole particle (*The physical properties of the Soil*, p. 13).

Tull's life was a long struggle against ill-health. He relates that his experiments were made and his book written 'in pains of the stone and other diseases as incurable and almost as cruel'. This no doubt made him irritable and querulous. Further, he was an innovator, and such people are rarely popular in the English countryside. He was constantly quarrelling with his servants and farm labourers, and they with him. His son turned out to be an extravagant spendthrift and ended his days in the Fleet Prison. He was annoyed, too, by the venomous criticisms of his work: his critics, he said, 'Seldom make use of any other logic than that of Billingsgate'. They nevertheless much esteemed his writings, which, Cobbett tells us, were 'plundered by English writers not a few, and by Scotch in whole bandittis': he might have added also that they were pirated in Dublin.

His book *The new horse houghing husbandry, or an essay on the principles of tillage and vegetation* was not published until 1731, 17 years after the experiments commenced. It was expanded in 1733, (with 'hoeing' in place of 'houghing' in the title): other editions followed, the most interesting being that edited by William Cobbett in 1822. Tull's work was favourably presented to continental scientists by Henri Louis Duhamel de Monceau in his *Éléments de Chimie* (Paris 1754); the first time an English agricultural writer had received that attention.

TOWNSHEND AND THE FOUR COURSE ROTATION

While Tull was experimenting and writing at his remote and solitary farm a large landowner was carrying out improvements of the greatest importance in Norfolk. In 1730 Charles, 2nd Viscount Townshend, retired from political life to his estate at Raynham and during the next eight years until his death he developed the four-course rotation which completely transformed the husbandry of the eastern counties and profoundly benefited the whole of British agriculture. Following Weston's advice he introduced folded turnips and clover in place of fallow, and achieved the successes for which Weston could only hope in vain. He adopted Tull's method of drilling turnips instead of broadcasting them, so got better tilth and good control of the weeds thereby increasing the yields. He also revived the ancient practice of marling which had become almost obsolete. Spectacular improvements were effected: Ernle records that one farm rose in annual rental value from £180 to £800 in thirty years; another rose from £18 to £240. The great merit of the new system was that it not only gave higher yields than usual; as in Flanders it constituted a continuously ascending spiral of increasing productiveness and it has proved capable of assimilating further improvements. The yields are still rising—a fortunate circumstance in an age when the human population is increasing far more rapidly than ever before. Those eight years can justly be described as among the most momentous in the history of British agriculture.

SCOTLAND JOINS IN

Agricultural improvement began later in Scotland than in England and there was little enclosure or interest in agricultural technique before about 1700. The first General Enclosure Act was passed in 1695, and the Society of Improvers in the Knowledge of Agriculture in Scotland was founded in 1723 but dissolved in 1745. Another organization, The Edinburgh Society for the Improvement of Arts and Manufactures, in 1756 took the practical step of offering a gold medal for the best dissertation on 'Vegetation and the Principles of Agriculture'. This induced Francis Home (1719–1813) to publish his *Principles of Agriculture and Vegetation* in 1757. He was at the time a doctor practising in Edinburgh, but later (1768) was appointed Professor of Materia Medica at the university till he retired in 1798 at the age of 79.

He was convinced that the principles of agriculture were based on chemistry and could not be understood without a knowledge of that subject: his book has therefore the distinction of being the first on agricultural chemistry, though he does not use that term. Its purpose, he stated, was to see 'how far Chymistry could go in settling the Principles of Agriculture'. It aroused great interest and passed through four editions besides being translated into French and German. As usual at the time, he regarded plant nutrition as the most important subject for investigation, and he made pot experiments with a number of substances including saltpetre, Epsom salt, vitriolated tartar (potassium sulphate) and olive oil, all of which increased plant growth. His list of plant foods included the four generally accepted: water, earth, air, salt, to which he added oil and fire 'in a fixed state', i.e. phlogiston. Oil, he wrote, was present in everything: in rain, snow, earth, manures; salt was not so universally distributed but occurred in the air and was taken up by 'attractors' and 'absorbents' in the soil. He discussed the various harmful factors. He could suggest no measures against insect pests and diseases, except the traditional steeping of seeds in a 'pickle of sea salt' to protect the grain against smut. He mentions certain supposed antipathies between plants preventing each from thriving in the other's presence: he instances cabbages and cyclamens, hemlock and rue, reeds and fern; 'the effects' he suggests, 'seem to be produced by the effluvia which are emitted by all organized bodies'.

Home was still thinking in terms of the old chemistry—the four ancient elements, earth, air, fire and water, and two later ones, oil and salt, of which all things were supposed to be compounded, and other errors of fact and theory—and there is little in his book that directly advanced agricultural science. One must agree with C. A. Browne[1] that it 'is more the picture of a disappearing epoch than the forecast of a new era in agricultural science'.

Home rendered great service by impressing upon Scottish agriculturists the need for experiments. 'The operations of "bodies" ', he wrote, 'are to be accounted for only from their known qualities ascertained by experiment. Reasoning on any other plan can never lead to truth. I shall not, therefore, proceed a single step without facts and experiments.' There was nothing new in this: it was the declared purpose of the 'Invisible College' and Boyle and the Royal Society of the 1660's; but Home did good service by again emphasizing its importance, though his suggestion that farmers themselves should make the experiments did not survive actual trial. He ended the book by appealing to the Edinburgh Society to appoint a committee for the purpose of raising 'a spirit of experimental farming over the country': premiums, either honorary or lucrative, should be offered to those 'who shall have delivered the most ingenious and useful experiments in agriculture'. There was an idealist

[1] A Source Book of Agricultural Chemistry, *Chronica Botanica*, 1944, p. 126.

streak in him, however; the experiments should not be on 'such subjects as the farmer is naturally led by his own gain to pursue; for such he will generally follow, to the utmost of his knowledge and abilities; but on such as are not so nearly connected with gain, and make him go out of the common road'.

It was many years before this proposal was taken seriously, and when in the end experimental fields were set up the experiments were made by professionals and for most of them the object was usually the pursuit of gain.

CHAPTER II

THE WAY BECOMES CLEARER
1750 – 1800

ONE of the great weaknesses of the early chemists was their inability to deal with gases, partly because the difficulties of manipulation had not yet been overcome, but mainly because of the fixed but entirely erroneous ideas about their nature. The start was made by Joseph Black (1728–99) of Glasgow—though born at Bordeaux, where his father was in the wine trade. He decided on a medical career, and entered the University of Edinburgh where in 1755 he published an English version of part of his Latin thesis on *Magnesia alba* (magnesium carbonate). He showed that when heated it became caustic, lost weight and gave off a gas (carbon dioxide) which he called 'fixed air'; but when the residue was recombined with the gas it lost its causticity and regained its original weight. Similarly mild limestone produced caustic lime on heating and gave off 'fixed air', but when the lime and 'fixed air' were recombined the limestone was reformed. The caustic lime was somewhat soluble in water, the limestone was not; he therefore identified 'fixed air' by ascertaining whether it turned lime water milky. In this way he showed that it was produced during fermentation and also by respiration of men and animals, and as he had already found it to be fatal to animals, he was able to explain why their breathing vitiated the atmosphere. Also he showed that it extinguished flame.

This was the first time that a gas had been studied in detail: previously all gases were regarded as consisting of an identical 'air', and differing only in the amount and nature of the impurities present. The importance of the work lay in the recognition that the gaseous condition was a form of matter in which many different substances might exist and which chemists should investigate. It was in doing this that modern chemistry and agricultural science both originated.

Joseph Priestley (1733–1804) brilliantly continued this work. He discovered a number of new gases and devised methods by which they could be collected and studied. He was one of the most remarkable men in the long procession of able British scientists. Like Boyle he was an amateur, and never held a university appointment; unlike him he was of humble origin and had to earn his living. His father was a woollen cloth dresser in the little village of Fieldhead near Leeds, and evidently an unusual person. He was a Nonconformist and, recognizing the exceptional ability of his son, sent him first to the local grammar school and then put him from the age of 16 to 19 under the charge of Mr Kirby, a minister at Heckmondwyke with whom he read an amazing assortment of subjects: Syriac, Chaldee, Arabic, French, Italian, natural philosophy, logic and metaphysics. In 1752 he entered the Daventry Academy where he spent three years training for the Nonconformist ministry. Then followed six years of ministry and teaching after which in 1761 he became classical tutor at a recently established Academy at Warrington.

Here he carried out important investigations on electricity and also attended chemistry lectures at Liverpool. Then in 1767 he became minister of the Mill Hill Unitarian Chapel at Leeds, and while there found leisure to make his first investigations on gases, beginning with 'fixed air' for the sufficient reason that a neighbouring brewery could supply him abundantly with it. He showed his ingenuity by inventing soda water, which won him the Copley Medal of the Royal Society: its highest award. In 1772 he left Leeds and for the next eight years was librarian and literary companion to Lord Shelburne of Calne. It was a fortunate move, for Lord Shelburne gave him every help and encouragement to continue his experimental studies, and those eight years were the most fruitful of his life. He discovered a number of new gases, the most important of which was oxygen in 1774, found by one of the simplest and most elegant experiments on record.[1] He also showed that men

[1] Commemorated by the statue now in Chamberlain Square, Birmingham originally set up on August, 1, 1874, the centenary of the discovery of oxygen. The present statue is a bronze replica of the original one in white marble.

and animals breathed out a poisonous gas (carbon dioxide), while the green leaves of living plants during the hours of sunlight reversed the process, taking the carbon out of the carbon dioxide and returning the oxygen to the atmosphere. He thus accounted for the stable condition of the atmosphere in spite of the considerable vitiation continuously going on.

He was less fortunate with his studies of plant and animal nutrition and of putrefaction, but this was the result of his adhesion to the phlogiston theory. He supposed that phlogiston[1] was the nutritive principle in animal and vegetable substances, and that when they putrefied it became an inflammable air. From the quantity thus produced 'it may be possible to determine the nutritive powers of different vegetable and animal substances, and also other problems in philosophy; though too much must not be expected from them'. The note of caution was wise: nothing came of them.

His attachment to the phlogiston theory cost him dearly. His discovery of oxygen was really a turning point in the history of chemistry, but he failed to see it. Soon after his discovery of oxygen he and Lord Shelburne were travelling on the Continent and met Lavoisier in Paris. Priestley told him of the discovery and he at once appreciated its significance: it played a great part in the founding of modern chemistry and agricultural science. When Priestley had done so much it seems a tragedy that he should have missed this crowning achievement.

In 1780 he left Lord Shelburne to become Junior Minister of the New Meeting (Unitarian) Chapel at Birmingham where he spent ten happy years among a congenial circle of scientific and literary friends. Unfortunately it all ended pitifully. He was always intellectually rather a rebel and his political sympathies brought him up against the Church and State Party. At the time of the Birmingham riots of 1791 the mob were so incensed against him that they burned down his chapel and his house,

---

[1] The phlogiston theory was set up by G. E. Stahl (1660–1734). All combustible substances were supposed to contain a combustible principle called phlogiston which escaped as flame when they burned, the violence of the burning depending on the amount present. Mercury like other metallic elements was a compound of a calx and the phlogiston. When heated in air it burned and lost its phlogiston becoming once more elementary calx. It was a false theory but it served some useful purpose during its lifetime. It fell to pieces when it was realized that the calx weighed more than the metal and therefore was the result of a gain of something, not a loss.

destroying all his apparatus and books, and, what he most deplored, his unpublished manuscripts. In a dignified letter of protest addressed to the citizens of Birmingham he writes regretfully of the valuable apparatus

'on which I annually spent large sums, with no pecuniary view whatever, but only in the advancement of science, for the benefit of my country and mankind. . . . But what I feel far more, you have destroyed *manuscripts* which have been the result of the laborious study of many years, and which I shall never be able to recompose; and this has been done to one who never did, or imagined, you any harm.'

He forthwith left Birmingham for London but stayed there only three years. Persistent ill-will against him even in scientific circles caused him in 1794 to emigrate to America where his sons helped him to build a house and laboratory at Northumberland in Pennsylvania. But his life's work was done: all he achieved was an elaborate defence of the outworn phlogiston theory which had already greatly hindered the progress of chemistry and had prevented him from realizing the far reaching implications of his work on oxygen and the growing plant. With touching fidelity (or out of sheer obstinacy) he refused to abandon a theory that he had supported all his working life. Like many other intellectual rebels, there were some loyalties he would not abandon. As A. D. Hall once wrote, 'We begin as iconoclasts, we end up as old fogeys.'

Priestley is interesting not only because of his scientific discoveries but still more because of the way in which he made them. His methods were simple and entirely empirical: one might almost call them haphazard: he would try an experiment, apparently out of sheer curiosity, merely on the chance that something might happen. It usually did, for he had the wonderful gift of achieving results by intuition, a gift not uncommon among other successful men of science. 'I do not think it at all degrading to the business of experimental philosophy' he wrote, 'to compare it, as I often do, to the diversion of hunting, where it sometimes happens that those who have beat the ground the most, and are consequently the best acquainted with it, weary themselves, without starting any game, when it may fall in the way of a mere passenger'. And as a concrete example he wrote in his *History of Electricity* (1767),

'It requires no great stock of particular preparatory knowledge: so that any person that is tolerably well versed in experimental philosophy, may presently be upon a level with the most experienced electricians . . . several raw adventurers have made themselves as considerable as some who have been, in other respects, the greatest philosphers. I need not tell my reader of how great weight this consideration is to induce him to provide himself with an electrical apparatus'.

The study of the atmosphere and its relations to plants and animals was continued in a series of meticulous experiments by Henry Cavendish (1731–1810), a wealthy amateur and almost a recluse, but their interest is much diminished through his adherence to the phlogiston theory.

THE BIRTH OF MODERN CHEMISTRY

For the next few years the lead passed to the Continent. The French chemist, Antoine Laurent Lavoisier (1743–94), finally cleared away the phlogiston stumbling block and gave the modern interpretation and arrangement of many facts already established. The first edition of his *Traité Elémentaire de Chemie présenté dans un ordre nouveau et d'après les découvertes modernes*, was published in two volumes in Paris in 1789. It captured the imagination of the scientific world and before long had been translated into English, German, Dutch and Italian. It made a clean sweep of transmutation, and gave Chemistry a quantitative basis.

'We may lay it down as an incontestable axiom, that, in all the operations of art and nature, nothing is created; an equal quantity of matter exists both before and after the experiment . . . nothing takes places beyond changes and modifications in the combinations of these elements.'

This of course is the nineteenth century law of conservation of matter. So with other of the false ideas that had cluttered up the subject: by careful quantitative experiments he was able to clear them away beyond recall. He carried inorganic chemistry as far as it could go until John Dalton's atomic theory was announced in 1807. Heat and light, however, were both included in his list of elements. He began the study of organic chemistry, made numerous agricultural investigations and in 1776 set up the first model farm.

Then came one of the greatest tragedies in the history of science. It was the time of the French Revolution, and in 1794 at the age of fifty one, while at the height of his powers, he was sent to the guillotine. '*La République n'a pas besoin de savants*', declared Coffinhal in pronouncing sentence: surely one of the most fatuous political *dicta* ever uttered.

Eight years later in Germany Albrach Daniel Thaer converted his estate into a forerunner of the Farm Institute and subsequently published a four volume treatise *The Principles of Rational Husbandry*,[1] one of the last books to be based on the old chemistry and interesting for its presentation of a view that still finds adherents. Humus, he wrote, is the cause of soil fertility and owes its special quality to the fact that it has been part of living plants. 'As humus is a product of life it is also a condition of life'. This life-giving property of materials that had formed part of living things extended also to the ash constituents, potash, lime, etc. which, he maintained, had better fertilizing value than the same substances obtained from purely mineral sources.

While the scientists had been striving to discover how plants feed and grow, the more enterprising farmers and landowners were continuing the efforts to improve their husbandry to which reference has already been made. These activities were stimulated towards the end of the eighteenth century by the personal interest of the King (George III) in farming, which naturally made it a fashionable pursuit. 'The farming tribe', wrote Arthur Young at this time, 'is now made up of all ranks from a Duke to an apprentice'. The period 1780 to 1810 was one of the most lively in the annals of British agriculture. The great improvers, Thomas Coke of Norfolk, and Francis, Duke of Bedford, had effected remarkable changes as described later, and their open days for farmers were well patronized. Un-

[1] *Grundsätze der rationellen Landwirtschaft* (1809–12).

fortunately like some of the other great improvers, notably Robert Bakewell (livestock) and Viscount Townshend, neither of them left detailed records of what they had done.[1] But the results were there for all to see.

Arthur Young (1741–1820), the best agricultural reporter we ever had,[2]—'that wise and honest traveller' John Morley called him—was busily collecting information about farming in the different English counties and a large part of France. When Pitt set up the Board of Agriculture in 1793 Young was appointed Secretary and, together with the President, Sir John Sinclair, he organized the remarkable series of county agricultural surveys which has never been equalled—though the Royal Agricultural Society is now engaged on the task. In 1784 he had started a monthly journal, *The Annals of Agriculture*, which he continued till 1809 when failing eyesight compelled him to stop work. The King contributed a few articles to it under the name of his shepherd, Ralph Robinson.

Another great character of those days was William Cobbett, a shrewd observer with a remarkable gift of vituperation, who during the years 1821–1832 travelled over much of England on horseback and recorded his impressions in his *Rural Rides*, denouncing all despoilers of agricultural land in fiercely uncompromising terms 'Which', as the polite editor of the *1885* edition points out, 'the refinement of the present day will condemn as bordering on breaches of decorum, if not as coarse and offensive'. But there was great distress in the countryside and Cobbett's sympathies were always with the labourer.[3] He hated London and towns with claims to gentility like Cheltenham, and at Oxford he fairly exploded when the exorbitant innkeeper presented his bill for two of them—4s for tea and 5s for beds.

---

[1] Coke left a notebook inscribed 'Book of Observations'' containing only a few records of weights of mangold roots and leaves.

[2] He was, however, afterwards very dissatisfied with his first efforts, *Farmers' letter to the people of England* (1767): 'A sin of the blackest dye, . . . nothing but ignorance, folly, presumption and rascality' was his mature judgment of it. He was always honest.

[3] So long as the labourer kept to the bread, cheese and beer of his fathers and avoided modern fads like tea and potatoes, two of Cobbett's particular abominations.

THE AGRICULTURAL SOCIETIES

Among the useful results of the intellectual ferment of the time was the formation, especially in the 1790's, of a number of agricultural societies, some purely local, others with a wider ambit—county or district. Much of their time was taken up with local affairs, but there were also discussions of new methods and ideas which helped to break down the resistance to innovation always to be found in the countryside.

Some of their activities had important results. The Odiham Society, (Hampshire), one of the oldest, can fairly claim to have started veterinary science and education in this country. One of its members, Thomas Burgess, the son of a local grocer, who became an Oxford don and a distinguished ecclesiastic, proposed on humanitarian grounds that action should be taken to replace the current very crude farriery used in the treatment of sick farm animals by better and more humane treatment based on fuller knowledge of their anatomy and diseases. Shortly afterwards Arthur Young described his visits in 1787 to the veterinary school recently established in Paris, and in 1788 the Odiham Society decided to send two students there for a course. The idea accorded with the British love of animals and it was taken up in London. Penn drew up a plan for a veterinary college based on that of the French Veterinarian St Bel, and carried it through so well that the London Veterinary College was opened in 1792 and St Bel was induced to join it as Professor.[1]

Among other county organizations must be mentioned Canterbury Agricultural Society founded in 1793, which later became the Canterbury Farmers Club. It claims to be the oldest of these in the country and it has a long history of usefulness in a region of high class farming. For many years it has been a powerful link between the scientific workers of Wye College and the farming community of East Kent.[2]

Beside these local societies there were others of much wider range. The Society for the Encouragement of Arts, Manufac-

[1] L. P. Pugh. From *Farriery to Veterinary Medicine*. Cambridge, Heffer, (for the Royal College of Veterinary Surgeons) 1962.
[2] Unfortunately its records were all destroyed in the German 'blitz' of June 1st, 1942.

tures and Commerce was founded in London in 1754 and in due course became the Royal Society of Arts. In its early years it was largely concerned with agriculture, but its other subjects gradually demanded more and more attention. It has, however, always remained helpful to agricultural science and practice by stimulating investigations and giving appropriate publicity to the results.

The Bath and West and Southern Counties Society (always called the Bath and West for short) owes its inception to the good example set by the Norfolk Agricultural Society in arousing interest in better farming and ensuring that it led to actual improvement. This was translated into action by a remarkable Norfolk man, Edmund Rack,[1] who, succeeding early in business, retired to Bath in 1775 at the age of 40. In travelling around he was much struck by the low standard of farming compared with that in Norfolk, and he wanted to raise it.

He proved to be emphatically the man for the job. He was born in 1735 at Attleborough in Norfolk, the son of an industrious weaver in humble circumstances, both parents were members of the Society of Friends and his mother, a remarkable woman, was an acceptable preacher among them. He had had to leave school early, but he continued his education while apprenticed to a general shopkeeper at Wymondham not far away. At the end of his time he became shopman to a lady at Bardfield in Essex whom after a time he married. She was well off, and they shortly retired.

He had early developed a flair for writing, and by the time of his retirement he had published a number of articles on agriculture and a variety of other subjects: his latest effort had been a volume of poems. Bath was then a favoured centre of literary coteries into two of which, headed by blue stocking hostesses of high social standing, Rack was admitted and he soon became a person of consequence.

Knowing the important part the Norfolk Agricultural Society had played in raising the agricultural standards in that county he conceived the idea of establishing a similar Society at Bath in the hope of attaining similarly good results:

[1] A full account of this interesting person is given by Thos. F. Plowman in *Journ. Bath & West Soc.*, Vol. 8. Series 5. 1914. I am much indebted to the Society's Secretarial staff for help with this section.

it was to be on a larger scale, however. He propounded his idea to a group of friends and in a series of letters to the local press pointing out that landowner farmers and the whole nation would gain by a fuller development of its agricultural resources. The Society was inaugurated at a meeting held on September 8th 1777. A persuasive announcement had been put out addressed 'to the Nobility and Gentry in the Counties of Somerset, Gloucester, Wilts and Dorset in general and the Cities of Bath and Bristol in particular' and it ended with the hope that 'as this Institution is intended for the benefit of all the above named Counties, it is humbly requested that the public-spirited Gentlemen residing therein will generally honour it with their countenance and protection'.

Bath may have been rather sated with such schemes: at any rate only 22 people attended the meeting. They were, however, enthusiastic enough to start a subscription list and elect a committee to draw up a plan of operations and submit it to a meeting at the end of October. This was even more poorly attended: only 18 people came and the prospect for the new Society must have looked rather dim. But Rack was not to be put off: like Siegfried of old:

'Never did he lose heart, nor of aught was he afraid.'

His optimism was justified: another meeting called in November attracted 39 people and things began to move.

The first business was to award premiums for a rather wide range of commendable achievements including good crop yields (including 'natural and artificial grasses'), good animals, long service, improved implements, planting trees, burning and collecting the greatest quantity of ashes from bracken and weeds—these ashes would neutralize soil acidity and were also the only potassic manure—and diverse miscellaneous services: destroying noxious vapours in coal mines and producing sufficient light to work there, and preventing boots and shoes from imbibing moisture in wet weather.

A few months later (June 1778) the Society's Committee of Correspondence and Enquiry, knowing that farmers always prefer example to precept in all things, decided that a general knowledge of the best modes of practice in all the different parts of the Kingdom was essential to the success of their land improvement schemes. Accordingly they drew up a list of questions on which they wanted information. Then follows a rather naive request.

'As this Society knows not the Persons to whom the said Queries might with the greatest Propriety be sent, a circular Letter (inclosing the said Queries) should be respectfully addressed to the High Sheriff of each County, requesting the favour of him to send them to some Person or Persons, whom he deems qualified to answer them from practical Experience, and transmit such answers as he may receive, to the Secretary of the Bath Society.'

The Royal Society more than a century earlier had likewise sought similar information:[1] the Bath Society was apparently more successful in collecting it; they published it in their *Letters and Papers*.

In February 1779 the Society acquired ten acres of land at Weston for conducting experiments under Mr Rack's management; this was the first experimental field to be established in Great Britain. Nothing of importance seems to have resulted, and before long it was given up as being 'on too contracted a scale and under a system of management too defective to be usefully continued'. Other societies had also tried to run experimental farms and failed.

Dr Alex Hunter of York had already in 1777 in a letter to the Committee stressed the desirability of publishing information it could obtain, and in 1780 there appeared the first of a series of *Letters and Papers* of the Society, the earliest publication of its kind in this country, which continued till 1829. Then came an interval of twentyfour years after which in 1853 the first volume of the *Transactions* appeared and successive issues have followed annually ever since.

Meanwhile, and almost imperceptibly at first, a change was beginning in the kind of experimental enquiry in agriculture. Hitherto the purpose in the main had been to get the facts clear; now the desire was to go a stage further and get more information about them. Chemistry offered the best means for

[1] See p. 22.

doing this, and it would also furnish the key to many of the farmers' problems. In 1784 some of the members of the Society raised the question of appointing a Professor of Chemistry. In the following year Dr Fothergill of the London Society of Arts and a well known scientist in his day wrote to the Committee of the Bath Society 'a very ingenious letter on the application of Chemistry to the use of agriculture'. The letter met with a not uncommon fate: it was referred to the Committee on Select Papers and nothing more was done.

It would be interesting to know why the idea of injecting Chemistry into Agricultural Science in England should have occurred just then. Many years earlier Francis Home (1757) had published his *Principles of Agriculture and Vegetation*[1] in Edinburgh, one purpose of which was 'to try how far chymistry will go in settling the principles of agriculture'; editions had been published in London in 1762 and 1776 and some recollection of this may have survived. Also it was the period when Lavoisier in Paris was revolutionizing chemistry and applying it to the solution of agricultural problems, and it may well have happened that information about his work may have set English scientists thinking on the same lines.

However the idea arose, nothing apparently was done by the Bath Society till 1805 when the Society took vigorous action. A 'Committee of Chemical Research' was set up and funds were collected for establishing and operating a laboratory to be made out of a vault in Hetling House. £100 was to be spent on apparatus by Dr Archer, who gave his services gratuitously, and £50 yearly was paid to Dr Boyd as Assistant: he asked also for some land for agricultural experiments but this at the time could not be granted. Farmers were invited to send in samples of soil, limestone, etc. for analysis, the results of which were published by the Society.[2]

Dr Archer's first lecture was given in March 1806; he died before completing the course; this was done by Dr Boyd. In 1808 a course was given by Dr Wilkinson. Boyd continued the analytical work on soils: some of his results are given below.

---

[1] See p. 45.
[2] They are in *Letters and Papers on Agriculture, Planting etc. selected from the Correspondence of the Bath and West of England Society*. Vol. II. 1807, 275–282. They are the earliest I have seen.

The analytical procedure used was Davy's who had described it early in his lectures[1] and he attached so much importance to it that he published it in a pamphlet printed and circulated in 1805. Davy was then at the height of his fame; the West Country claimed him as one of their own people and the Bath and West Society can hardly have failed to receive a copy.

Analytical data for two soils from the same farm; (a) the best (b) the worst on the farm. Quantities present in 400 grains.

		Best	Worst
Water dried off at 300°		26	24
		—	—
Sieved	Fibre	1	2
	Coarse or stony	137	241
	Fine	262	157
		—	—
In fine part	Siliceous sand	228	232
	Finely divided matter	40	32
	Alumina	42	56
	Carbonate of lime	28	18
	Sulphate of iron and animal matter *	4	2
	Fibre (vegetable)	1	2
	Animal matter	22	26
	Water	26	24
	Loss	9	8
		—	—
		400	400

* Dissolved in the lixivial water. On ignition there was a smell like burning feathers.

Nothing is said about the recommendations, if any, for improving the poorer soil, nor was the poverty explained: indeed it is difficult to see what advice could have been given on the basis of the information supplied. In some cases the specific gravity of the soil was determined by weighing a cubic foot of it. Neither potash nor phosphate is mentioned in either of the above analyses although some small quantities of potassium sulphate are recorded in several soils. Some soils were examined for 'phosphate of lime and magnesia' but no traces of either could be detected. Davy was not a good analyst and in any case good methods had not yet been devized.

The Chemical Research Committee felt that farmers would appreciate soil analyses better if they did some simple ones

[1] See pp. 67 & 74 Footnote 1 & Appendix p. 307.

themselves and accordingly Dr Boyd describes the preparation of a nitric acid extract of soil and the determination therein of alumina, magnesia, lime. Carbonic acid was determined by loss of weight when the soil was treated with acid and silica. The residue after acid extraction was called silex.

Another paper deals with blight in wheat; it differs markedly from the earlier accounts. By now Sir Joseph Banks had shown that the cause was a fungus—another plant—and the author sets out to prove that only the weak plants are attacked. He indicates measures by which he claims that weakness will be avoided and the crop will escape attack.

The question of running an experimental farm was raised again in 1807 and the volume of *Letters etc.* for that year contains an account of the discussion and report of a committee approved to look into it. The need was admittedly increasing, more and greater rural improvement having become necessary. The difficulty was financial; Committee management in those days being apparently no more successful than in these. The proposal was to invite some able young man to run the farm at his own cost but under the aegis of the Society; this would assure him readier and more remunerative sales of the superior livestock and other commodities that presumably he would produce. Also he could take rich gentlemen's sons as farm pupils—but with the warning that some of these were dissolute young men and special care would in certain circumstances be needed. Among the problems needing investigation were economy of labour, modes of culture, courses of cropping, comparative advantages of various implements and of the drill and broadcast husbandry—all except the last are still on the appropriate programmes of the research institutes.[1] But again no action was taken.

Another great society, the Highland and Agricultural Society, was founded in 1784, seven years after the Bath and West. Its original purpose was the development of the Highlands with, however, due attention to the preservation of the language, poetry and music. By 1789 the Society was offering gold medals valued at ten guineas for essays on the economy and management

[1] My thanks are due to Major the Lord Darling, Secretary to Bath and West Society, for enabling me to obtain the above information about the activities of the Society during this period.

of black cattle farms under a breeding stock; the kinds of grass and green crops suited to the soil and climate of the Highlands; the proportion and degrees in which 'inclosures' were proper and expedient under a breeding stock. The first volume of its *Journal* was issued in 1799. The second volume (1803) announced a change. The membership had so much increased in numbers and distribution that the Society decided no longer to restrict its activities to the Highlands but to extend them to the whole of Scotland: the name was amended accordingly and the range of subjects dealt with was widened. The further history will be given in a later chapter.

So far only two British botanists, Stephen Hales and Nehemiah Grew, had made any notable contribution to agricultural science. Another, Richard Bradley, Professor of Botany at Cambridge from 1724 to 1732, achieved much popularity and his name not infrequently crops up in the agricultural literature of the period. Some of his botanical work has been defended by no less an authority than Dr Hamshaw Thomas, also of Cambridge, but no one has tried to defend him personally. He must surely be the most extraordinary professor Cambridge ever had. Elected on a fictitious recommendation and an empty promise to found a botanic garden at his own expense, he soon caused a great scandal through his complete ignorance of Greek and Latin and his failure to deliver the prescribed courses of lectures. The authorities seem to have been extremely tolerant, but after seven years 'he was grown so scandalous that it was in agitation to turn him out of his professorship'. But this was unnecessary, a year later (1732) he was dead.

Before the century closed, however, another botanist, Erasmus Darwin, (1731–1802), was attempting to apply the chemical and botanical knowledge of his day to the problems of plant physiology with special reference to effecting improvements in agriculture and horticulture. He was not only a scientist but also a poet: his first book *The Botanic Garden* (1792) was in verse of no special distinction. Later (1799) he wrote *Phytologia or The Philosophy of Agriculture and Gardening*. He held certain unusual views: among others that plants had sensation and volition, like animals. His contributions to agricultural science related mainly to plant nutrition. The chief food of plants, in his view, was carbonic acid which was normally taken up by the roots from the soil solution. They could also take up sugar and mucilage and these might be useful manures. Water was an important nutrient: it was decomposed in the plant, the oxygen being liberated from the leaves and the hydrogen taking part in reactions within the plant. Nitrogen appeared to be essential: it probably combined with water in the soil to form 'nitrous acid' and ammonia both of which are taken up by the plant roots. Phosphorus was a universal constituent of plants and probably essential for them. It could be supplied by bone ash, decaying animal and vegetable matter, liquid manure, and some types of 'calcareous earth'. He suggested that search should be made in this country for phosphate of lime for use as manure. This is the earliest statement by a British scientist I have seen that nitrogen and phosphate are essential for the growth of plants: it was a remarkable piece of intuition. Before long deposits of calcium phosphate were found in Suffolk in the form of coprolites and were used for the manufacture of superphosphate in its early days. He discussed soil analysis, but quite rightly did not consider it sufficiently advanced to be of help in dealing with soil fertility problems. He suggested, however, that farmers should be able to determine by chemical tests the main properties of the different primary earths: calcareous, argillaceous, silicious etc.

Looking back over the 250 years of scientific labour recorded in these two chapters there may seem little return for all the effort put into it. This was not for want of trying. Some of the ablest men of their time sought scientific explanations of the phenomena of plant growth, which they recognized as the basic problem in agriculture. They approached the problem first on one hypothesis then on another, but without success. Each like Helen Waddell's Wandering Scholar:

I seek all roads, but find my road in none.

But there had been progress. Methods and appliances gradually improved, making possible the identification and study of gases, while quantitative measurements became more practicable and trustworthy, allowing chemical reactions to be more closely studied. Most important had been the clearing away of long established false ideas, especially the idea of transmutation of one element into another, e.g. water into the entire plant substance including the ash. Another had been the belief that all gases—'airs'—were identical, differing only in the various contaminants. This idea extended also to salts. One universal salt was supposed to appear under many guises as the result of different accompanying agents. There still remained many difficulties in regard to the soil, especially in assessing its fertility. Little advance had been made on the ancient method of rubbing a moist clod between fingers and thumb: if the soil stuck it was good, but not otherwise, or Virgil's advice to dig a hole in the ground and then put the soil back again and stamp it down: it was poor if it did not fill the hole, but good if it more than filled it.

Considering the difficulties, however, it is surprizing that so much had been accomplished. Chemistry in the modern sense, on which so much of agricultural science is based, did not exist. Scientific research was not yet a paid profession, but a voluntary activity by men of means like Boyle or spare time occupations of professional men like Hales. There was no co-ordination or continuity in the work: each man had his own research programme and it ended when he ceased to carry it on. The continuity which a University Chair of Agriculture might have facilitated was not yet available, the Edinburgh Chair was not founded till 1790 and the Sibthorpian Chair at Oxford six years later: neither sufficed for a full-time scientist, indeed the Oxford appointment had to be held over for a number of years before it could be filled.[1]

Nevertheless there had been progress; jerky and spasmodic but real. The early years of the nineteenth century saw chemistry established on a sound basis and agricultural chemistry well on the way to more fruitful development than ever before. For pure chemistry the final touches had been the announcement of the atomic theory by John Dalton of Manchester in 1807; and for agricultural chemistry it was the work of a gifted Swiss chemist, Theodore de Saussure of Geneva (1767—1845), who in a beautiful series of quantitative experiments, using better appliances and more accurate eudiometric methods than were available to his predecessors, had been able to work out more clearly than they the parts played in the building up of plant

[1] See p. 86. Footnote 1.

material by oxygen, carbon-dioxide and water in light and in darkness respectively. He also studied the up-take of salts from the soil and showed that so long as the roots were alive the process was selective, some salts being taken more readily than others. He was the first to tabulate with some degree of accuracy the ash constituents of plants and he endeavoured to discover the principles governing the differences between them. He still retained the belief however, that plants derived an important part of their nourishment, including almost all of their nitrogen, from the soluble organic matter of the soil. But most of the gross errors of the past had been cleared away and the road was open for the progress that the new century was to see.

CHAPTER III

THE EARLY NINETEENTH CENTURY, SCIENCE FOR USE IN AGRICULTURE

1800 – 1843

THE new century opened badly for the ordinary citizen. France declared war on England in February 1801, and it dragged on for fourteen years. T. H. Baker's *Records* show that a number of the early seasons were difficult. The average price of wheat which for many years had ranged between 40s and 50s per quarter jumped in 1799 to 69s and in the two succeeding years to 113s 10d and 119s 6d respectively: these were long remembered as 'Famine Years'. For forty years thereafter the fluctuation was commonly from about 60s to 80s a quarter.

These high prices emphasized the need for greater output than current methods could produce. Empirical attempts at raising productivity had already yielded good results and were still doing so. Coke of Norfolk continued his improvements and his annual demonstrations thereof—the 'Holkham sheep shearings'—with lavish hospitality to the multitude of farmers who came to see them. He lived till 1842, but he wrote nothing about what he was doing or hoped to do, and he left few records: Edward Rigby, in 1817 and later years, gave a short description in *Holkham, its agriculture;* there is also much later a short account in the *Journal* of the Royal Agricultural Society by Walter Pye.[1] But the results were there for all to see. Many of the visitors must have remembered the time in 1776 when as

[1] (Vol. 6. Series 3, pp. 1–15, 1895). Coke's life was written by his great-granddaughter, Mrs A. M. W. Stirling: *Coke of Norfolk and his Friends* (2 vols. 1910). Coke himself left only a small 'Book of Observations' containing little but the weights of some mangold roots and leaves.

a youth of 21 Coke had come down from London to take possession of his large but poverty-stricken inheritance where 'two rabbits were fighting for every blade of grass'. Two of his tenants refused to renew their leases at existing rents whereupon he, totally ignorant of agriculture but young and obstinate, decided that he would farm the land himself and forthwith began the experiments which ended by raising his annual rent roll from £2,200 in 1776 to £20,000 in 1816.

Naturally, other landowners sought to follow his example. The Dukes of Bedford had always been progressive agriculturists, and the Duke of that day (John, the 6th Duke) carried on the tradition: he organized similar 'sheep shearings' at Woburn, the memory of which has been perpetuated in an interesting print by George Garrard in 1811:[1] one of a number of remarkable agricultural prints published in the first half of the nineteenth century.

While these practical developments were proceeding an important step was taken by Arthur Young, Secretary to the Board of Agriculture. It will be remembered that the founders of the Royal Society had as one of their objects the improvement of agriculture (p. 21). Nothing very striking had resulted compared with what farmers and landowners had achieved empirically: agricultural science in Britain had fallen into rather a dull period, and was not attracting as much attention from scientists as it had done. The Board of Agriculture, which had been set up in 1793, gave the idea of scientific help to farmers a new start by arranging with Humphrey Davy, the brilliant professor of Chemistry at the newly established Royal Institution in London, that he should deliver annually a course of lectures on agriculture. This he did in each of the ten years 1803–1812. The material was published in 1813 under the title *Elements of Agricultural Chemistry*. It was the first time the name had been used in England, though it had already appeared in Germany.[2] Davy's definition still remains one of the best:

'Agricultural chemistry has for its objects all those changes in

---

[1] It bears an inscription typical of those times: 'Dedicated by permission to His Grace the Duke of Bedford by His Grace's most obedient and very humble servant George Garrard.'

[2] S. F. Hermbstadt's new Journal *Archiv der Agriculturchemie*, 1803. He was Professor of Technology in Berlin.

the arrangements of matter connected with the growth and
nourishment of plants, the comparative values of their produce
as food; the constitution of soils; the manner in which lands are
enriched by manure, or rendered fertile by the different processes of cultivation.'

There is no reference to livestock problems: he regarded these
as the business of the animal physiologists. He justified the
linkage with chemistry because 'It is scarcely possible to enter
upon any investigation in agriculture without finding it connected, more or less, with doctrines or elucidations derived
from chemistry'. The name continued in use throughout the
nineteenth century until incursions of other subjects made a
more comprehensive title desirable and the name 'Agricultural
Science' was adopted.

Davy was neither an agriculturist nor an agricultural
chemist, but an electro-chemist whose remarkable discoveries
made in rapid succession had raised him to the highest eminence
in the scientific world. He was also a very popular and most
attractive lecturer, holding his large audiences spell-bound,
and he gave the subject a status which it had never enjoyed
before, and which, indeed, it has hardly regained yet.

He had a remarkable career; perhaps its most remarkable
feature being that he was ever discovered. He was born in
Penzance in 1778[1] of 'humble but respectable parents', educated
at the grammar school there and at Truro, but showed no sign
of interest in science. His father having died he was apprenticed
to a surgeon apothecary and started studying metaphysics,
ethics and mathematics. He did no chemistry till 1797 at the
age of nineteen, but he then made such progress that in 1798 he
was introduced to Dr Thomas Beddoes, who was setting up a
Medical Pneumatic Institute at Bristol for studying the medicinal properties of various gases, and at the end of the year he
appointed Davy as Superintendent. Within a few months Davy
had discovered the curious intoxicating effects of nitrous oxide
which gave it the name 'laughing gas', and brought him into
much prominence.

In 1801 Count Rumford was founding the Royal Institution
and appointed him Assistant Lecturer in Chemistry; he rose

[1] Commemorated by a bronze statue in Market Jew Street there.

quickly and in May 1802 was appointed Professor. His most important scientific work was on electro-chemistry in which he achieved some great triumphs, notably the isolation of sodium and potassium. He resigned his professorship in 1812 and married a lady of means, went on to the Continent for three years, and soon after his return invented the safety lamp. In 1823, however, his health began to fail and after three years, he returned to the Continent for the last time. He died at Geneva in 1829 at the age of 51.

He was not only a brilliant lecturer, but a good writer, and not confined to prose: Coleridge, indeed, declared that if he 'had not been the first chemist he would have been the first poet of his age'—which need not be taken too seriously.

British science can hardly find a parallel to his meteoric career. An unknown apothecary's apprentice at nineteen knowing little or no chemistry; discovered almost by accident; Professor of Chemistry at the Royal Institution and a Fellow of the Royal Society at twenty-five; knighted and married at thirty-four to a rich, well established and pretty but sharp-tongued blue-stocking with whom he was not infrequently quarrelling; a baronet and President of the Royal Society at forty-two—all richly deserved by the amazing brilliance of his chemical discoveries. But along with his successes he seems to have developed some unattractive features and to have become rather a snob: Wordsworth described him as a sensualist and a slave of rank and worldly station, while Coleridge, who had known and admired him as a young man, described him as having become a 'theo-mammonist'—worshipper of God and Mammon.[1] Sir Harold Hartley describes him as a complex character, but a countryman devoted to the land and a keen sportsman, appreciating invitations to the large country houses.

Up to Davy's time the literature of agricultural chemistry in Great Britain had consisted in a number of disconnected publications, some written in terms of the new chemistry, others earlier. In his lectures on agricultural chemistry Davy collected this scattered material, set it in orderly array and built it up into a coherent subject. He consulted over a hundred works during

[1] See Miss Anne Treneer's life of him: *The Mercurial Chemist* (Matheson 1963) and Sir Harold Hartley's biography (Nelson).

his search for material, and made numerous experiments to
test statements that seemed to need it.

The lectures present in attractive form the best of the
knowledge of the seventeenth and eighteenth centuries, passed
on to the nineteenth century by the best chemist of the time. He
pointed out the small number of chemical elements important in
agriculture: only twelve out of forty-seven then known.[1] He
emphasized the necessity for knowing the composition of soils
and crops and described methods of analysis of both. For soils
the chief constituents determined were silica, lime, alumina,
magnesia, oxides of iron and manganese, vegetable and animal
matter, and soluble saline compounds: common salt, sulphate of
magnesia, sulphate and carbonate of potash and sulphate of soda.

The silica, he said, is usually combined with alumina and oxide
of iron, or with these two bases and oxides of lime and magnesia.

The list of plant constituents was much longer, it included
nineteen groups: (1) gum, (2) starch, (3) sugar, (4) albumen,
(5) gluten, (6) gum elastic, (7) extract, (8) tannin, (9)
indigo, (10) narcotic principles, (11) bitter principles, (12)
wax, (13) resins, (14) camphor, (15) fixed oils, (16) volatile
oils, (17) woody fibre, (18) acids, (19) alkalis, earths, metallic
oxides, and saline compounds. Methods of determination and
analytical results obtained in his laboratory for thirty-seven
different crops were given as well as analyses made elsewhere.
He attempted also to assess the feeding value of the ninety-
seven different grasses grown by the Duke of Bedford at
Woburn; the criterion was the percentage of water soluble
matter, which is now known to be inaccurate.

Apparently Davy did not regard these substances as rigidly
fixed in composition: 'No two compounds procured from
different vegetables are precisely alike', he wrote; 'and there are
even differences in the qualities of the same compound, according to the time in which it has been collected and the manner in
which it has been prepared.'

Unfortunately he is not very clear about the food of plants
and seems sometimes rather to shift his ground. The 'mucila-
ginous, gelatinous, saccharine, oils and extractive fluids, and
solutions of carbon dioxide in water . . . in their unchanged

[1] The number known is now 102.

state contain almost all the principles necessary for the life of plants, but there are few cases in which they can be applied as manure in their pure forms'. 'Water, and the decomposing animal and vegetable matter existing in the soil constitute the true nourishment of plants.' The most important property of a manure was that it should 'afford as much soluble matter as is possible to the roots of the plant, and that in a slow and gradual manner, so that it may be entirely consumed in forming the sap or organized parts of the plant'.

The roots cannot take up solid particles no matter how minute they may be: solid substances must be changed by fermentation or the action of lime or other process to liquid or gaseous substances before plant roots can assimilate them. During this process 'the principal elastic (i.e. gaseous) matter disengaged is carbonic acid with some ammonia, and both these, if retained by the moisture in the soil, are capable of becoming an useful nourishment of plants'.

The most important plant foods, however, were the nutrients present in the atmosphere which were absorbed by the soil and taken up by the plant roots: a perpetual and apparently inexhaustible process. 'In supplying animal or vegetable manure', he wrote in his little tract on soil analysis, 'a temporary food only is provided for plants, which is in all cases exhausted by means of a certain number of crops; but when a soil is rendered of the best possible constitution and texture, with respect to its earthy parts, its fertility may be considered as permanently established. It becomes capable of attracting a very large portion of vegetable nourishment from the atmosphere, and of producing its crops with comparatively little labour and expense.'

The leaves also played an important part in plant nutrition. He accepted de Saussure's proof that the green leaves of plants take in carbon dioxide from the air and under the influence of sunlight decompose it, retaining the carbon in the plant and returning the oxygen to the air from which it has originally been taken. He thus accounted for the constancy of composition of the atmosphere—already recognized in those days—in spite of the oxygen absorption and carbon dioxide evolution resulting from the vast amount of respiration, combustion, putrefaction, fermentation, etc. always taking place. 'The principal consumption of the carbon dioxide in the atmosphere', he wrote, 'seems to be in affording nourishment to plants, and some of them appear to be supplied with carbon mainly from this source.'

He was much less clear about the source of nitrogen—azote in his day—or even the need for it. He repeatedly hints at the value of ammonia as a plant food. In the section on manures, especially farmyard manure and urine, he constantly refers to a copious formation of ammonia, and he describes a remarkable experiment he had made in October of 1808. He filled a retort with hot fermenting manure (litter and dung of cattle) and pushed its beak into the soil amongst the roots of some grass in the borders of a garden; 'in less than a week a very distinct effect was produced upon the grass; upon the spot exposed to the influence of the matter disengaged in fermentation, it grew with much more luxuriance than the grass in any other part of the garden'. He watered the grass with dilute solutions of ammonium carbonate and found that growth was improved,[1] a result that 'might be expected, for carbonate af ammonia consists of carbon, hydrogene, azote and oxygene'.

Soot, he stated, owes part of its efficacy to the ammoniacal salts it contains, and he went on 'the liquor produced by the distillation of coal contains carbonate and acetate of ammonia, and is said to be a very good manure'. He had already in 1805 examined samples of guano sent over from South America and found that on heating they gave off 'strong ammoniacal fumes'. He knew also that 'putrid urine abounds in ammoniacal salts, and though less active than fresh urine, is a very powerful manure'. Yet only rarely, and then only incidentally, does he describe ammonia as a 'useful nourishment of plants'. It is strange that he did not attach more importance to it as a source of nitrogen in plant nutrition.[2] Instead, he states that 'the species of urine that contain the most albumen, gelatine and urea are the best as manures'.

Equally strange is the complete oblivion into which the knowledge of nitre in the soil and its significance possessed by the Elizabethan scientists had fallen. In spite of the many soil analyses made as the result of Davy's initiative nitrates were

---

[1] Ammonium nitrate was ineffective, but the solution was acid. Nitrate of soda was a little better, but apparently not promising: there was no following up.

[2] His early experiments had indicated that human beings could assimilate gaseous nitrogen.

not found in soil till 1856, and their rediscovery was rightly hailed as a great event.

He was much in advance of general opinion in regard to the mineral constituents of plants. Belief in transmutation was still widespread. Many believed that plants constructed their ash constituents out of water or other substances as they were needed: even Lavoisier thought that the alkali metals were produced during plant growth. Davy, on the other hand, maintained that the plants 'took them up through their roots from the soil'. 'It has been generally supposed', he wrote, that these materials act in the vegetable economy in the same manner as condiments on stimulants in the animal economy and that they render the common food more nutritive.' 'It seems, however, a much more probable idea, that they are actually a part of the true food of plants and that they supply that kind of matter to the vegetable fibre which is analogous to the bony matter in animal structures.' And elsewhere: 'The ashes of plants contain some of the earths of the soil on which they grow. . . . If they be considered as necessary to the vegetable, it is as giving hardness and firmness to its organization', and he instances the 'epidermis, principally of silicious earth' carried by wheat, oats and hollow grasses 'to strengthen them and defend them from the attacks of insects and parasitical plants'. He does not mention phosphates.

Of the four chief vegetable and animal constituents the carbon, hydrogen, and oxygen could be derived from the carbonic acid and water in the atmosphere and the soil, but the nitrogen could not. 'When glutinous and albuminous substances exist in plants the azote they contain may be suspected to be derived from the atmosphere, but no experiments have been made which prove this: they might easily be instituted upon mushrooms and funguses.' However, he did nothing about it, nor did anyone else for some long time. His statement seems to suggest that there are plants free from 'glutinous and albuminous substances' in which case they would presumably contain no nitrogen. He is always vague on this subject and does not discuss it. Strangely enough he failed to realize that his observations on the effects of ammonia on plant growth provided the key to this problem.

He attached great importance to soil analysis, and regarded
c*

it as the proper guide to soil improvement. A whole lecture was devoted to this subject and he had it printed and circulated as a separate pamphlet long before the rest of the lectures were published.[1] Another important new feature of his lectures was the inclusion of some of the physical properties of the soil among those to be studied, for which purpose he gave suitable methods. They included specific gravity, heat capacity and absorptive power. He attached special importance to the absorptive power, partly as an indicator of the quantity of decomposable organic matter, but chiefly because, as already stated, he regarded absorption by the soil of nutritive vapours from the atmosphere as the chief source of food for plants, manures playing only a secondary part.

Another observation by Davy has provided copious material for research workers and still does so. 'The earths, and even the earthy carbonates, have a certain degree of chemical attraction for many of the principles of vegetation and animal substances', hence soils rich in these constituents are very effective in conserving farmyard manure. For this reason he recommended ploughing the manure under while it is fresh: the heat of fermentation would be useful and the fertilizing constituents would be conserved. The observation is quite correct: the agents concerned, however, are not the 'earths' but the clay and some of the organic matter. Soils well supplied with these are rightly called rich because 'vegetable nourishment is long preserved in them unless taken up by the organs of plants'.

The manures used to supply the nutrients were of three kinds: vegetable, animal, and mineral. Those of vegetable origin included straw, green manures, oil seed cakes, sea weed, peat, peat ashes and wood ashes: 'cole ashes' no longer appear, otherwise the list is unchanged since the late seventeenth century. Manures of animal origin included dung, urine, guano, bones, horn and hair: again the same as of old except for guano, which was only recently known and not yet available in any quantity. The mineral manures included calcium carbonate, lime,

[1] *On the analysis of soils as connected with their improvement:* 1805. The other lectures were not published till 1813. While the analytical procedure is fully set out the connection with soil improvement is not very clear. Dr Boyd almost certainly used this pamphlet in his analyses for the Bath and West Society. (p. 60). *See also* Appendix, p. 107.

dolomite, gypsum (for clover and sown grasses), calcium phosphate, and various salts of sodium, potassium and ammonium.
No reason is given for the inclusion of calcium phosphate:
apparently Davy had not seen, or did not accept, Erasmus
Darwin's view that phosphate is an essential food constituent
for plants (p. 63) though he knew Darwin. Investigation must
have been difficult, however, as the analytical procedure for
estimating phosphate was very unsatisfactory (p. 60). Lime
is useful because it brings any hard vegetable matter into a
state of more rapid decomposition: there is no mention of soil
acidity.

The course finished with a lecture on the chemical principles
involved in pasture management, and in the improvement of
land by paring and burning, (Devonshiring or Downshiring),
irrigation, fallowing and crop rotation.

The book had great success; it had passed through six English
and two American editions by 1839 and had also been translated
into French, German and Italian. It remained a standard text
for some fifty years.

Davy retained his interest in the book to the end. In both
the third edition (1821) and the fourth (1827) two years before
his death, he refers to the considerable improvements in
chemical science which had made many alterations and additions
necessary.

It was not without its detractors, however. John Donaldson
in his *Agricultural Biography* (1854) states that it 'enjoyed some
little popularity, but scarcely added anything to our previous
stock of knowledge. It was hailed as a grand beginning, but
nearly half a century has not shown any advancement.' Very
charitably he blames nobody: it results from the severe limitations of the subject. 'Agriculture and chemistry', he continues,
'are connected in the single article of manures only; the other
uses are very widely different.'

Davy rendered agricultural science the great service of
making it respectable again; under his patronage its prestige
stood where it had done in the better days of George III. Any
scientist, however distinguished, could devote time and energy
to the subject without exciting comment. By building the
scattered information into a coherent whole he showed up the
gaps that needed filling, and the subjects that needed re-

examination. He was the first British chemist to draw up a method of soil analysis which included both chemical and physical properties, and to show—though not very clearly—how the results could be used to indicate methods of soil improvement. He also pointed out the manurial value of ammonia, and the ability of some of the soil constituents to retain certain fertilizer materials, notably farmyard manure (i.e. ammonia and phosphate), and hold them against loss by drainage. Studies of this power of retention later developed into an important new branch of science. He recognized clearly the way in which new knowledge of the growth of plants would be obtained: in his introductory lecture he stated:

'They receive their nourishment from the external elements; they assimilate it by means of peculiar organs; and it is by examining their physical and chemical constitution and the substances and powers which act upon them and the modifications they undergo, that the scientific principles of Agricultural Chemistry are obtained.'

In spite of analytical difficulties he studied the calcium phosphate in soil and noted that while insoluble in pure water it became soluble on addition of acid. He thought it was probably necessary for 'corn' crops and other 'white crops'. Finally he was the first in this country to controvert the view that the alkalis and alkaline earths in the soil were only stimulants: he maintained that they were true plant nutrients.

Lectures are not always as interesting to read as to hear, and modern readers may find Davy's large quarto volume of 386 pages (including 63 on grasses) rather prolix in places and would have preferred a more compact text book. But he had his contemporaries in mind and the notable success of the book showed that it was what they wanted.

Then followed some twenty years of intellectual stagnation for agricultural science in England and of great suffering in the countryside. During a period of twenty-three years, from 1793 to 1815, there had been fourteen bad harvests but only two good ones. When at last the war ended with victory in 1815 there remained the dreadful burden of a huge National Debt, very heavy taxation, much unemployment and grave discontent among the workers which the Poor Laws of the time could not much alleviate. Several select committees of the House of Commons had inquired into the depressed conditions of agriculture. The 1833 Report was very gloomy. Scarcely a solvent tenant farmer remained in the Wealds of Kent and Sussex, and many farmers, having lost everything, were working on the roads. Wages were pitifully low: a usual good rate of pay was two shillings per day of ten hours for a man, one shilling for a youth, sixpence for a child.

There was an equally barren period in the development of agricultural science. One interesting book appeared but it attracted no attention although well praised by a few who had seen it. It was written in 1819 by an obscure apothecary, William Grisenthwaite of Wells, Norfolk, and although only small he gave it a high sounding title: 'A new theory of agriculture in which the nature of soils, crops, and manures is explained, many prevailing prejudices are exploded, and the application of bones, gypsum, lime, chalk, etc. is determined on scientific principles.' It was published in Wells, and apparently had only a small circulation perhaps because Wells was then regarded as a remote country town out of which little of importance could be expected. In 1830 a second edition was published, this time in London by Simpkin Marshall and others, but this seems to have fared little better although it was highly praised by John C. Loudon in his *Encyclopaedia*, (1825) and by H. R. Madden in the *Journal* of the Highland & Agricultural Society for 1841 (Vol. 13). But when John Donaldson published his very useful *Agricultural Bibliography* in 1854 he could find no copy, nor could he obtain any information about the book on the new theory. Fortunately the Rothamsted Library possesses a copy of each edition, which I have been allowed to use.

The interest of the book lies in its foreshadowings of some general principles enunciated twenty years later by Liebig; it shows also the serious errors in the composition of crops prevalent in the days before sound and practicable methods of analysis had been devised. Soil is described as 'that mixture of earthy bodies which is calculated to furnish support to plants and serves as a medium through which nourishments may be conveyed to them'. He regarded its role as purely passive: 'the stomach of the plants', he called it, containing certain salts which they required but not otherwise contributing to their nutrition. Holding this view he naturally disagreed entirely with Davy's insistence on the importance of soil analysis. He saw no point in it. Some of the salts were needed for producing and maintaining a proper physical condition in the soil, enabling it to hold by capillary attraction an adequate supply of water for the needs of the plant.

He divided the life of the plant into two stages: growth and seed production. For growth its requirements were few: it consisted chiefly of carbon, hydrogen and oxygen, all of which came from the atmosphere, and a small proportion of saline bodies from the soil. A few plants (or very few: he is vague about this) contained nitrogen; wheat was the chief of these. For seed formation the requirements were more complex. The plant made new substances which required new materials and those must come from the salts already in the soil or to be supplied in manure. Wheat, the chief crop in his district, was his main example: it made gluten during ripening, and this contained much nitrogen which must be supplied from outside: 'the constancy of its presence' he added, justifies the conclusion that it answers some necessary purpose in the grain and that therefore it (i.e. nitrogenous manure) ought always to be provided when that grain is to be 'grown'. It was an age of teleological thought, when men sought evidence of design or purpose in Nature. The grain contained phosphate of lime which likewise must come from either the soil or manure.

It is in regard to manuring that he is most interesting. 'Agriculture', he wrote, 'may be considered to be a system of operations calculated to convert manure into vegetable matter.' The manure must supply the materials for building up the substances required for the functioning of the plant.

'It is evident, therefore, that the substances employed as manures should be composed of these elements, for unless they are, there will be a deficiency of some of the elements in the vegetable itself, and it is probable that such dependence may prevent the formation of those substances within it for which its particular organization is contrived and upon which its healthy existence depends.'

He several times reverted to the importance of those substances responsible for the proper functioning of the plant—the earliest premonition I can find of the complex chemical activities in the plant revealed by modern science. The proper manuring for a crop, he insisted, could be discovered by analysis of the adult plants—a clear foreshadowing of Liebig's ash analysis procedure. Thomas Thompson in the vegetable section of his *Chemistry of Organic bodies* (1838) had expressed the same view: 'Plant food can only be decided by attention to what they are composed of.' Clover, lucerne and sainfoin all contained gypsum, which should be reserved especially for them and not used as a general manure as he had seen done at Holkham.

Unfortunately his analytical procedure was pitifully inadequate. Peas contained ('demanded' was his word) 'super oxalate of lime', but 'as the oxalic acid is seldom found in large quantities in a state of nature so as to be applied as a manure, it is probable that the pea plant has the power of forming it'. He pointed out that large groups of plants probably have similar manurial requirements and a succession of cropping will remove so much plant food that the productiveness of the land is lowered. The remedy, he wrote, is to replace the useful material so taken. Farmers try to get over this difficulty by crop rotation but this only puts off the evil day; if the substances removed from the soil are duly returned each season the soil will retain its productiveness indefinitely. Rotations then become unnecessary and the area under wheat could be increased. Another remarkable foreshadowing was his declaration that 'when one specific substance needed by a plant is absent, no excess of others can supply the deficiency'.

Determination of nitrogen and of phosphate presented great difficulties then and for many years later, and he went sadly astray about barley grain which, he stated, contained neither the one nor the other; in which respect, he pointed out, it differed profoundly from wheat. He then contradicted himself by stating that its characteristic component was nitrate of potash or of soda, either of which could therefore be used as manure. The former was available in crude form, being used for the manufacture of gunpowder; the latter was not yet available but he gave a recipe for making it from Glauber's salt and nitre.

He associated nitrogen with the animal rather than the vegetable kingdom; it was present in urine, but not in the solid excreta—what he called the alval part—also in flesh, wool, etc. It was the characteristic manure for wheat, for which it should be reserved. He condemned the common practice of applying animal manure, bones, woollen rags etc., to growing grass: at this stage, he maintained, it served no purpose, the grass was still growing and consisted of carbon, hydrogen and oxygen only without nitrogen. He was of course quite wrong, as he would have discovered had he ever studied a meadow so treated. He also condemned the common practice of manuring wheat with broken up oil cake on the grounds that it contained no nitrogen, which again was wrong.[1] The solid nitrogenous manures, like the equally essential phosphate of lime, are insoluble in water and therefore cannot be assimilated by plants until they are made soluble: he does not explain what happens to wool or oil cake, but 'it is not a little remarkable', he wrote, 'that phosphate of lime is soluble in no known fluid unless there be also in that fluid a portion of some animal matter'— which again is completely wrong.

It is a curious book, not easy to read, but very interesting, and the neglect which was its fate is hard to understand.

After Evelyn's *Terra* no other book devoted entirely to soil appeared till 1838 when John Morton (1781–1864) produced one that in spite of its interest has been strangely overlooked. He was born in 1781 at Ceres, Fifeshire, and farmed at Kilmany in the same county; the farming system allowed him considerable leisure which he spent in walking repeatedly over the English counties observing the systems of farming, the soils, and the geological formations, which were then beginning to attract attention as the subject of a new science, fostered by a new scientific society, the Geological Society, founded in 1807. In 1810 he moved to Dulverton in Somerset and may well have met William Smith, the Somerset canal engineer now remembered chiefly as 'the father of British geology' whose famous map made in 1815 of the geological formations of Britain is almost valid today except for the oldest formations in Wales.

[1] It commonly contains about 5 per cent.

Lawes' First Laboratory
Outside
Inside

3. *Lawes' Testimonial Laboratory*
   Outside
   Inside

Morton remained in Somerset for eight years, and then transferred to Gloucestershire in 1818 as Agent to Lord Ducie's
estates there; he held this post till 1852 when he retired to
Nailsworth, also in Gloucestershire, where he remained till his
death in 1864 at the age of 82.

While with Lord Ducie he had established and conducted
the Whitfield Example Farm and started the Uley Agricultural
Machine Factory: he also wrote, apparently from copious notes,
an account of his observations during his earlier peregrinations
in the English counties. His descriptions of the geography of
the different geological formations are so clear that one feels
he must have been looking at Smith's geological map when he
wrote them.

The book was published in 1838, a small volume with a
somewhat ponderous title: *On the Nature and Property of Soils,
their connection with the Geological Formation on which they rest,
the best means of permanently increasing their productiveness, and
on the rent and profits of agriculture.*

Hitherto soils had been classified only on a textural basis as
sands, loams, clay, etc., and in the octavo volumes reporting
the county agricultural surveys organized by Arthur Young[1]
there were accounts usually accompanied by sketch maps showing the distribution of those types over the region concerned.
This classification, however, was very rough, and Morton
wanted a classification that would

'identify their peculiar properties, also the kind of crops they
are best fitted to produce and the mode of culture best calculated
for each. . . . We shall therefore associate together the soils on
those formations the nature and properties of whose materials
are nearly alike, although they may differ in the proportions of
the materials of which they are composed.'

He set up three main groups of soils: aluminous, calcareous
and silicious; each containing a number of sub groups. The
table on p. 82 summarizes the type of classification: it is not
complete.

[1] See p. 54.

Morton's Classification of Soils (1838)

ALUMINOUS

(1) Little or no calcareous matter. — London clay, plastic clay (all the clay between the London clay and the Weald clay), Weald clay, clay, clay of coal measures.

(2) Considerable calcareous matter—but less silicious than (1); all particles are minute. — Gault, blue lias.

CALCAREOUS

(1) Abundant lime. — Lower chalk marl, some of the gault, oolite clay.

(2) Much clay but little or no silicious matter.

(1) and (2) are formed of 'impalpable' matter.

(3) Calcareous gravelly soils: fragments of calcareous rock, with little or no silicious matter. — Diluvium on Oxford clay and blue lias. Upper chalk and oolite.

(4) Fragments of calcareous rock and considerable silicious matter. — Coral rag, lower oolite, magnesian lime, carboniferous lime.

SILICIOUS

(1–6) Friable dry sands: Sand of the plastic clay, iron sand (Hastings beds), coal formation, millstone grit, old red sandstone and granite.

(7–10) Diluvium on plastic clay, gault, new red sandstone and coal formations.

(11–17) Some of these are on the palaeozoic rocks. Old red sandstone, etc., some fragmentary, some calcareous.

'The surface of the earth', he wrote, 'partakes of the nature and colour of the subsoil or rock on which it rests.' Starting from the most recent formations he described the overlying soils attaching particular importance to their colour and state of moisture, and giving also their agricultural characteristics. The details recorded show that he was a close observer and must have taken and preserved voluminous notes.

The most recently formed soils were exceptions to the rule connecting the soil with the underlying rock. Soil at the bottom of a slope might have no connection with the underlying material but could simply have been washed down from the higher ground as an alluvial deposit. Or it could be a diluvial deposit formed in a great deluge—Noah's flood was still accepted as an historic event. Unlike the alluvium this might be a considerable mass of soil, sand or gravel on high ground where there were no longer any hills from which it might have come.

The alluvial soils were the richer but some of the diluvials of the Eastern counties were very good especially after they had been dressed with the underlying chalk or clay which could be dug out of the corner of the field.[1] He quoted the Holkham results: land formerly a rabbit warren had by this treatment been made to produce thirty to forty bushels of wheat and forty to sixty bushels of barley per acre and the rents raised from the former 1s to 20s per acre. Peat soils also came into the most recent group showing no relation with the subjacent rock; they were more widely spread in those days than now and varied greatly in agricultural value, no distinction having yet been drawn between peat and fen. Some (the fen soils) became very productive when treated with the clay that underlay them, others (the peats) were more difficult. Dartmoor was hopeless except for growing larch. The agricultural properties of these various groups are set out, but no chemical analyses are given.

The rest of the book is interesting as a coherent record of views held in the period before strict chemical examination had begun to penetrate the different sections of agricultural science. Like Grisenthwaite he states that 'the materials of which the soil is composed only seems to afford the plant a proper supply of moisture to the roots for its nourishment'. The work of de Saussure was comprehended only in parts: '(Plants) give out oxygen when the light of the sun is on them, retaining the hydrogen and forming carbon for the increase of the plant, but when the light is absent, they receive oxygen, and hydrogen is given out.' But on the same page he states that 'in sunshine carbon is received by growing plants from the air and oxygen is given out . . . but in the dark, carbonic acid gas is thrown out into the atmosphere, and oxygen is absorbed. The decomposition of water and carbonic acid gas is perpetually going on during vegetable life, and forming the organs and the materials of plants.' And further on: 'Animal and vegetable matter deposi-

[1] He mentions 100 cubic yards per acre.

ted in the soil as it were digests it, and forms a solution which it conveys to the plants.' But he sums up in words that can hardly be bettered: 'The process of the growth and decay of vegetable matter goes on in a continual succession, and the decay of one crop becomes the nourishment of the next'. The decay was brought about by 'insensible fermentation.'

Similarly manure 'must be dissolved and form a chemical combination with water before the organs of the plant can receive it'. Free water in the soil, however, does not serve: but 'that portion only which is adhering to it by cohesive attraction'; in modern terms, capillary attraction. Free water was harmful. 'Complete or perfect drainage is the foundation of all improvements in husbandry', he wrote, and he commended the work of James Smith of Deanston, Perthshire, who in 1823 had drained a bog and converted it into a garden: he described the method in his *Remarks on Thorough Drainage & Deep Ploughing* (1831). There were as yet no pipes and his method was to cut trenches $2\frac{1}{2}$ feet deep and 16 to 21 feet apart, nearly fill them with stones and then finish with soil, finally to connect the drains with a ditch to allow the water to get away. Morton quotes with approval from Smith's book.[1]

He noted that 'light sandy soils have been greatly improved by the adoption of a new system of culture'—which he does not specify but is presumably the Norfolk system[2]—'but the poor clays remain in the same state they were in a century ago'. Some thought they could not be improved; he did not agree: his golden rule was 'to change its constituent parts by the addition of those earthy materials of which it is deficient, so as to bring it nearer to the nature of those soils which we know to be fertile. The remedy for poor clay was to add sand, chalk, marl, or burned clay and light unfermented manure, or perfect pulverization to make the soil friable'—also to carry out perfect subsoil drainage. He accepted Davy's standards for productive soils: they should contain 50—75 per cent silicious material, 20—40 per cent aluminous, and 10—20 per cent calcareous.

[1] This was not the first book on drainage. Joseph Elkington had already in 1797 published An *account of the most approved Mode of Draining Land according to the system practiced by Mr Joseph Elkington*, and long before that Stephen Schwitze in the *Weekly Miscellany* for the Improvement of Husbandry, August 24, 1777.

[2] P. 66.

His short section on manures contains several interesting passages. He was one of the earliest writers to use the expression 'artificial manures'; nothing that goes by that name today was yet known to agriculturists. He applied it to bone dust, soot, rape and other oil seed cakes. He quotes also an interesting passage on manures from one of James Anderson's books:

'Writers on agriculture have been too long in the custom of dividing manure into two classes; viz. enriching manures, or those that tended direct to render the soil more prolific, however sterile it may be . . . and exciting manures, or those that were supposed to have a tendency to render the soil more prolific merely by acting on those enriching manures that had been formerly in the soil, and giving them a new stimulus, so as to enable them to operate anew upon that soil which they had formerly fertilized.'[1]

Morton did not accept this view, as he held that lime has a directly beneficial effect on the soil: not being a chemist he did not specify it, though he suggested various possibilities. At the end he reverted to the question of the food of plants which many had tried and concluded that 'it is not so much any particular substance, or any combination of substances as a condition of the soil': manure 'may tend to give it this condition for a time, but its effects will be transitory compared with other mineral matter applied to alter its textures'. Morton's final advice to farmers is that they should pay more attention to the nature and state or condition of the component parts of the soil; and whenever they find it too loose and light, to give it the addition of some substances that will make it more adhesive and firm; and when it is too tenacious, to apply to it some light porous substance that will make and keep the soil in the condition which will best promote the absorption and transmission of moisture for the use of plants.'

He was thus one of the pioneers in soil physics.[2]

[1] James Anderson, *Quick lime as a manure*, in *Essays relating to agriculture & rural affairs*, 3 vols., 1797. Dung was the best example of the first group and lime of the second.

[2] An interesting account of Morton's ideas on soil is given by B. T. Bunting of Birkbeck College in the *Geographical Journal*, 1964, Vol. 130, pp. 136-9. My thanks are due to Mr. Bunting for bringing this forgotten pioneer to my notice. The Rothamsted Library possesses the first edition of his book but I had inadvertently overlooked it.

Neither of the books just described seems to have had any effect on the barren period in the development of agricultural science to which reference has already been made. It was brought to an end, however, by one of the most scholarly and versatile men of his time, Charles Giles Daubeny. He was born in 1795 at Stratton, Gloucestershire, the son of the Rev. James Daubeny, and was educated at Winchester (1808—10) and Magdalen College, Oxford (1810—15), where he distinguished himself by gaining the Chancellor's prize for a Latin essay. In 1815 he proceeded to London and then to Edinburgh to study medicine, but he did not confine himself thereto: at Edinburgh he attended Prof. Jameson's lectures on Geology and Mineralogy which aroused in him a lively interest that he never lost. He was well off financially, and after taking his medical degree in 1819 he travelled leisurely through France studying the geological and chemical history of the earth. He returned to Oxford in 1822 as Aldrichian Professor of Chemistry; his department was then housed in the basement of the old Ashmolean Museum, now part of the Museum of the History of Science. Here he studied natural mineral waters to obtain information about the chemical processes going on below the surface of the districts from which the waters came. With the same object he made extensive journeys across Europe to Transylvania, taking always his testing apparatus with him, and studying also the extinct volcanoes on the way.

The 1830 journey was to Geneva, where he attended the course of lectures delivered annually before the Academy by the distinguished Swiss botanist, Augustin Pyramus de Candolle. They were a revelation to him. 'It was at Geneva', he wrote, 'that I first began to estimate at their true weight the pretentions of Botany to be regarded as a science, and not merely as an ingenious art for discovering the name of any plant that might be put before us.' He continued his botanical studies with such good effect that when in 1834 the Oxford Chair of Botany fell vacant he was appointed to it while still holding the chemistry chair till his successor settled in. He then transferred his work and his home to the Physic Garden—now the Botanic Garden— which he enlarged and greatly improved.[1]

---

[1] In 1840 he collected another Professorship, the Sibthorpian Chair of Rural Economy. The Sibthorpian, however, was not then a full-time post. It had been

He was an enthusiastic supporter of the British Association from its foundation in 1831 onwards, and he served on its Botanical Committee set up to arrange for investigations on important problems needing further study. In 1833 John Lindley, Professor of Botany at University College, London, but born and bred in rural Norfolk, reported that some plants are incapable of healthy growth in soil in which plants of the same species have previously been grown, no matter how much manure they are given. In explanation he quoted experiments by Macaire of Geneva, a chemical colleague of de Candolle's, which he thought showed that 'all plants part with a kind of faecal matter by their roots . . . the nature of such excretions varies with the species or large natural orders . . . they are thrown off by the roots on account of their presence in the system being deleterious'. He probably got this idea from de Candolle's book *Physiologie Végétale* published in Paris in 1832, in which the author expressed his conviction held since 1805 that specific toxic excretions from the roots of plants were the cause of the superiority of rotations over continuous successions of the same crop; he had tried to interest chemists without success till Macaire had volunteered to assist.

Daubeny forthwith undertook the investigation and made it one of the classics of agricultural science. Eighteen different crops were grown for ten years in two groups. In one the same crops followed consecutively on the same plots; in the other the succession varied so that no crop ever followed another of the same kind. No manure was given. In almost every instance the yields decreased, and generally the decrease was greater where the crops were grown consecutively than where the sequence varied. The differences, however, were insufficient to justify the assumption of toxic root excretions, except perhaps in the case of *Euphorbia lathyris* which has a very acrid sap. For the other plants the fall in yields was attributed to the more rapid removal from the continuous plots of the mineral nutrients required by the plant.

Daubeny did not stop there, however. He analysed the soils

founded in 1796 by the Will of John Sibthorp, Professor of Botany, but with a prior claim that his magnum opus, *Flora Gracca*, must first be published. This was a costly work and there was no money available for the chair till 1840. Daubeny was thus the first to be appointed.

and the plant ash. Important results soon emerged. The plants were unable to extract more than a fraction of the nutrient elements—potassium, phosphate, etc.,—contained in the soil. Digestion with hot hydrochloric acid for four hours extracted not only all that any one generation of plants could take up, which he called the *active* part, but it extracted also the *dormant* part which only slowly came into action. The two together he called *available*, and the residue not dissolved by the acid he called *unavailable*. He separated the active from the dormant fractions by digesting the soil with a solution of carbonic acid, and assumed that while this could dissolve the active part it could not affect the dormant.[1]

It was the first time the distinction had been recognized and it made possible the development of soil analysis which, as will appear later, has proved to be one of the most useful services chemistry has rendered to agriculture.

LAWES AND ROTHAMSTED
(*a*) FIRST PERIOD. 1814—1842

Meanwhile one of Daubeny's pupils, John Bennet Lawes, was starting on a career that was destined to have a profound and lasting effect on British agriculture and agricultural science.

John Bennet Lawes was born on December 28, 1814, at Rothamsted near Harpenden, Hertfordshire: an ancient manor, rather remotely situated between two of the roads leading northwards out of London: the Watling Street to the west, and the unnamed and less important Luton and Bedford road, on which stands Harpenden, to the east. Its long and entirely uneventful history goes back to the year 1212; it is not, however, in Doomsday Book. Only four families have occupied it during the whole of that time, and only two or three of its long procession of occupants ever emerged from manorial obscurity into the light of history. Human occupation began much earlier than 1212, however: the remains of a Romano-British shrine of the first century AD were opened up in 1936, and Belgian pottery and earlier stone implements have periodically been found.

The fourth owner, ancestor of Lawes, was Dame Anne Myddleton, daughter of a Flemish refugee; who, starting as a

---

[1] Royal Society *Phil. Trans.*, 1845, 179–253.

rich heiress, made two wealthy marriages, first to Jacob Wittewronge, son of another refugee who had acquired wealth as a brewer, by whom she had a son John; and the second to Sir Thomas Myddleton, sometime Lord Mayor of London who, however, did not long survive. She wanted John to become an English country gentleman, and in 1623 she bought Rothamsted from its bankrupt owner, whose family had held it for nearly 300 years, and installed him in it.

He completely fulfilled his mother's ambition. He lived at Rothamsted for more than seventy years, became a model country squire, interested in his farm, keeping records of crops and weather, discharging his magisterial and other local duties, and serving as Member of Parliament. He was clearly very tactful, for he passed through the most difficult period of English history without loss of dignity or property. He was knighted by Charles I in 1641, helped Cromwell's army, was pardoned by Charles II in 1660 for this disloyal association, and made a baronet two years later. Direct male heirs ceased in 1763 and the estate passed first to a cousin, John Bennet, and then to a nephew, John Bennet Lawes, who was a friend of the Prince Regent: a costly distinction in those days which nearly reduced the estate to bankruptcy. He died in 1822, leaving one son, also John Bennet Lawes, born in 1814, the great agriculturist.

Being only eight years old when his father died he was brought up by his mother. She followed the lines then customary for young squires; public school and University: in his case Eton and Brasenose College, Oxford. He showed no early promise. At his private school he was always in trouble and often in disgrace, learning little; at Eton, he wrote, 'I learnt just enough to escape punishment, but no more':[1] he went at fourteen and left before he was seventeen. He read with a tutor in preparation for Oxford but spent most of his time fishing and shooting; he entered Brasenose College in 1832 at the age of eighteen 'where I remained two years learning little or nothing and following no particular pursuits, I did not go up for my degree'. His biographer, R. Warington Jun. however, states that he attended Daubeny's lectures.[2] Rothamsted had

---

[1] The brief Eton record, however, indicates a bright boy, well advanced for his age.
[2] *Proc. Roy. Soc.*, vol. 75, (1905), pp. 228–35: reprinted in A. D. Hall's, *Book of the Rothamsted Experiments* (London, 1905, pp. xxi–xxxii).

meanwhile been let, but the tenant became insolvent. He and his mother therefore returned to live there in 1834, and as the home farm of 250 acres was vacant he left Oxford to manage it. The task was not easy. Times had long been bad and still were. 'In 1837', wrote Lord Ernle,[1] 'the farming industry had passed through a quarter of a century of misfortune, aggravated by a disordered currency, bank failures, adverse seasons, labour difficulties, agrarian discontent.'

Somehow as a boy he had acquired a taste for making chemical experiments, which had to be done at home, chemistry not being as yet a school subject, but it was all very desultory. On returning home from Oxford he resumed his chemical experiments with some enthusiasm, fitting up one of the best bedrooms for the purpose, much to the dismay of his mother. His experiments were not, however, concerned with agricultural problems, but with the active principles of medicinal plants: poppies, hemlock, henbane, belladonna, etc., which he grew on the farm for the purpose. 'At that time', he states, 'I almost knew the pharmacopoeia by heart and I was not satisfied until I had made the acquaintance of the author.' This was Dr Anthony Todd Thomson, Professor of Materia Medica at University College, London, who became his chief instructor and adviser. An old barn at the top of Agdell field and Barnfield transformed into a laboratory replaced the bedroom in the house. For a while the manufacture of the chlorides of mercury was attempted by Dr Thomson's new process, but this was abandoned after wasting much time and money on it. Before long the pharmaceutical work was also abandoned: his chemical activities had had nothing to do with farming and in any case nothing came of any of them. Nor did he appear to have any great interest in farming or any new ideas about it. At the age of twenty-one he must have appeared rather a hopeless and aimless young man.

Two factors seem to have influenced him in changing over from pharmaceutical to agricultural chemistry. He had become acquainted with Theodore de Saussure's work on plant nutrition, in particular his conclusion that plants derive most of their carbon from the carbon dioxide of the air, but were unable to assimilate gaseous nitrogen and therefore could obtain none

[1] *English Farming Past and Present*, third ed. 1922, p. 347.

from the air apart from the small fraction derived from the atmospheric ammonia. Supplies could come only from some nitrogenous compound in the soil. Lawes thought he would like to find out what this was.

The other factor, which finally prevailed, arose out of the changing economic situation in the country. The long years of poverty and depression were ending and England was becoming more prosperous. Industry was developing and creating more wealth in the towns; this led to increased demands for more food and better food. More meat was wanted, necessitating increasing numbers of better livestock. Railways were being made, thus facilitating transport of farm produce to the towns. Farmers met this situation by enclosing and cultivating more land and striving for higher yields. There was a growing interest in manures. The value of bones had long been known and the demand for them speedily exceeded the home supply, necessitating larger and larger imports. In 1823 these had been valued at £14,395, by 1837 they had risen to £254,600. Liebig declared in what looks like a fit of petulance that England was robbing the battlefields of Europe in its ghoulish search for more.[1]

Farmers were, however, greatly puzzled by the apparently erratic behaviour of bones whether crushed or finely ground. On some soils they acted well; on others they had little or no effect. Some of the local agricultural societies tried to get an enquiry started. The Doncaster Agricultural Association had in 1829 issued a report showing that bones were very effective on dry sands, limestone and chalk soils, light loams and peats, but not on clays and heavy loams; 'a very considerable proportion of the soils of Great Britain', it added, 'would therefore be excluded from the profitable employment of this valuable manure'. Ten years later the problem occupied a prominent place in a well considered programme of research drawn up by a Committee of the English Agricultural Society. Nothing, however, had been done.

Some time after Lawes' return from Oxford a neighbouring landowner, Lord Dacre of Kimpton Hoo, raised this question

---

[1] South America supplied a good deal. In the early days of the cattle industry on the pampas there was no refrigeration or important meat trade; instead the animals were boiled down to provide tallow and bones for export.

with him. Each knew that bones were ineffective on his soil, though very effective on certain others. Lord Dacre suggested that as Lawes was fond of making chemical experiments he should try to find out why.[1] Lawes accepted the challenge. Unfortunately the date of this conversation is not known so that it cannot be placed in the suite of events, nor are the full details of what followed known with certainty: no diaries of Lawes are known and the note book recording his experiments is very scrappy and gives few dates. There are three sources of information about Lawes' early experiments with bones: his note-book recording what he actually did; sworn testimony given by himself and his laboratory man King in lawsuits of 1850 and 1853 described later; and two statements written by himself: one undated, the other a letter published in the *Agricultural Gazette* of January 2, 1888; these two statements, however, contain nothing of interest.

Unfortunately only one note book can be found; the one for the experiments of 1841 and 1842. Very little detail is given, but the broad outlines are clear. The plan of the 1841 series suggests that a considerable amount of sorting out had been done during the two preceding years and that Lawes knew that treatment of the bones with sulphuric acid made them effective as manure, and he knew also approximately in what quantities they should be used. The summer field experiments were on turnips on plots of 1/30th of an acre and the scheme included: Series 1—phosphate of lime (source unspecified) plus sulphuric acid in several diminishing doses; Series 2—as 1, with addition respectively of carbonates of magnesia, lime, potash, soda; Series 3—as 1, but bones instead of phosphate of lime; Series 4—as 2, but bones instead of phosphate of lime; Series 5—as 1, plus sulphate of ammonia or nitrate of soda; Series 6—various substances, e.g. sulphate of ammonia; soot, used alone; and unmanured.

The purpose was clearly to discover how much acid was necessary to obtain the most effective result, and whether anything was gained by neutralizing the superphosphate with an alkaline carbonate bringing about 'reversion'. The good

[1] Mr Marlborough Pryor, a neighbouring landowner who knew both Lord Dacre and Lawes well, told me in 1913 of this conversation.

effects of sulphate of ammonia and of nitrate of soda had also evidently been established.

The 1842 experiments are much more extensive, and include pot experiments testing many simple salts, and a large number of field experiments testing various mixtures of sulphuric acid with phosphate of lime, bones, and apatite. The influence of Liebig is indicated by the facts that the ashes of straw, hay and farmyard manure were also tested, and the rain water was collected and analysed to see how much ammonia it contained.

The lawsuit papers are the most detailed and presumably completely reliable. In his evidence Lawes stated that in 1836, 1837 and 1838 he had used considerable quantities of bone dust on turnips without results; in 1839, 1840 and 1841 he had experimented with bones, burnt bones, and mineral phosphate decomposed by sulphuric and other acids to form the soluble phosphate then known to chemists as superphosphate of lime. The 1839 trials were on a small scale only, made in pots or on small numbers of plants in the field; apparently however, the total number was large, for in the spring of that year he had brought over from Oxford his old 'scout', King,[1] to help him with them. The results, particularly those with turnips, were striking. The treatment with acid completely overcame the inertness both of the bones and the mineral phosphate, and both now gave notable increases in crop. The result was important for two reasons. It solved the problem of the ineffectiveness of bones on great areas of farm land: they need only be treated with sulphuric acid and they became active. Further, it opened the way to the utilization of the large supplies of mineral phosphate which geologists were beginning to find in various parts of Europe, which in their natural condition had little manurial value, but after treatment with acid acted well.

The explanation is quite simple; one wonders how Lawes came to miss it in the 1836 trials: it could have been found in

[1] King was of humble origin but a very remarkable man and a great character. He much impressed his fellow workers and became known as 'the Professor'. He remained at Rothamsted all his life—till 1879—working as laboratory assistant and meteorological observer, and satisfying Gilbert's rather exacting requirements. Unfortunately he fell into disfavour towards the end for committing the unforgivable and quite unprofessorial sin of conspiring with two or three others to steal and drink the beer intended for the allotment holders' New Year Festivities. (E. Grey, *Rothamsted Experiment Station: Reminiscences, Tales and Anecdotes 1872–1922*, privately printed.)

any chemistry text book. Bones owe most of their characteristic fertilizer value to their calcium phosphate, the insoluble tricalcic compound. This, however, is inert; before it can act it has to be transformed into the soluble monocalcic salt. Some soils contain acidic substances that can effect this change: the bones then act well. Other soils contain no such component: on them the bones cannot become soluble and they remain ineffective. Any acid would serve to bring about the changes but sulphuric acid was in practice the most convenient.

The second valuable result of the experiments was to show that the mineral phosphate while itself, like bones, inert on many soils only more so, becomes a valuable manure on treatment with acids. All this, however, was for the future.

Lawes' reaction to the 1839 results was to repeat the experiments on a larger scale. In the spring of 1840 he engaged a chemist, Dobson, from University College, London to help, and he used the superphosphate on half an acre or more of land, applying it to grass and other crops. Further, he found another source of phosphate: the charred bones used for the decolourizing of sugar and discarded after a few operations. In 1841 he bought 30 tons of this, made and used 20 tons of superphosphate and was so impressed with the result that he proposed to take out a patent for its manufacture, but was deterred by his friends. 'As I had no male relation,' he wrote in 1873, 'my Mother was the only person to influence me in my pursuits, and she was violently opposed both to science or business.' She wanted him to be an ordinary country gentleman, and in the 1840's gentlemen did not engage in trade, least of all in the manure trade. But he was so pleased with the 1841 results that he applied for and on May 23, 1842, obtained a patent for:

'(1) Chemically decomposing for purposes of manure by means of sulphuric acid of Bones, or Bone Ash or Apatite or Phosphorite or any other substances containing phosphoric acid;

(2) Compounding and use for purposes of manure of a mixture of phosphoric acid with any particular alkali, as Potass or Soda or Magnesia or Ammonia, or any earth containing such alkalis:

(3) Production and use for purposes of manure of a combination of Silica in the state of ground flint or same with

either of the alkalis Potass or Soda, or of the application for purposes of manure of crystall or glass ground to a state of powder.'

Lawes then began to act vigorously. He purchased a factory at Deptford Creek, London, and accomplished so much that on July 1, 1843, there appeared this modest advertisement in the *Gardeners' Chronicle:*—

J. B. LAWES PATENT MANURES composed of Super Phosphate of Lime, Phosphate of Ammonia, Silicate of Potass: etc. are now for sale at his Factory, Deptford-Creek, London, price 4s 6d per bushel. These substances can be had separately: the Super Phosphate of Lime alone is recommended for fixing the Ammonia of Dung-heaps, Cesspools, Gas Liquor, etc. Price 4s 6d per bushel.

For superphosphate this works out at about £7 per ton.

At first Lawes used bone ash as his chief source of phosphate. Some mineral phosphate was available from the Suffolk Crag and the Surrey Greensand, but it was too costly for general use. With the increasing scarcity of bones Lawes might soon have run into difficulties. Fortunately for him, however, large deposits of mineral phosphates were being found in France, Spain and elsewhere. Those at Estramadura in Spain had been known since the eighteenth century, but in 1843 Daubeny visited the district to ascertain whether the material had fertilizer value, and if so, whether sufficient was available to make it of interest to British farmers. He confirmed that it was there in very large quantities, showed by a field trial that it acted well on turnips, especially after treatment with sulphuric acid, and was indeed comparable with bones as fertilizer material.[1] There was difficulty of access, but the Spanish Government undertook to remedy this by building a railway.

Clearly there was no reason to fear any shortage of material for making superphosphate and Lawes was able to go ahead with an easy mind. And not only Lawes. Phosphates were supposed to nourish the brain. There was already a haunting fear of what would happen to mankind when the supplies of phosphatic manure could no longer satisfy world needs. An

[1] *Journ. Roy. Agric. Soc.*, Vol. VI., Pt. II, 1846.

imaginative French writer presented a lurid account of progressive degeneration as the human brain continuously deteriorated, becoming less and less capable of finding a solution as this terribly important problem gradually but inescapably became more and more difficult. Happily vast deposits of mineral phosphate were soon discovered and all fears of that particular catastrophe were put at rest.

Lawes made his discovery in 1839 but did not publish it. Liebig in his book published in 1840 and described later suggested that bones should be treated with sulphuric acid before use as manure, and has therefore been given the priority:[1] some of the continental writers even on this score credit Liebig with having founded the fertilizer industry. Liebig's recommendation, however, was singularly unhelpful: it was that the mixture of bones and sulphuric acid should be stirred up in water and sprayed on to the land before ploughing—a proposal so impracticable that it was ignored by farmers and was not mentioned by Daubeny in his comprehensive lecture on manures in 1841.[2] Even Liebig himself did not follow it up: when mineral phosphates were discovered in quantity he recommended that they should be burned and ground before use as manure. But the published statement played a part in the lawsuit to be described later.

In founding this new industry Lawes had two great strokes of luck. He started making superphosphate in the early days of a long period of rising prosperity for agriculture; also it quickly found favour with farmers because of its wonderful effects on turnips, then vitally important as the cornerstone of the four-course rotation, and an essential food for sheep and cattle during the winter.

Meanwhile another development was going on which was destined profoundly to affect the Rothamsted experiments. It was widely believed by scientists that the changes and processes in the bodies of plants and animals were brought about by a special agency, a vital force, different from the ordinary chemical forces governing the changes in mineral substances. Hence

[1] This action of sulphuric acid had already been announced by Escher in 1835. The priority question is discussed by W. G. T. Packard in *The Chemical Age*, January 23, p. 63, 1937.

[2] *Journ. Roy. Agric. Soc.*, 1841, Vol. 2, pp. 232–58.

had arisen the distinction between organic substances, producible only by vital agencies, and inorganic substances, producible by ordinary chemical agencies. The distinction broke down in 1828 when Wöhler synthesized urea, a typical organic substance, by purely inorganic reactions, involving no vital agencies. Justus von Liebig (1803–1873) Professor of Chemistry at Giessen University from 1824 to 1852[1] had made many investigations on the preparation and properties of other organic compounds. He widened the scope of his enquiries in order to discover something about the processes of life, or as he called it, 'the organization' of plants and animals, and proceeded to try and interest plant and animal physiologists in the matter. In 1837 he attended the Liverpool meeting of the British Association to read a paper urging British scientists to study organic chemistry 'which when taken in connection with the researches on physiology both animal and vegetable, which have been so successfully prosecuted in this country, may be expected to afford us the most important and novel conclusions respecting the functions of organization'.

Even at that early date the method of dealing with such a request was well understood: he was invited to prepare a report on the state of organic chemistry and organic analysis. No such report seems to have arrived; instead there appeared in 1840 a book dedicated to the British Association and entitled *Organic Chemistry in its application to Agriculture and Physiology*,[2] which can fairly claim to be the most important book ever published on the subject. Within eight years it had gone through seventeen editions and translations, four each in English and German; by 1876 there had been nine German editions.

Liebig was purely a laboratory worker. Many analyses were made in his laboratory by improved methods, notably those of Will and Fresenius on the mineral constituents of plants, which were much in advance of anything previously done. For most of his material he had to depend on his predecessors, Theodore de Saussure, Sprengel, Schübler, and others. The great value of the book lay in its shrewdly critical assembly of the

---

[1] He then transferred to Munich University but his most important work was already done.

[2] Edited by Lyon Playfair, one of his many pupils. The book was published simultaneously in Germany.

D

knowledge already gained, and building it up into a subject that accorded with the best chemical science of the day. It corresponded in a way to Davy's *Agricultural Chemistry* to which he pays high tribute. 'I have endeavoured to follow the path laid out by Sir Humphry Davy', he wrote, 'who based his conclusions only on what was capable of inquiry and proof.' In the thirty years since Davy wrote there had been further great advances in chemistry and the time was ripe for another critical survey. Liebig was ideally suited for the task. He was the leading chemist of his time, a brilliant writer, fierce and devastating in controversy in an uninhibited age when men spoke their minds freely, there being as yet no Laws of Libel to restrain them.

His views on plant nutrition were the first to attract attention in England. He himself made no experiments on the subject, but from existing knowledge he drew some revolutionary deductions. He pointed out that the carbon, the chief constituent, comes from 'carbonic acid' (carbon dioxide) most of which is taken from the unlimited supplies in the air by the green leaves of plants in daylight, though a small part formed by oxidation of the soil organic matter dissolves in the soil water and enters the roots where it is assimilated. This is specially important for the young plant which has as yet only very small leaves; as the plant grows, however, it becomes more important for the health of the soil. Ploughing and other cultivations increase fertility by allowing greater access of air and 'change the putrefaction of its organic constituents into a pure process of oxidation; and from the moment at which all the organic matter existing in a soil enters into a state of oxidation or decay its fertility is increased. The oxygen is no longer employed for the conversion of the brown soluble matter into the insoluble coal of humus, but serves for the formation of carbonic acid.'

The nitrogen, like the carbon, comes from the atmosphere where it occurs as ammonia and is brought down by the rain. In the first edition of his book he states that the quantities are insufficient and must be supplemented—which is quite correct. In later editions he altered this and stated that the quantity is sufficient. The hydrogen and oxygen in the plant substance come from water. None of these elements therefore need be supplied in the manure; organic manures, farmyard manure and the like, are at best superfluous. But the case is entirely different for the vitally important ash constituents of the plants: potassium, sodium, calcium, magnesium, phosphate, and in the case of cereals, silica.[1] These are obtained from the soluble mineral substances in the soil formed by weathering the rocks, but this process is extremely slow and quite inadequate to keep pace with the demands of well yielding crops. Supplies therefore have to be added to the soil.

Liebig assumed that the chemical analyses of the ash of a normal crop would show the need of the crop for the various mineral constituents, and analysis of the soil would show whether it contained sufficient; if not, the deficit must be made up. Manuring was no longer a matter of giving impressive doses of dung; it became an exact science, a matter of chemical analysis and arithmetic; attractive in its simplicity but devastatingly revolutionary. Had they come from anyone less distinguished than Liebig these new ideas would probably have been ignored: farmers could hardly be expected to believe that the value of farmyard manure lay, not in its richly smelling organic matter, but only in the ashes left after it was burned.

Liebig repeatedly emphasized that organic matter was quite unnecessary for soil fertility. 'It is the greatest possible mistake', he wrote, 'to suppose that temporary diminution of fertility in a soil is due to loss of humus: it is the mere consequence of the exhaustion of the alkalis.' The manurial action of solid excrements is due to their mineral constituents: human faeces supply phosphates of lime and magnesia, horse dung supplies phosphate of magnesia and silicate of potash. Straw supplies silicate of potash and phosphates. 'We could keep our fields in a constant state of fertility by replacing every year as much as we remove from them in the form of produce; but an increase in fertility and consequent increase in crop, can only be obtained when we add more to them than we take away.'

Phosphate supplies to the plant can be increased by dressings

[1] The function of the first four—they were called the alkalis and alkaline earths—was supposed to be the neutralization of the various acids that occur in the plant juices: they were therefore regarded as interchangeable: nevertheless they all occurred in all plants. In due course, however, Daubeny adduced massive evidence that sodium and potassium were not interchangeable in barley except to a very limited extent. (*Journ. Chem. Soc.*, 1853.)

of ground bones, and these act better after treatment with sulphuric acid.

Meanwhile three nitrogenous fertilizers, hitherto known only in small quantities, were becoming available on a commercial scale. Imports of nitrate of soda from the immense deposits in Chile began in 1835 just before Lawes started his experiments. But there was nothing in the nature of an Extension Service in those days and it still remained a novelty till 1850.[1] Sulphate and muriate of ammonia had long been obtainable in small quantities sufficient for small scale experiments, but large quantities for farm use came much later. It first appeared as a bye product in the manufacture of coal gas, by the distillation of coal. This started near the end of the eighteenth Century. Ammonia was one of the by products removed by washing with water. This gas liquor as it was called, was soon found to possess fertilizing properties, but the results were very erratic. The remedy was suggested by Dr Fownes in a prize essay written in 1842 and published in the Royal Agricultural Society's *Journal* for 1845.

'The only purely azotized (i.e. nitrogenous)manure' he wrote 'is the ammoniacal liquid from the gas works . . . this liquid has been tried by many farmers as a manure for corn (i.e. wheat) but with variable success as may be expected from its indefinite nature. . . . The best mode of using this substance will certainly be to reduce it to an impure ammoniacal salt, sulphate or chloride, then to apply such salt scattered over the ground in a sparing manner.'

Unknown to Fownes and the *Journal* editors this procedure had already been adopted by the Gas Light & Coke Company in 1815 but the product was unsatisfactory. Further attempts in 1833 were more successful. The first published field experiments were made in Scotland in 1841 by Mr Maclean of Penicuik Pentland Hills, and other more comprehensive ones followed. Farmers recognized the value of the improved product; by 1849 Way reported that a considerable number of them were using it. The sulphate was cheaper to produce than the muriate

[1] Ernle, *English Farming Past and Present*, 3rd edn., 1922, p. 366.

and was therefore chosen for large scale manufacture. The price was usually about £12 per ton: it was applied at the rate of about 1½ cwt. per acre on wheat, barley, oats and grass. It was usually mixed with common salt to increase the bulk, thereby facilitating broadcasting. It was less satisfactory for turnips in the low rainfall conditions of the Eastern counties where they were chiefly grown, but it acted well in the cooler moister conditions of the Northern counties. By 1879 about 40,000 tons per annum were being produced.[1] Lawes appears to have tried both sulphate of ammonia and nitrate of soda for the first time in 1841. Guano, the sun and air-dried droppings of the birds nesting on some of the small rainless and uninhabited islands off the coast of Peru, was also first imported in 1835. It was the richest fertilizer our farmers had ever known and they readily took to it, objecting only that its price was high. Lawes does not seem to have experimented with it, but he did with the other two nitrogenous fertilizers and obtained very good results.

This did not accord with Liebig's mineral theory of plant nutrition, and Daubeny, always seeking a path of peace, put forward an ingenious suggestion which, if it could have been established, would have reconciled the apparently conflicting views. In a paper before the British Association in 1841 entitled 'On manures considered as stimulants to vegetation' he raised the question whether these substances, instead of serving as nutrients, acted by stimulating secretion of the root agents that were supposed to dissolve the mineral nutrients in the soil and facilitate their absorption by the plant roots. It was claimed by some who had tried them that sodium nitrate and potassium salts were less effective in subsequent applications than in the first. Daubeny's explanation was that the first application had stimulated a large absorption of other essential salts, and if these were present in only limited quantities in the soil the supplies would soon be exhausted. He suggested that these ill effects could better be avoided by the addition of bone manure and if necessary other nutrients—soil analysis would show what these should be—rather than by discontinuance of the nitrate. It was the first hint that the total nutrient supply should be

[1] Further details are given by W. G. T. Packard in *The History of the Fertilizer Industry in Britain*, Fertilizer Society Proceedings, No. 19, 1952: London: and E. H. Tripp and S. W. Cheveley, *A Century of Fertilizer Progress*, 1939.

properly balanced in accordance with the requirements of the crop.

Although it was correct, Daubeny's answer did not dispose of the question whether fertilizers like superphosphate, sulphate of ammonia, nitrate of soda, etc. are plant foods or stimulants, or, in the more homely language of the farmer, beef steaks or glasses of whisky. That question continued to be raised and endlessly discussed at innumerable farmers' meetings throughout the rest of the 19th Century and spasmodically even later still.

Daubeny's further activities are described in a later chapter.

GILBERT JOINS LAWES.
THE ROTHAMSTED EXPERIMENTS BEGIN: 1843.

Meanwhile Lawes' factory was prospering and although it promised to give him a busy industrial life he wanted also to maintain his interest in agricultural science. To this end he invited a chemist, Joseph Henry Gilbert (1817–1901), three years his junior, to join him, which he did on June 1, 1843.

Gilbert was born at Hull on August 1, 1817, and came of a literary family. His father was Classical Tutor at the Divinity College, Rotherham, and afterwards became a well-known Congregational Minister at Nottingham whither they had moved in 1825. His mother, Ann Taylor before her marriage, was a well-known writer of children's verse—'My Mother' and 'Meddlesome Matty' are not yet forgotten. Both parents are given a place in the *Dictionary of National Biography*, a distinction accorded to none of Lawes' ancestors.

He went first to an elementary school taught by a very able blind lady, then to a school at Mansfield. While still a boy of fifteen a serious gun-shot accident destroyed one eye and injured the other. His general health suffered considerably and it was some years before he could resume his studies. In 1838 he entered Glasgow University and studied analytical chemistry under Prof. Thomas Thomson, botany under Sir W. J. Hooker, and Materia Medica. He remained only a year, however: in the autumn of 1839 he went to University College, London, where he attended the chemistry lectures and laboratory course of Prof. T. Graham; he also worked for a time in the laboratory of Prof. A. T. Thomson, who, it will be remembered, had been Lawes' chemical adviser. He spent the summer session of 1840 studying under Liebig at Giessen and obtained his Ph.D;—a matter of weeks only in those days—then on returning to University College he became assistant to Prof. A. T. Thomson where he met Lawes. In 1842 he was appointed consulting chemist to a calico printer in Manchester, but after a few months he came to Rothamsted.

Lawes and Gilbert were almost the exact counterparts of each other. Lawes was the shrewd, far seeing, practical man of affairs, laying down the broad outlines; very able in business, insistent on what he believed to be his rights, yet, these once acknowledged, prepared to offer compensation or even to waive them if they injured others; having also the strong sense of responsibility towards the village, and especially his own work people, that was so characteristic of the old country squires. Among the farm workers he organized and helped to run a savings bank, a pig club, a group of allotments, and other activities. He was not an active politician, nor did he attend scientific meetings. He was a country gentleman; hospitable, deeply attached to his farm, and he much enjoyed his autumn holiday deer stalking and salmon fishing in Scotland. He had shrewd scientific insight, could see a problem in its proper perspective and devise a direct way of dealing with it. But he was impatient of detail and lost interest in an enquiry once he was satisfied that a solution had been found. An old farm worker told me that he once gave the order to discontinue the Broadbalk wheat experiment on the grounds that nothing more was to be learned from them. Only after a most urgent appeal by Gilbert was the order countermanded.

Gilbert on the other hand was a born student, much devoted to detail, and meticulously accurate; very loth to change. He would have no truck with short cuts, like logarithms or slide rules, nor would he ever use the metric system. For use in the laboratory he devised a fluid measure based on the gallon and the one-thousandth part thereof, and had burettes made for it, also he used grain weights and fractions thereof. He was unperturbed by the fact that all other chemists of repute were using the metric weights and measures and would not adopt his. He travelled a great deal and regularly attended scientific meetings.

He was extremely methodical and from the time of his arrival at Rothamsted he kept full records of crop yields and analytical, meteorological, and other data, which, once begun were never discontinued. Throughout his fifty-eight years at Rothamsted there are hardly any gaps in the records. The work involved was excruciatingly dull and dreary: it nearly wrecked the only trained scientific worker that kept to it permanently; the others remained only a short time. Instead of trying to keep young scientists Gilbert took boys from the village school and had them taught the various processes, one process only per boy. They became extremely competent, each at his particular job. No blame attached to a mistake provided it was reported in full and at once, but any attempt at concealment or evasion was severely dealt with. As they grew up the successful boys were retained on the staff, becoming thereby a village élite; they trained other boys to succeed them, passing on to them the feeling of pride in their work, and pride, too, in being part of the great Rothamsted organization.

Gilbert was somewhat of a martinet: he was also of jealous disposition and did not like to have younger scientists working at the laboratory for fear they should steal some of the credit that he felt was his due. His work was his life, and he kept at it till he died in 1901 at the age of eighty-four. He knew his fellow scientists, but otherwise did not greatly cultivate the social graces. A lady whom his hostess on one occasion had allotted to him as dinner partner felt honoured at the choice, but was soon desperately bored because his sole conversation was a long and dreary criticism of Liebig's mineral theory. He was a great character: one of those about whom stories and legends grew up and clustered, to be remembered long after he was gone. He owed much to his second wife Maria ('Ria to him), a very kind lady who was often able to smooth over difficulties that his rather stubborn nature had created.

1843. PREPARATION FOR THE CLASSICAL FIELD INVESTIGATIONS

With the arrival of Gilbert the experimental programme at Rothamsted changed completely both in direction and in character. The work on superphosphate ceased, and henceforward the field experiments were kept quite apart from the factory and its problems: indeed Gilbert stated in his evidence at the lawsuit that he went there only two or three times a year. Gilbert's purpose was, in his own words, 'the investigation of the scientific problems involved in agricultural processes'.

The work fell into two divisions: field experiments on the arable part of the farm, and laboratory investigations. Lawes' busy life often kept him away from Rothamsted, but whenever he was at home he and Gilbert had long conferences daily about the work. Field experiments were new for Gilbert and for most of the farm staff; many little details had to be worked out. For the first few years the programme was slender. The earliest recorded experiments were with wheat and turnips in 1843.

Those on wheat were on Broadbalk field, which had had no manure since 1839 when the four year rotation started, and was due to receive farmyard manure in the current year. One plot remained unmanured, another received farmyard manure at the rate of fourteen tons per acre which became the standard dressing, and a third, added two years later, received the mixture of ammonium chloride and ammonium sulphate which was called ammonium salts. The other experiments were on turnips in Barnfield. For the first three years the comparison was simply between farmyard manure and no manure: after that, however, the plots instead of being set in adjoining rows as on Broadbalk were set out chess-board fashion, the different mineral dressings in rows side by side, and the nitrogenous dressings in rows crossing them at right angles. It was entirely new, and suitable farm workers had to be picked for training in the experimental technique; they remained an *élite* as long as the ordinary farm lasted.

The turnip experiments gave such interesting results that they were published in the *Gardeners' Chronicle* for June, 1845, first of the 174 Rothamsted papers to be issued in Lawes' and Gilbert's time. It was, however, in Lawes' name only: Gilbert's name did not appear, nor did it on most of the papers published during the next ten years. After 1855, however, all papers appeared in both names.

Meanwhile Liebig's book on *Agricultural Chemistry* was being widely read. It had contained various statements which

D*

he later amended. Lawes set out his views in his first important paper[1] and in a later one jointly with Gilbert[2] to which there was a lively rejoinder by Liebig in his delightful book *Familiar letters on Chemistry*. As foundation of a research programme there is nothing better than a controversial hypothesis, and it may be counted part of Lawes' good fortune this was ready to hand.

Like many of their contemporaries, Lawes and Gilbert were keen controversialists and loved to assail a hypothesis. They began with an attack on Liebig's 'mineral theory' of the nutrition of crops. They accepted his view that plants draw their carbon from the atmosphere, but they vigorously controverted his idea that nitrogen also came from the air and therefore need not be supplied in the manure. Lawes' early experiments had shown the great fertilizing value of sulphate of ammonia and nitrate of soda, and Gilbert's analyses soon showed that atmospheric ammonia contributed nothing appreciable to the crop; the nitrogen came from the soil or the fertilizer, and the size of the crop depended on the amount supplied.

But there was a troublesome exception. Clover and other leguminous plants growing in the field not only required no nitrogenous manure but actually enriched the soil in nitrogen. For twenty-five years Lawes and Gilbert sought an explanation of this surprising phenomenon but in vain. As was often to happen, a problem in agricultural science was brought to a stand-still for want of new ideas that could come in only from another branch of science, and this had not yet been developed. The problem was solved in the end, but by two German investigators, Hellriegel and Wilfarth, and not at Rothamsted.

Lawes and Gilbert's second quarrel with Liebig was about the relation between the fertilizer requirements of the crop and the composition of its ash. They recognized the need for supplying the various mineral elements, but did not agree that the quantities required could be deduced from analysis of the ash: if it proved anything a small proportion in the ash did not indicate a small requirement but a great difficulty in ex-

[1] 'Agricultural Chemistry', *Journ. Roy. Agric. Soc.*, vol. 8, 226, 1847.
[2] 'Agricultural Chemistry, especially in relation to the Mineral Theory of Baron Liebig', *ibid.*, vol. 12, 1, 1851.

tracting from the soil what might be a very important element.

The laboratory in which Gilbert worked was the barn which Lawes had converted in 1837. It was the first of its kind in Great Britain and was only three years younger than the oldest of all, Boussingault's laboratory at Pechelbronn, Alsace, set up in 1834. It was a low single storey building about forty-five feet in length. Gilbert's mother visiting it one evening in 1850 found it

'a wild, rambling laboratory, surrounded, or rather crammed, with implements and objects, that looked more like the fossil remains of extinct species than anything else. . . . He (Henry) stuck three lighted candles in some sort of putty or other, about the walls, and then took leave of us for two hours of dismal, and rather nervous-looking solitude, with just the possibility of an explosion before he had done.'

APPENDIX TO CHAPTER III

Davy's methods of soil analysis. (1805)[1]

200 to 400 grains (13–26 gms) of air dried soil are needed. Determine the specific gravity (sp. gr. bottle method). This gives an indication of the quantity of animal and vegetable matter present, then:

(1) determine loss of water at 300 °F. by heating in a basin over an Argand burner. If no thermometer is available the discolouring of a chip of wood at the bottom of the basin is a sufficient indication of the temperature. If 50 grains weight are lost the soil is highly absorbent and therefore rich in vegetable or animal matter or aluminous earth. If 20 to 10 are lost the soil is only slightly absorbent or retentive and is probably mostly siliceous earth.

(2) Bruise gently in a mortar, sieve out and weigh (*a*) vegetable fibre, (*b*) stones; note whether these are calcareous (effervesce with acids); siliceous (scratch glass when freshly broken) or aluminous (easily cut and do not effervesce).

(3) Boil the soil in three or four times its weight of water and when its 'texture' has broken down let it cool, 'agitate the parts together', and leave to rest; the coarse sand separates out in one minute, the finer in two or three. Collect these fractions from the bottom and weigh the COARSE SAND.

(4) Evaporate the water. The residue consists of SALTS and SOLUBLE ANIMAL AND VEGETABLE MATTER.

[1] From his *Elements of Agricultural Chemistry*, 1813, pp. 138–154; also his small treatise *On the analysis of soils as connected with their improvement*, 1805.

(5) Collect and weigh the fine residue of (3), transfer to evaporating basin, add twice its weight of muriatic acid diluted with its volume of water, stir often, filter, dry and weigh the residue (a). Loss — ACID SOLUBLE MATERIAL.

(6) To the solution add a little 'prussiate of potasse and iron' (potassium ferro-cyanide). The blue precipitate is a compound of IRON. Add the 'prussiate' drop by drop till no more precipitate forms. Collect, heat to redness: the residue is IRON OXIDE and perhaps some MANGANESE oxides.

(7) To the filtrate add a solution of 'neutralized carbonate of potash' till effervescence ceases. The precipitate is CARBONATE OF LIME. Collect, dry and weigh.

(8) Boil the filtrate for a quarter of an hour: the precipitate is CARBONATE OF MAGNESIA.

(9) Go back to (5): ignite the residue (a) in a crucible 'over a common fire' till all blackness disappears. Loss is ANIMAL AND VEGETABLE MATTER. It is impossible to separate these 'without very refined and difficult experiments'. A smell of burnt feathers indicates animal material and a blue flame vegetable material.

(10) The residue is 'earthy matter': alumina, silica, and combined oxides of iron and 'manganesum'. To separate these boil for two or three hours with sulphuric acid diluted with four times its weight of water: for every 100 grains of solid allow 120 grains of acid. Filter. The residue is SILICA.

(11) To the filtrate add a solution of ammonium succinate: this precipitates the OXIDE OF IRON.

(12) To the filtrate add soap lye: this precipitates the ALUMINA. Iron and alumina precipitates must be heated to redness, each is then converted into the oxide. No method is given for determining the manganese.

The above technique suffices for all ordinary purposes, but if 'very great accuracy' is required a modification is used. In (10) instead of boiling with sulphuric acid the residue is fused with four times its weight of dry potassium carbonate in a silver or porcelain crucible. The mass is dissolved in muriatic acid and the solution evaporated nearly to dryness, distilled water is added. The residue is silica. The solution contains the iron, alumina, and other bases as chlorides and these are separated as before.

This is the process usually adopted by 'chemical philosophers' for the analysis of stones.

There was no simple means of estimating calcium sulphate or phosphate. If either was suspected 400 grains of soil mixed with one third its weight of powdered charcoal was heated to redness in a crucible for half an hour. The mass was then boiled for a quarter of an hour in half a pint of water, filtered, and the filtrate exposed to the air in an open vessel for some days. A white precipitate forms if any notable quantity of gypsum is present. For the determination of phosphate 'muriatic acid must be digested upon the soil, in quantity more than sufficient to saturate the soluble earths: the solution must be evaporated, and water poured upon the solid matter. This fluid will dissolve the compounds of earths with the muriatic acid and leave the phosphate of lime untouched.'

Analysis of a good siliceous sandy soil (*Davy*)

	Grains
Water of absorption	18
Stones and siliceous gravel	42
Undecomposed vegetable fibres	10
Fine siliceous sand	200
Carbonate of Lime[1]	25
Carbonate of magnesia	4
Matter destructible by heat	10
Silex	40
Alumine	32
Oxide of iron	4
Soluble matter chiefly sulphate of potash and vegetable extract	5
Gypsum	3
Phosphate of lime	2
Total	395
Loss	5

[1] Estimated from the volume of carbon dioxide evolved on treatment with acid.

CHAPTER IV

FOUNDATION AND EARLY YEARS OF THE ROYAL AGRICULTURAL SOCIETY OF ENGLAND

1837 – 1867

THE year 1837, one of great landmarks in the history of the old British Empire, is also an important landmark in the history of British agricultural science and practice, for it was then that the first steps were taken to create a permanent organization for encouraging cooperation of farmers in all parts of Britain with agricultural scientists. Both parties stood to gain: the farmers empirically discovered new facts unknown to the scientists and were able to check (and not infrequently disprove) some of the scientists' deductions, while the scientists could and did solve many problems which had long defeated the farmers, and as time went on they were able to provide new appliances considerably better than anything previously known.

The first step was taken in December 1837 when Earl Spencer, one of the leading agriculturists of the time, speaking at the Annual Dinner of the Smithfield Club then at the beginning of its fortieth year, suggested the formation of an Agricultural Society of England to complete the group of Societies that for long had been doing much useful work among farmers. He instanced in particular the good work of the Highland and Agricultural Society as an example to be followed and stressed the importance of applying science to agriculture.[1] The idea proved acceptable: The English Agricultural Society was duly formed. One of its declared objects was 'To encourage men of

---

[1] A detailed account of the formation of the Society was given by its Secretary B. Clarke in Vol. 51 of its *Journal*, 1890.

science in their attention to the improvement of agricultural implements, the construction of farm buildings and cottages, the application of chemistry to the general purposes of agriculture, the destruction of insects injurious to vegetable life, and the eradication of weeds'.

The Society held its first London meeting in May 1839 and its Committee presented a list of problems on which more information was wanted. Among them was the classification of soils: 'it being obvious that a correct knowledge of the various soils of this country is the only solid foundation of English Agricultural science'. Plant diseases were also on the list: little was known of their real nature and 'still less of any mode of prevention or cure'. The bone problem[1] was as yet unsolved and one of the questions related to it: 'What is the constituent element of Bones which promotes vegetation on some soils, and how is that element rendered inoperative elsewhere?'

The first volume of the Society's *Journal* was in two parts issued in 1839 and 1840. The first paper was by Philip Pusey, one of the great farming land owners of the day, who had taken a very active part in founding the Society. He described the present state of agricultural science and practice and indicated promising lines of improvement. Further advances, he stated, would require careful observation and well considered experiments on a number of large farms provided with ample resources and located in different climatic and other regions. Another paper by John Morton on the relative values of several varieties of wheat is interesting because of the great amount of information it was planned to provide. The plots were very small, 1/440 acre only. The seeds were sown to an exact depth and uniform spacing, a special hand dibbler being used, and full records were taken of (1) the number of seeds planted (792 for each of 16 varieties), (2) number of survivors, (3) number of heads, (4) heads per root, (5) grain yield, lb. per plot and tons per acre, (6) straw length, (8) weight of roots. Observations were also made on the incidence of attack by insect pests. Such thoroughness was extremely rare and remained so for many years.

In March 1840 the Society received its Charter and thereupon changed its name and became the Royal Agricultural Society of

[1] P. 91.

England. Its aim was re-stated:—'The Royal Agricultural Society of England has been founded for the object of perfecting the System of English Agriculture by the union of practice with science. . . .'

These last three words became forthwith the motto of the Society, they were printed on the title page of the new Society's *Journal* and on all succeeding issues. The *Journal* rapidly became the medium for publication of papers on agricultural science, and a study of its pages shows clearly the course of developments during the next fifty years. Most of the important investigations made in England are reported there, even when a fuller account had been published by the Royal Society or the Chemical Society.

In the early years problems relating to plant nutrition and fertilizer use attracted most attention. At the time of the first volume guano and nitrate of soda were the only fertilizers known: both were of recent introduction (1835); later volumes deal with other fertilizers as they were introduced and the new problems arising therefrom. As time went on other subjects gradually crept in until a new and much more complex science had developed. This process began in the second volume of the *Journal* (1840) where John Stevens-Henslow, (1796–1861), Professor of Botany at Cambridge, writing on the diseases of wheat had to admit that most of his information was from Continental sources, no proper research having been carried out in this country.

Already problems were arising in regard to nitrate of soda, and Philip Pusey writing in the same volume about its alleged erratic behaviour as a fertilizer appealed to 'men of science who are competent to do it justice . . . to assist us by investigating the question of manures and the food of plants.' This was written in November, 1840 after he had already read Liebig's book which apparently had not altogether satisfied him.

The position of sulphate of ammonia was uncertain. Gas liquor had been known to be a good fertilizer almost from the outset in the early days of the century and the effect was attributed to the ammonia. The fertilizer value of sulphate of ammonia was known in the late 1830's to Lawes and the agricultural chemists but not generally to farmers: as late as 1843 Fownes wrote[1] 'I beg once more to call attention to the salts of ammonia. Should these really be found to produce the beneficial effects anticipated, we shall possess at home, within the limits of our own island, resources for the improvement of agriculture, compared with which guano, and nitrate of soda, and all such things are insignificant'.

James F. W. Johnston (p. 130) had a paper about guano controverting Liebig's view that its high fertilizer value lay in its alkalis and alkaline earths in spite of the difficulty that the quantities present were very small. Johnston found practically no potash in his samples, but 7 per cent of Ammonia (NH_3) and 29 to 43 per cent of phosphate of lime: these two in his view fully accounted for the high manurial value.

Later (Vol. 3, 1843) Daubeny emphasized the need for more agricultural education and research in this country, and showed how far we were behind some of the continental countries, France and especially Germany. He recognized the willingness of many of our farmers to undertake empirical trials with a new manure, but continued: 'it would be highly useful if a course of experiments were set on foot to determine the exact mode in which it (the manure) operates upon the soil and upon the crop. And I know not how such experiments can well be instituted, except it be on an experimental farm, established for the purpose, and placed under scientific hands'—a theme to which he frequently recurs.

Daubeny rendered further valuable service by urging the need of improving soil analysis. Chemists were still using Davy's 1805 method,[2] but it is difficult to see what guidance the results could have afforded. At the meeting of the British Association in 1842 he declared emphatically that the method was too crude and should be improved: determination of phosphate should be refined to take cognizance of quantities of the order of $0 \cdot 1$ or even $0 \cdot 01$ per cent. Further, the subsoil should also be analysed. Ploughing was now deeper than formerly, but there would be no advantage in this unless the subsoil contained substances needed by the crop, but not present in optimum quantities in the surface soil. In Vol. 3 of the Society's *Journal* (1843) Pusey in a paper on the 'Progress of the Agricultural Knowledge during the last four years' joins in the

[1] *Journal Roy. Agric. Soc.*, 1843, Vol. 4, p. 498.   [2] See p. 107.

condemnation and complains that soil analyses published by Davy and later agricultural chemists are all 'so superficial, and in most cases so inaccurate that we possess no means of ascertaining the composition or nature of English arable land'.

The methods of analysis of soils and plant ash, and some typical results, are set out in detail by Dr Fownes in Vol. 4, p. 498, 1843. One example will suffice. An old grassland soil after drying contained 51 per cent of siliceous sand rich in iron oxide and 49 per cent of finely divided matter removed by elutriation: this contained per 100 parts:—

Silica	68·4
Alumina	10·2
Oxide of iron	11·8
Carbonate of lime	0·8
Carbonate of magnesia	0·4
Organic matter	3·6
Potash (by lime process)	4·08[1]
Loss	0·72
	———
Total	100

There was direct evidence of the presence of nitrogen and phosphate but no estimate of their amounts.

The procedure was apparently identical with that used in 1807 by Dr Boyd of the Bath and West Society (p. 60) and a modern advisory officer would find it equally unhelpful in trying to draw up a fertilizer *régime*.

At the Anniversary Meeting of the Society on May 22, 1843, it was announced that Dr Playfair, widely known as the translator of Liebig's great book on agricultural chemistry,

'having resolved to devote his attention to the study and practice of agricultural chemistry, and to establish at the Royal Institution at Manchester a laboratory for the pursuit and investigation of this subject, the Council have gladly availed themselves of the opportunity of appointing him Consulting Chemist to the Society'.

The post was honorary and carried no salary; the duties were to advise the Society on chemical matters, and to undertake analy-

[1] No comment is made on this apparently high figure.

ses of soils and other substances for members on a scale of charges.

Lyon Playfair was born at Chunar, Bengal Province, in 1818 and educated at the Universities of St Andrews, Glasgow, and Edinburgh; he then proceeded to Giessen where he worked under Liebig: he was fellow student with Gilbert. After taking his doctor's degree he returned to England, became Chemical Adviser to the Primrose Print Works at Clitheroe (Lancashire), in 1841 and '42, and then in 1843 he was appointed honorary Professor of Chemistry to the Royal Institution, Manchester.

He was very able and might have done much for agricultural science but he was soon tempted away. In 1845 he was appointed to a professorship in the newly established Royal School of Mines, South Kensington, and also as chemist to the Geological Survey, and was much in demand by various public departments for help in chemical and gas inspections. It was a great loss for agricultural science.

The 1845 and 1846 *Journals* (Vols. 6 and 7) contain papers by John Hannon on Liebig's 'great discovery of dissolving bones in sulphuric acid' for making them effective as fertilizer over a wider range of soils. He had made experiments with solutions as Liebig suggested and also had prepared some dry superphosphate.

He had heard of Lawes and obtained from him directions for making superphosphate—though why Lawes should have given them is not explained. Pusey on the other hand seems not to have heard of Lawes or his superphosphate factory, for in discussing the results of experiments with home-made superphosphate in the 1845 *Journal* he states that 'nothing seems now to be wanted but some plan for bringing it within the ordinary routine of farming'.

During this period there was terrible destruction of the potato crop in Ireland for which neither cause nor remedy could be found. Playfair discussed the subject at length in two papers in Vol. 6. (1845); some thought the cause was a fungus, others that it was of chemical nature. He made no helpful proposals in regard to the disease, and could only suggest the abandonment of potatoes and search for alternative cheap foods. Vol. 7 (1846) contains a detailed account of the disease by

F. J. Graham, and a correct description of the climatic conditions favouring its spread. He also made microscopic studies of the fungi isolated from diseased tubers, including *Phytophthora infestans*, the actual cause of the disease, though he did not realise this and thought it was only a secondary infection.

The papers presented to the British Association for reading at its Annual Meetings were generally more scientific in character though some of them had quite a sound practical bearing. There was the proud boast of Sir Roderick Murchison, the distinguished geologist, President of the 1846 meeting at Southampton, in reminding agricultural members of the Association to make use of its staff for the solution of their problems: 'and if, above all, they wish us to solve their doubts respecting the qualities of soils and the results of these mixtures, or the effects of various manures upon them, our chemists are at hand'. At the same meeting there was the warning of W. C. Spooner, that most recommendations of chemists are too costly to be of practical value to farmers.

Daubeny was long an important figure at their meetings. His papers are too numerous for individual discussion, and a number were also read elsewhere.

A new contributor appeared in Vol. 7 (1846) who in a short career played an important part in the development of agricultural science. He was James Thomas Way, then Professor of Chemistry at the Cirencester College of Agriculture. He was born in 1821, the son of a doctor at Tunbridge Wells. In 1841 he entered University College, London and studied chemistry under Thomas Graham, afterwards becoming his assistant. He did not remain long in London, but in 1843 went to Oxford as assistant to Daubeny to analyse the ashes of agricultural plants in order to furnish the Royal Agricultural Society with data needed for manuring according to Liebig's views then widely held. In 1846 he was appointed Professor of Chemistry at the Royal Agricultural College, Cirencester. His paper, 'The fairy rings of pasture as illustrating the use of inorganic manure', was of no great importance in itself, but significant as showing him to be not only a good analyst but also capable of thinking about his experimental results. He rightly associated the good growth of grass on the fairy ring with the growth of the fungus. The mineral constituents left on its death contained 55 per cent of potash and 29 per cent of phosphoric acid, while for dead grass the figures were only 35 and 6·5 respectively. The fungus thus concentrated within itself these two essential nutrients and when it died they served as a manurial dressing. This paper was followed by a longer and more detailed one on the ash constituents of the grain and straw of a number of varieties of wheat with recommendations about the mineral manures needed to replace the nutrients thus removed from the soil. A second paper in the next volume dealt on the same lines with swedes and a still later one with pasture grasses;[1] this was followed by one on the relative nutritive and fattening properties of different 'Natural' and 'Artificial' grasses.[2]

This same volume (Vol. 8 1847) is important as containing Lawes' first scientific paper: it is entitled 'On Agricultural Chemistry' and is in his name only—although Gilbert had been at Rothamsted for four years. It contains his first announcement of the purpose of his experiments: 'For some years past', he wrote, 'I have been engaged in a very extensive series of experiments upon my farm with a view to determine some of the more important questions which are constantly arising in the minds of agriculturists.' The paper is the first round in the long controversy with Liebig about the source of nitrogen for plants: 'It cannot be too generally known', he wrote categorically, 'that the elaboration of carbon bears a very constant relation to the supply of ammonia in the manure', and he goes on: 'In my experiments upon wheat it required 3 lb. of ammonia to produce a bushel of corn'—a statement based on the yields for the first three seasons of the Broadbalk experiments. In a note added to this paper Philip Pusey makes the first reference to the Rothamsted experiments to appear in the Society's Journal. He had been to see them and was greatly impressed

'. . . my confidence in the scrupulous accuracy of those gentlemen (Lawes and Gilbert) has been strengthened by a visit to Rothamsted . . . . The extent of the experimental ground—the expenditure at which it has been kept up—the perseverance with which, year after year, it has been maintained, are such as

[1] Vol. 11. p. 497.
[2] *Ibid.*, Vol. 14, p. 171, 1853. 'Natural' grasses were wild and self-sown, 'artificial' were sown, generally with seed from some other farm or district.

might rather be expected from a public institution than a private landowner, and render Rothamsted, at present, the principal source of trustworthy scientific information on Agricultural Chemistry.'

The same volume contained a long account of the three years' experiments on turnips at Rothamsted, also in Lawes' name only, of which Lawes had already given a preliminary account in the *Gardeners' Chronicle* for June, 1845—his first publication.

Considering how important drainage was to English farmers of the mid-nineteenth century, and how much money some landowners were spending on it, a number of papers might have been expected on the subject. Actually there was only one of importance: it was by Josiah Parkes, the drainer of Chat Moss, who had in 1843 been appointed Consulting Engineer to the Society. In it he discussed the influence of water on the temperature of soils, and the quantity of rain water and its discharge by drains. The data were obtained from King's Langley about ten miles west of Rothamsted and showed that about 42 per cent of the rain water (26·6 inches per annum) percolated through three feet of soil carrying grass, as against about 50 per cent through bare soil at Rothamsted.

In 1847 Way was appointed Consulting Chemist to the Society and he held the post for the next ten years. His first paper after his appointment gave the results of his search for soft mineral phosphates which could be used direct as fertilizer, thus saving the cost of acid treatment which the harder minerals required. He examined samples of the phosphatic fossils and marls from the upper and lower greensand: unfortunately the deposits were too small to be of any commercial interest. When softer minerals were later found in quantity they proved less effective than superphosphate and did not come into common use.

Way re-examined his methods of analysis. As already mentioned, the German chemists, notably Will and Fresenius in Liebig's Laboratory, had introduced considerable improvements, including ways of avoiding losses of certain elements, e.g. potassium and sulphur in the incineration which formed part of the analytical procedure. Way admitted that some sulphur had been lost, but nothing else. British agricultural science owes a great debt to those chemists, mostly German, who spent their lives in the dreary monotonous task of improving qualitative and quantitative chemical analysis.[1]

A group of papers by Way in the next volume of the Society's *Journal* (Vol. 10. p. 849) is of interest as showing the marked improvement he had effected in presentation of analytical results. Imports of guano were increasing, but the different lots varied a good deal in composition and value. The older analysts following Liebig had assumed that the fertilizer components were the phosphates and alkaline salts and earths, and reported these only, or if they did more, included ammonium urate. Way gave a much more modern presentation: ammonia, phosphate of lime, and potash. Further, and greatly daring, he calculated the money values of the different samples from the cost per pound of the fertilizer constituents in sulphate of ammonia, coprolites and sulphate and muriate of potash. The result might have been rather unfair for the vendor but it would have afforded some guidance to the buyer.

Later he made the method more precise and used it for valuing mixed fertilizers on the basis of the prices of single nutrient fertilizers like nitrate of soda. Knowing the percentage of the nutrient in the fertilizer and the price asked, the value of 1 per cent per ton was calculated. The values thus obtained for nitrogen, phosphate, and potash[2] indicated a fair price for a mixed fertilizer, subject to any special factor that might justify a higher price. This is the Unit System, and has proved very useful. It was not at once adopted, and there was an interval of years during which there was much over-charging. Already dishonesty was appearing in the manure trade and some of the samples analysed were worthless.

Way was an industrious analyst and in successive issues of the *Journal* published numbers of ash analyses of crops with the expectation of getting guidance for their manuring. He had already dealt with numerous varieties of wheat grain and straw and with roots (Vols. 7 and 8 of the Journal): to these he added pasture grasses in 1850 (Vol. 11). As a result of Liebig's insistence on their vital importance, analyses of the ashes of crops

[1] Fresenius' textbook on the subject was in use in British chemical laboratories as late as the 1890's.

[2] N P_2O_5 and K_2O in these days.

were much in vogue during this period: the palm must go to E. T. Hemming, an otherwise unknown person, who appended 113 pages of tabular matter to his prize essay on 'The neglect of Chemistry by Practical Farmers, its causes and remedies', all of which were published *in extenso* in the *Journal*, Vol. 13, 1852.

Way's paper on the relative nutritive and fattening proper-ties of different natural and artificial grasses illustrates the advances in the evaluation of crops since the time of Davy who, it will be remembered, assessed the relative feeding values of the twenty-nine varieties of the Woburn grasses by estimating their respective contents of water soluble material—which had proved entirely fallacious. The analytical methods used by Way represented a great advance and have almost a modern look: they included determinations of '(1) Water, (2) Albuminous Principles, (3) Fatty matters, (4) Heat producing Principles: starch, sugar, gums, (5) Woody Fibre, (6) Ash': in modern terms, water, protein, fat, carbohydrates, fibre, ash. The correspondence is not exact, but the difference is not great. Way added that neither Woody Fibre nor Ash had nutritive value, which is not correct.

These and other papers show that Way served his generation faithfully but he did more. Two investigations opened up entirely new subjects of great scientific interest and technical importance. The first was suggested to him about 1848 by a Yorkshire gentleman, H. S. Thompson, who three years earlier, working with Mr Spence, a chemist of York, had discovered that when a solution of ammonium sulphate is shaken with soil the ammonia is fixed by the soil and calcium goes into solution. Potassium sulphate in solution behaved similarly: potassium was absorbed and calcium liberated. The result explained why drainage water from land fertilized with ammonium and potassium salts contained no ammonia and only little potash. He recognized the important bearing of this discovery on fertilizer practice and continued to follow it up: meanwhile he told Way about it.

Way saw that the significance of the discovery was not con-fined to fertilizer practice but had important relations with the soil. He found that the amount of calcium liberated was equivalent to the amount of ammonia fixed: it was therefore a chemical reaction between the ammonium sulphate and an insoluble 'salt of lime' in the soil. He then tried to find this 'salt of lime'. It was neither the calcium carbonate, the sand, the undecomposed rock however finely ground, nor the organic matter. It was in the clay fraction, but it formed only part of the clay and it lost its power on ignition. No known simple silicate possessed these properties, but he prepared a number of 'double silicates' by putting another base into aluminium silicate (which he regarded as the basis of clay) and showed that the lime and alumina silicate reacted, like clay, with ammonium salts to form an almost insoluble double ammonium silicate and a soluble calcium salt; also, like clay, it lost this property after ignition.[1] He found that these double silicates could be arranged in order: the bases of the higher members being able to displace those of members lower down but not *vice versa*. Although he did not establish the existence of such double silicates in the soil, their resemblance to the reactive 'salt of lime' was so close that he considered himself justified in assuming their identity.

The idea of double silicates held the field for many years, but in the end it proved too simple, as has often happened in the history of agricultural science. When sixty years later methods became available for opening up the clay complex a wonderful structure was revealed and the full significance of Way's discovery became manifest. By that time, however, Way had long since been dead—as also has not uncommonly happened to agricultural scientists.

The significance of his other important discovery was also not fully recognized at the time. In 1856 in analysing drainage water from soils variously fertilized he found as he expected practically no ammonia and very little potash, but to his surprise nitrate was present, though none had been supplied as fertilizer: it could only have been produced in the soil from added ammonium salts or other nitrogen compounds. This discovery[2] lay for some twenty years before it could be understood;

---

[1] Thompson's paper is in Vol. 11. p. 68–74, 1850 of the Society's *Journal*, Way's are in the same volume pp. 313–379 and Vol. 13. 123–143 (1852).

[2] Really a rediscovery. The presence of nitre in the soil was well known in Elizabethan times (p. 17) but had apparently been forgotten.

the mystery could not be solved until the important science of soil bacteriology was born.

Unfortunately in the next year (1857) Way resigned his appointment with the Royal Agricultural Society and silently abandoned agricultural science. This was a great tragedy, for it is impossible to say what he might have done had he continued as he had been doing. No other worker of his time had opened up so much new ground, so little appreciated at the time but so rich in consequences which, however, were not realised till long after his death.

He gave up agriculture to work on the problems of London's sewage disposal. Liebig had never tired of condemning the method, all too common in those days, of running the sewage into the nearest river, greatly to the detriment of the downstream inhabitants. But what Liebig most fiercely denounced was the waste of the mineral nutrients which the crops had taken out from the soil; although at the time these were renewed by imports—robbing other countries, he declared—an end would come and 'the consequences might be incalculable. Bloody wars have sometimes sprung from causes of much less importance'. Liebig's suggestion was that superphosphate should be added to the sewage and the resulting mixture used as fertilizer. This recalls Lawes' claim in his first advertisement, that superphosphate can be used for absorbing ammonia in manure heaps. Way's first paper on London sewage appeared in the Society's *Journal* for 1859: later he collaborated with Lawes in producing the third Report of the Royal Commission on Sewage (1865). During the rest of his active life he worked for various official bodies but his health was not good and he died at the age of sixty-four in 1884.[1]

Way was succeeded by John Christopher Augustus Voelcker: always known as Augustus Voelcker. He was born in 1822 at Frankfort-on-Main, left school at the age of sixteen and worked for six years in a pharmacist's shop, then in 1844 he entered the University of Göttingen where he studied chemistry under Wöhler and took his Ph.D. degree two years later. He managed also to attend some of Liebig's lectures at Giessen. He then went to Utrecht University as assistant to Prof. Jan Mulder who was

---

[1] An Obituary Notice appeared in the *Journal of the Chemical Society* (*Transactions*) for 1884, p. 29, but none in the *Journal of the Royal Agricultural Society*.

working on physiological chemistry, especially in its relation to vegetable and animal production. He stayed only a short time, but it decided his future career.

In February, 1847, he transferred to Edinburgh as assistant to J. F. W. Johnston, then Chemist to the Agricultural Chemistry Association of Scotland (p. 131). Here he remained for two years, getting familiar with the ways and problems of the farmers, periodically lecturing at Durham University in place of Johnston, and cultivating the friendship of George Wilson, Regius Professor of Technology at Edinburgh University, which became an important influence in his life.

In August 1849 he was appointed Professor of Chemistry at the Royal Agricultural College, Cirencester, and then began to strike out his own line, a combination of field experiments on the college and other farms with associated scientific work in his laboratory. In those early days he was not a voluminous writer though he became one later on when he felt more sure of his ground. His first paper in the Royal Agricultural Society's *Journal* (Vol. 13, 1852) recorded analyses of carrots and parsnips; he recommended the latter for cultivation for fodder because of their high content of dry matter and their resistance to frost. His second paper in the Society's *Journal* was in 1855 (Vol. 16) and deals with his field experiments on swedes, the first outside Rothamsted to be recorded in England though there had been earlier ones in Scotland. They were the first of a long series made by him on the farmer's own land; he may have got the idea while working in Scotland under Johnston, but while the aim in Scotland had been in part to develop a mental attitude towards experiments Voelcker's sole purpose was to discover the effects of the fertilizer on plant growth.

There was great need for careful field experiments with fertilizers, for although they had been copiously talked about and written about, actual knowledge concerning their effects in the field was very scanty. Only few were as yet on the market; chiefly nitrate of soda, guano, superphosphate and salt as distinct from the well-known animal and vegetable waste products used as manure. The countryman's ignorance about them is vividly portrayed by C. W. Wren Hoskyns in his *Talpa, or the chronicles of a clay farm* (1852) where he sets out the difficulties of a progressive farmer with his slow moving staff. Voelcker states that many of the trials previously made with fertilizer had little value and could mislead. In this 1855 paper he discussed the many snags in field experiments and indicated ways of avoiding them.

In 1856 he published in the Society's *Journal* the most complete studies yet made of the composition of farmyard manure and the changes it undergoes on storage in different conditions, and he followed this in 1857 by similar studies of liquid manure. Gilbert described these masterly papers as embodying the 'Chemistry of Farmyard Manure'. In 1857 also he published his studies of the effects of paring and burning, then a common way of reducing the stickiness and intractability of heavy clay soils.[1] Some decomposition of the insoluble silicates occurred, increasing the amounts of potash and soda that plants could take up. This explained the suitability of the process for 'potash-loving' crops like potatoes, turnips, carrots and 'other green crops'. Over-burning, however, spoiled the effect, and moreover, it reduced the ability of the soil to absorb moisture and ammonia from the atmosphere—a property to which Davy had attached great importance.

Davy also had studied the effects of paring and burning, and a comparison of his conclusions with those of Voelcker shows how great had been the advance between 1813 and 1852. Davy attributed the improvement partly to the decreased tenacity of coherence of the clay (with which Voelcker agreed) and partly to the destruction of inert and useless vegetable matter with formation of charcoal which 'being very finely divided and imposed on a large surface of the field, 'must have been gradually converted into carbonic acid'—which he recognized as a most important plant food.

Voelcker recognized at once the significance for fertilizer practice of Way's investigations on the fixation of ammonia by soils, and he showed that the potassium and phosphate ions were similarly fixed. He continued to make field experiments on farmers' own land for a number of years, but at Cirencester he carried out a series to obtain more detailed information than a field experiment could give. Field and laboratory experiments were made in which the control plants received all elements

[1] Drainage later displaced it, being much better, but it was not at that time a common practice.

taken up by the crop from the soil, and the effects of omitting individual elements were studied. The results were reported to the British Association in 1859 and 1861. Mineral manures without nitrogen increased the yields of leguminous crops but failed to increased yields of non-leguminous crops. On the other hand, ammoniacal salts increased growth of gramineous but not of leguminous plants.

The fourteen years at Cirencester had been very fruitful for him. He had made a good reputation among farmers for his sound knowledge of the new science of manuring, and in 1855 he was appointed Consulting Chemist to the Bath and West of England Agricultural Society. When in 1857 the corresponding post at the Royal Agricultural Society fell vacant he was the obvious successor, and was duly appointed. He still remained at the college, however, and widened his interest in field experiments. In 1861 he summarized the results of some he had started in 1855 which had behaved abnormally, but he attempted no evasion or suppression: 'I do not attempt to explain these discrepancies', he wrote, 'but have no doubt the experiments were carefully made, and can only say that for some reason or other which often escapes our notice, some strangely anomalous results are sometimes obtained in field experiments.' He elaborated this theme in a lecture before the Society's Council in 1865 on the conditions to be observed in carrying out field experiments in which he pointed out that they must be prepared if necessary 'to throw the result of three or four years' labour into the waste paper basket', before there is 'any appearance before the public'. But again he urged, as his old chief Johnston had done before him, that 'it is experiments which establish general principles that we require much more urgently than what are commonly called practical experiments which have for their avowed object simply the profit of the farm'. Way had returned to the Society for the occasion, and in the discussion he advocated the establishment of experiment stations on the German model where systematic research could be carried out.

Hitherto supplies of potassium salts for prospective fertilizer use had been small, and chiefly derived from wood ashes got by burning forest trees in America. In 1851, however, the Stassfurt mines were opened and three years later in 1854 Voelcker visited them. He found about 14,000 workmen extracting common salt, but the potassium salts were almost unwanted, and he left Germany uncertain whether they were of much value in farm practice.

In 1863 he decided to leave the Royal Agricultural College and set up in London as Consulting Chemist, a new profession called into existence by the growing complexity of modern business which created chemical problems outside the experience of the business man and on which he needed guidance from an expert on whose integrity he could rely completely. Farmers also needed such help; they were now extensive buyers of fertilizers, feeding stuffs and other commodities the value of which they could not possibly assess till months after the purchase had been made. Already adulteration and other dishonest practices were widespread, against which farmers were helpless.

Voelcker was admirably suited for the work: he was forty-one years of age, at the height of his powers and reputation, trusted by farmers as the best adviser they had and of unimpeachable probity.

His new commitments, however, did not quench his interest in field experiments and the scientific problems involved. His first experiments were with low grade potash salts, and reported in the *Journal* for 1867; they were unpromising. By 1871, however, he had discovered where the need for potash lay: on light sandy soils and peat soils, especially for potatoes, turnips, swedes and clover, and for worn-out pastures. It was long, however, before potassic fertilizers were extensively used.

He still found time to study problems of purely scientific interest. The Broadbalk field had fairly recently been drained for practical reasons and Voelcker wished to discover how the absorptive power of the soil for various ions affected the composition of the drainage water. In his Report in 1868 he states that he had already spent much time on analysing samples 'with very interesting results' and the investigation was likely to open up 'quite a mine of theoretical enquiry'. His final paper justified this expectation; it appeared in the *Journal* for 1874.[1]

For the first thirteen years in London he had no farm on which he could carry out long-term experiments. He still made field experiments on outside farms, the last important ones recorded were those in 1870 on potatoes which finally decided his views

[1] Vol. 10, Series II, p. 138.

in regard to the value of potassic fertilizers. By this time his technique had so developed that little if any improvement in field trials was effected for some 50 years, apart from those resulting from better design of implements and condition of fertilizer. The results were:—

Yields of potatoes at four centres, light soils, 1868–9, tons per acre

	I	II	III	IV	Mean
With fertilizer	8·2	9·10	12·25	8·15	9·42
No fertilizer	3·3	5·75	6·55	6·55	5·54
Increase given by fertilizer	4·9	3·35	5·70	1·60	3·88

The dressing was 2 cwt. sulphate of ammonia, 4 cwt. super-phosphate and 2 cwt. potash salts per acre.

From 1876 onwards he made his field experiments at the Woburn Experimental Farm generously provided by the Duke of Bedford.[1]

His numerous and widespread field experiments gave him an exceptional knowledge of fertilizers and he may fairly be said to have put their efficient use in farm practice on to a sound basis. Unfortunately he never recorded his knowledge systematically in a book. But his example was followed, and some particularly interesting experiments are recorded in the Royal Agricultural Society's Journals. One on potatoes by George Maw of the Royal Agricultural College, Cirencester, in Vol. 3, 2nd series, 1867, shows the effects on yield of seed size, planting distance, cut setts, etc., with a discussion of variability of the results of such trials and the pitfalls in their interpretation. Another in Vol. 6, 1870, was by John Wrightson in his best days: a group of experiments organized by him on farms around Cirencester on wheat, barley and swedes with all the plots in duplicate, the results ably discussed, and the percentage of the applied nitrogen recovered in the wheat calculated.

Voelcker was happy in his home life. He had married in 1852 and had one daughter and four sons, two of whom as they grew up joined him in his consulting practice. He died in 1884, but his name lived on and his work was continued after his death; the sons carried on the practice and the eldest, also John Augustus, followed him as consulting chemist to the Society.

[1] See p. 136.

His sterling qualities and outstanding services to British agriculture and agricultural science had deservedly earned for him widespread admiration and respect. He had come to this country as an unknown youth of twenty-five and devoted the remaining thirty-seven years of his life to the development of agricultural science and practice here. Gilbert writing the obituary notice in the Society's *Journal*[1] described him as 'my most intimate scientific friend' and set out his achievements: elucidation of the chemistry of farmyard manure and of land drainage water; the absorption of potassium, sodium and other ions by soils; the large number of field trials and the vast number of analyses of fertilizers and feeding stuffs made in his laboratory, many of the results being published—which had the effect of up-grading the various products for the farmer's benefit. He also made many analyses of milk and milk products, developing standards of quality for the benefit of the consumer. His critical attitude to field experiments and the improvements he effected had much increased their value to farmers and scientists alike, and had encouraged a much wider use of them than had previously been attempted. The value of his scientific work was recognized by his election to the Fellowship of the Royal Society in 1870, he being one of the few agricultural scientists so honoured during the nineteenth century.

THE HIGHLAND AND AGRICULTURAL SOCIETY

The founding and early years of this Society have already been described (p. 61): It continued to accept Home's view that the greatest impediment to Scottish agriculture was the lack of experiments on which a national system could be based, and believing that this should be rectified by the farmers themselves it sought 'to increase the spirit of experiment-making over the country'. The Society began by seeking out the weaknesses of Scottish agriculture, and offering premiums to farmers and others who would find ways of correcting them. Fertilizer problems were the obvious first choice, since 'in this part of the island the subject has been less attended to and less understood than on the other side of the Tweed'. The first experiments were on the fertilizer value of salt by various farmers

[1] Vol. 21, 1885.

during the years 1818 to 1821: they were rather primitive and difficult to interpret, also the results were usually expressed in strange units and narrated; only occasionally tabulated. A better set was made in 1823 with turnips: the plots were one Scotch acre in size and the manures were farmyard manure 12 tons, bone dust $1\frac{1}{2}$ tons, ground bones and lime compost with herrings: eight barrels at 2s 6d. There was no untreated plot and no duplication. In another experiment (1831) 'nitre' (nitrate of soda) was tested on grass and on wheat: on the grass it was a great success but it caused the wheat to lodge: the season was very wet.[1] 12 cwt. had been obtained from London at a cost of £1 7s 0d per cwt. It was applied at the rate of $1\frac{1}{4}$ cwt. per Scotch acre (= 1·26 Statute acres).

Farmers were much impressed by the results with bones. 'The efficiency, cheapness and portable nature of bruised bones', wrote a contributor, 'have of late years in a particular manner directed the attention of agriculturists in Scotland to this species of manure; and have led to the construction of powerful machines for the purpose of bruising or pulverizing bones.' Some strange mixtures were used in the experiments: one farmer compared herring compost with a mixture of 'coal ashes',[2] hen dung and horn shavings. The absence of an untreated plot restricted the information that might have been obtained. The Society's council was, however, anxious that the investigations should not be confined to problems of immediate practical interest but should include more fundamental studies, and in the *Journal* for 1839 a section on agricultural science was added to the premium list, and essays were invited elucidating certain problems in soil fertility and plant growth. It was hoped that scientists would be attracted and would at their own expense carry out the necessary investigations while the farmers were working at more practical problems. This, however, did not happen.

1841 was a busy year for the Society: no less than 80 pages of the *Journal* are occupied by matters relating to the premiums. In Maclean's 1841 experiments on top dressings of rye grass and clover laid in for hay there were no less than 28 plots, two

[1] Robert Bruce of Kennet, *Jour. Highland and Agric. Soc.*, New Series, Vol. 11, 195, 1831.
[2] Probably Charcoal ashes: see p. 24.

E

of them untreated. The fertilizers included nitrate of soda, sulphate of ammonia,[1] muriate of ammonia, ammoniacal (gas) liquor, guano, urine, rape dust, gypsum, sulphate of magnesia, soot and other manures. The plots were 1/20 imperial acre in size.[2]

Fortunately with this change in the atmosphere came the man who could ensure wise use of the new opportunities. He was James Finlay Weir Johnston (1796–1855), born at Paisley. His education was scanty but he supplemented it by private study and got into the University of Glasgow. Here he supported himself by private tuition and obtained his M.A. degree. He early became associated with Durham and opened a school there in 1825. Five years later, having married a wealthy lady, he proceeded to Sweden to study chemistry under Berzelius. When Durham University was established in 1833 he was appointed Reader in chemistry and mineralogy and held that post till his death in 1855.

Except for the last seven years of his life he continued to live near Edinburgh and took great interest in the efforts of the Highland and Agricultural Society to induce farmers to do experiments on their own farms. But he recognized the deceptive simplicity of such experiments, and their inevitable unreliability because farmers did not know how to conduct them properly. Moreover the premium system was not suited to the sustained efforts and continuous expenditure required for scientific investigations. Farmers might still be encouraged to make experiments on practical problems, but they should receive written instructions showing how to do them. Scientists however, should be paid for their work—which really meant that the Society should itself establish and maintain a research institute. This the Society refused to do.

Meanwhile Johnston continued his efforts to instruct farmers in experimentation and in 1841 he brought out for their use a pamphlet: *Suggestions for Experiments in Practical Agriculture*, which he revised periodically, and in order to give a connected account of the subject he wrote *Elements of Scientific Agriculture*

[1] The first field experiment with sulphate of ammonia that I can find. Lawes already knew of its action and was using it.

[2] The 1843 vol. 14 devotes much space to manures and the application of principles of vegetable physiology and chemistry to agriculture. The plot technique had improved.

and Geology: a farmers' edition of his massive book *Lectures on Agricultural Chemistry and Geology,* (1841–4). His most popular book was his *Catechism of Agricultural Chemistry and Geology* (Edinburgh, 1844), which passed through thirty-three editions in his lifetime and was translated into a number of European languages. He also published *Instructions for the Analysis of Soils* in 1847, and other books.

He showed so clearly the value of soil analysis and of properly conducted manurial trials that a demand arose for a laboratory operated by the Society. A committee appointed early in 1842 to look into this possibility recognized its value but turned it down on the grounds of expense. The promotors thereupon founded The *Agricultural Chemistry Association of Scotland* and in 1843 appointed Johnston as its chemist. A very enlightened programme was drawn up: its purpose was 'the enlargement of our present knowledge . . . to establish general principles' not to confine itself to analyses for immediate profit.

Such analyses however, were increasingly necessary—242 were in fact made in the first year—for fertilizers were becoming important articles of commerce and serious overcharging and adulteration had begun. Johnston drew up standards of quality and price to which fertilizers should conform, a very valuable service to farmers so long as it was well founded.

It was some years before the Scottish agricultural scientists showed much interest in Liebig's new ideas. His book was published in England in 1840 but even as late as 1845 it was hardly mentioned in the Society's *Journal.* It was a contributor from Gloucester, A. Gyde, who first gave Liebig his due position. In the *Journal* for 1843–5 he wrote:

'the Report of Liebig to the British Association on the application of Chemistry to Agriculture, and the work of Sprengel, who has made so many analyses of the ashes of plants and soils, have given a new stimulus to this branch of science, and the subject is now in a fair way of receiving that share of investigation it deserves, and which promises to be of so much benefit to mankind. Prior to that', he went on, 'the chemistry of agriculture was involved in considerable obscurity; few men of science directed their attention to it, and those few met with so little encouragement to pursue the subject that they preferred following the more beaten track of science.'

In Scotland they were years of increasing interest in farmers' field experiments with manures of very varied kinds. Vol. 15 of the *Journal* (1843–5) contains no less than 27 papers on this subject.

A group of papers during this period is of special interest as showing the views then current on plant nutrition. They are by H. R. Madden and the first is in Vol. 13 (1841) and may well have been written before he could have seen Liebig's book. Plants required organic food in the form of farmyard manure or some similar material, and by some process not completely understood it must be made soluble otherwise it could not find entry. He stresses the importance of mineral nutrients, basing this, however, not on Liebig's Mineral Theory, which he did not mention, but on Grisenthwaite's Special Manure Theory already described[1] according to which the manure must supply the same elements as are contained in the crop and in the same proportions—which Liebig's mineral theory also required. Madden was enthusiastic about this. 'It is the addition of these saline matters to the soil so as to render their supply to the various plants an absolute certainty—if adopted will in all probability constitute the greatest improvement hitherto promulgated with reference to agriculture.'

In the next volume (Vol. 14. 1842) Madden discussed the advantages which had been derived, or seemed likely to accrue to agriculture from the application of the principles of physiology and chemistry. Hitherto, he admitted, science had served only to explain existing practice: it had not introduced to farmers anything new. As it progressed, however, it would lay down new principles, which would take the risk out of farming. He set out the position as it then stood. A fertile soil must contain a sufficiency of decomposable organic matter. Physiologists did not agree about its precise relationships with plant growth: some attributed its value to the mineral matter, always associated with it, some to its nitrogen: the quality in the soil, however, was in general a good indication of the soil's fertility. Land under vegetation gained fertility because of the slowing down of the decomposition of its organic matter and the direct gain of organic matter resulting from the growth of vegetation 'at the expense of the atmospheric supply of nourishment'. Cultivation increased the loss of nutrients, especially the alkalis and alkaline earths.

Madden's own contribution to the subject was his discovery that the soil organic matter contained 'ulmic acid' which combined with ammonia and in that form he regarded it as the true food of plants. Those that had a high nitrogen content might take up so much that their need for carbon was also largely satisfied leaving very little to be obtained through the leaves. For practical purposes he recognized dung as the best manure, but refers also to bones, and the nitrates of soda and potash.

The Agricultural Chemistry Association contributed a number of papers to the *Journal*, mostly analytical. The subscribers wanted the work developed on these practical lines; Johnston on the other hand wanted a more vigorous search for general principles. Also he lost faith in experiments conducted by farmers; only those by 'professional experimenters', he maintained, could be trusted. Experiments were better done on small garden sites near the laboratory than on farms. Fundamental research was essential, but an agricultural society was not the proper body to carry it out. Nor did he think an agricultural college would be better. 'The proper business of a college is to teach—not to investigate: to diffuse existing knowledge the first—to enlarge that knowledge only the second consideration.' He put up no proposals for the organization of fundamental research, however.[1]

Johnston retired from the Association in 1848 and it was dissolved: he left Edinburgh and made Durham his permanent home. He travelled a good deal. He was in North America from August, 1849, to April, 1850, and helped in the development of agricultural science, then in its infancy there.[2] He also visited the Continent. Returning home, he gave up agricultural research and devoted himself to his last and some think his best book,

[1] 'The present state of agriculture in its relations to Chemistry and Geology,' *Journ. Roy. Agric. Soc.*, I, 200–36, 1848. An interesting and stimulating lecture delivered at the York meeting of the Royal Agricultural Society in 1848.

[2] High tribute is paid to him by H. C. Knoblauch and his co-editors in their *State Agricultural experiment stations. A history of research policy and procedure.* (U.S.A. Dept. of Agric. 1962.)

The Chemistry of Common Life.[1] His influence was felt for long after he retired. It was he who had found Augustus Voelcker as an unknown assistant in Utrecht, brought him over to Edinburgh as his own assistant and gave him the basis of a philosophy of scientific development of agriculture that enabled him to become one of the leading figures in British agriculture of his day.

The Agricultural Chemistry Association had served the useful purpose of showing that farmers appreciated the help of chemists, and on its dissolution the Society reversed its earlier decision in 1848 and appointed Dr Thomas Anderson, Regius Professor of Chemistry in the University of Glasgow, as their Chemist.[2] He contributed a paper on the composition and value of superphosphate in the 1851–3 issue, and a long review on the recent progress of scientific agriculture in which he discussed the work of Lawes, Way and others. There was a certain element of comedy about his treatment of the nitrogen problem. Lawes, who had castigated Liebig for declaring that nitrogenous manuring was unnecessary for farm crops, had himself been guilty of the statement that turnips receiving superphosphate need no nitrogenous fertilizer. Lawes thereby put himself in the wrong and Anderson dealt faithfully with him. Lawes ought to have explained that the varieties of turnips he used could not in his conditions of soil and climate make growth greater than that for which his soil could provide the nitrogen, and there was consequently nothing gained by supplying more nitrogen. Growth limits of turnips and swedes are higher in southern Scotland than in southeast England and nitrogen fertilizers are usually necessary to attain them.

Anderson made a good start with a long report on recent progress in scientific agriculture which showed what could be done by the infusion of scientific methods. He also emphasized the need for improving the methods of field and other experiments 'so that precise and conclusive results may be obtained from them'. He started field experiments on a uniform plan to be made on several farms, the plots being $\frac{1}{112}$ acres in size arranged systematically in two blocks. He also tried various

---

[1] 2 vols., 1853–5; revised and continued after his death by G. W. Lewis in 1859 and again by A. H. Church, 1879.
[2] A full account is given in the Society's *Journal*, 1847–49, p. 674.

arrangements for overcoming soil variations but without much success.[1]

Like Johnston, however, Anderson was uneasy about the field experiments as they were done. In a paper 'On the methods of Agricultural enquiry' in the 1857–9 volume he wrote: 'There is no subject which more deeply merits the attention of the agriculturist than the mode of conducting his experiments so that precise and conclusive results may be obtained from them.'

Dr Anderson resigned his post as Chemist to the Society in 1874 and was succeeded by his assistant, J. Dewar, who, however, shortly afterwards became Jacksonian Professor of Chemistry at Cambridge, where he had a distinguished career.

In the next volume (1859–61) a Royal Warrant for a charter for the Society was announced. One of the objects of the Society was declared to be the encouragement of proper education for farmers, and this, 'in the opinion of the Society, may best be afforded by directing young agriculturists to a suitable course of study, and by examining and certifying their successful prosecution thereof'. It was clearly realized that a proper standard of education would be essential if farmers were to obtain the full benefit of the possibilities opened up by the new and advancing science.

This was the beginning of the diploma examination system adopted later by the English Society: in 1900 the two were combined. The system has proved of great value in raising the British farmer from his old position as a lay figure for *Punch* who had little use for science to his present position as a helpful colleague in discovering facts which agricultural science has to interpret.

The *Journal* for 1868 has an interesting article on the dietaries of Scottish agricultural labourers, which were claimed to be considerably better than those of the corresponding classes in England or Ireland.

Dr Anderson ceased to be chemist to the Society in 1874; his assistant Dewar acted till 1877, when Andrew P. Aitken was appointed. In 1878 Alex Leslie, writing on 'Agricultural Experimental Statistics', urged the desirability of making experi-

---

[1] *Journ. Highland Ag. Soc.* Series 4, Vol. 2, 1866–7. p. 391. Other experiments with larger plots were marred by comparing the manures on equal money values.

ments similar to those at Rothamsted at a number of different points in the British Islands, since 'it is still uncertain to what extent the results thus accurately ascertained for a particular soil and climate would hold good for other varieties of soil and climate'. The suggestion that other stations should be founded had been made before, and had been finding favour, for in the same volume it is announced that agricultural experiment stations had been established at Longniddry and Pumpherston in 1878.

This time, however, the honours were with the Royal Agricultural Society: the Woburn Experiment Station was established in 1876.

DAUBENY'S LATER WORK

During the middle years of the nineteenth century the only scientist of note outside of Rothamsted and the big Agricultural Societies to carry on investigations was Charles Daubeny (p. 68), whose earlier work has been described in Chapter III, and he was active almost to the end of his life in 1867. His last investigation was into the question whether plant roots must take up any and every substance dissolved in the soil water or whether they had any power of selecting useful substances and rejecting others. Two views of the constitution of plant roots had been put forward. According to one the roots consisted of groups of cells each surrounded by a semi-permeable membrane of the ordinary type as studied by Thomas Graham, possessing no unusual properties, and allowing entry of any diffusible substance presented to the roots. The other view was that plants were built up on a definite chemical pattern specific to each species, and the roots could reject, or were unable to admit, substances not conforming thereto. Some scientists having given up the idea of a special 'vital force' objected to this second view on the grounds that it implied possession of volition by plants; others accepted it on the grounds that a beneficent Creator would naturally endow created things with properties that were good for them. The difficulty about the absorption of a poison like copper sulphate was overcome by showing that the poison killed the root and the power of rejection therefore disappeared.

Daubeny collected the evidence and discussed it in a paper presented to the Chemical Society in 1862. He admitted that the idea of non-selective absorption by the roots was more widely held, but he set out his reasons for accepting the alternative idea of a 'chemical constitution'. Different samples of the ash of a particular species of plant showed similarities suggesting a pattern: it was not possible fully to replace any of the bases or acids usually present by any other not usually present in the plant even if it belonged to the same chemical series. Even when partial replacement was possible it never proceeded far. Granted that every species of plant possesses a 'chemical constitution' different from every other, it follows that 'of several species grown in the same soil, each one must exercise a kind of selection, in order to extract from the same material the several ingredients which it requires for 'its separate organizations'. Variation, however, is only to be expected. The 'proximate principles' of which the plant is composed (e.g. gluten, starch, etc.) vary greatly in amount with variations in the conditions of growth, and as each of these 'principles' has its accompaniment of associated minerals the total will change also. Further, the plant contains indefinite quantities of minerals circulating in the sap and not yet captured by any of the 'principles'. All variations in the mineral composition of the ash could thus be explained without assuming free entry for all diffusible substances.

Accepting the fact that abnormal substances cannot replace normal ones in the plant one can only suppose that either they are not taken up by the plant or they are taken up and then excreted. He preferred the former view while recognizing its difficulty. As he saw it, it implied some power of selection or form of volition for which the ordinary natural forces could not account: he therefore fell back on Vital Force although this was becoming more and more discredited as chemists were more and more using purely inorganic procedures for making organic compounds, always hitherto supposed to require the intervention of the living cell.

He concluded rather tentatively that 'the spongioles[1] of the roots have residing in them some specific power of excluding

---

[1] Spongioles, diminutive of spongia, terms no longer used for the absorbing extremities of roote, i.e. root hairs.

E*

those constituents of the soils which are abnormal, and, there-fore, unsuitable to the plant, but they take up those which are normal in any proportions in which they may chance to present themselves; the redundant portion, however, left after the necessities of the organism have been provided for, being again excreted'. He further adds: 'whenever abnormal substances are taken up by a living plant it is in consequence of some inter-ference with the vital functions of the roots, caused, in the first instance, by the deleterious influence of the agent employed'.

Another subject interesting Daubeny and also the British Association Committee at that time was the longevity of seeds. Among other reasons for their interest was the fact that travellers in Egypt were frequently offered—at a price—seeds of wheat alleged to have been found in ancient tombs, which still germinated and produced good plants. Daubeny relates that 'wheat is now commonly grown in this country to which the name of "mummy wheat" has been given, from its having survived from ancient Egypt', and he also gives instances of persons of 'unimpeachable integrity' testing grains which they themselves had collected from ancient coffins, or in one instance a sealed alabaster vase, and growing plants from them. Un-fortunately for their authenticity the seeds sometimes produced maize plants, which were quite unknown outside America till comparatively modern times, but in a sufficient number of instances their claims to be genuine appeared to be well-founded.

The British Association accordingly set up a special com-mittee in 1840 to investigate the question, appealing to museums, botanical gardens and other reliable custodians for samples of seed of known date and history. It functioned for seventeen years, from 1840 to 1857, and tested large numbers of seeds of 288 different genera (or species: the two words were used indiscriminately) and of these, seeds of only 34 genera survived for more than 10 years, only 20 for more than 20 years and only two for more than 40 years: both were legumi-nosae.[1] The 'mummy wheat' story has occasionally been resuscitated but no authentic support has ever been obtained.

To the end of his days Daubeny was Liebig's most ardent

[1] An interesting account of the findings of the committee and other observations was given by Daubeny in a lecture on Rural Economy at Oxford in 1863 and recorded in his *Miscellanies*, Vol. I, p. 135–50.

advocate in Great Britain. I have found only two points of disagreement. Liebig supposed that the function of the alkalis and alkaline earths in the growing plant was to neutralize the various acids in the plant juices; he therefore regarded them as interchangeable. Daubeny could not agree. He grew barley supplied with different proportions of sodium and potassium salts and reported to the Chemical Society in 1853 that he had found no evidence of any great substitution of potassium by sodium.[1] Also, in spite of Daubeny's destructive evidence[2], Liebig accepted de Candolle's hypothesis that plants excrete substances from their roots which are toxic to other plants of the same kind but not to plants of a different kind; he thus accounted for the advantages of rotation. He seems to have regarded the process as analogous to excretion by animals.

Daubeny was President of the British Association in 1856. In his Presidential address he emphasized Liebig's view that soil organic matter plays no part in plant nutrition except to increase the supply of carbon dioxide from which the plant would derive more carbon; and if the soil contained sufficient of the necessary minerals the plant would obtain from the atmosphere all the nitrogen it needed.

No record has been found that Daubeny ever saw the Rothamsted experiments, but he made a characteristic attempt to show that both Rothamsted and Liebig were right. 'The practical question remains', he said, 'whether allowing for theoretical proof of Baron Liebig's position, a larger expenditure of capital will not be required for bringing a given farm into a condition to dispense with ammoniacal manures, than by procuring those materials which contain that ingredient ready for use. And here experimental researches such as those conducted on so extended and liberal a scale by Mr. Lawes and Dr Gilbert, come in aid of theory. They stand, as it were, midway between the abstract principles which Science points out to the farmer, and the traditional usages with respect to his art, which have been handed down to him from one generation to another.'

Which put Rothamsted in its place.

Daubeny also tried to defend the agricultural chemists against Philip Pusey's taunt five years earlier (1851) on the

---

[1] He does not, however, make a very strong case.　　　　[2] See p. 87.

meagre benefits they had so far conferred on farmers: 'nothing, except to use sulphuric acid with his bones, and to take advantage of the refuse flax liquor, formerly thrown away and wasted'. Daubeny claimed only two 'infallible recipes', though without stating precisely what they were.

It must be admitted, however, that Liebig's insistence, with Daubeny's powerful support, that nitrogen was not a necessary fertilizer ingredient created difficulties for English chemists. Voelcker investigated the question whether nitrate of soda owed its effectiveness to the nitrogen or the sodium; and some of the early analyses of guano reported only the phosphates, alkalis and alkaline earths but not the nitrogen, and so gave a completely misleading idea of its value. The more independent minded chemists, however, Johnston, Way and others, included always the nitrogen, to which along with the phosphate they rightly attributed its fertilizer value. Daubeny also accepted Liebig's view that it was unnecessary to attempt conservation of ammonia in stable manure, dung heaps, etc: 'every soil', he declared, 'absorbs from the rain water or from the atmosphere more of this ingredient than is required for any ordinary crop'.

The disposal of town sewage was then attracting much attention, particularly the need to ensure complete protection of public health. A common method was simply to tip it into the nearest river where, of course, all its plant nutrients were lost. Liebig had been very scathing about this: Daubeny was, also, in a more polite way.[1] He pointed out that, although the losses thus incurred were at present being counteracted by importing the mineral nutrients from abroad in the form of guano and mineral phosphate, the supplies of these were only limited: indefinite continuance could not be assured. He was not altogether satisfied with the irrigation system and preferred the much more effective methods used by the Chinese and Japanese, of which the earth closet was an example. He admitted that the problem had not yet become urgent, but argued that

[1] In a lecture to the Oxfordshire Farmers' Club in November 1863, Daubeny thus described Oxford's method: 'In Oxford a large portion of the sewage is made to empty itself into the bed of a river, often nearly destitute of water, under the most public of its thoroughfares, and in close contiguity to many of its dwelling houses and some of its collegiate buildings', and he goes on to repeat the warnings of what may happen if this draining away of plant food resources continues unchecked. (C. G. Daubeny, *Miscellanies*, Vol. 2, p. 132.)

advantage should be taken of this quiet period to find a solution.

Later (1863), he quoted the example of both China and Japan as further evidence of the non-necessity for supplying nitrogen in manure. Their farmers were regarded as leading the world in getting the maximum manurial value out of human excrements; with them, he reported 'the volatile or azotized (i.e. nitrogenous) portion of the manure is left exposed to the sun and air, until it becomes desiccated, and all its animal matter is destroyed'. Davy had already reported much the same thing: 'the Chinese, who have more practical knowledge of the use and application of manure than any other people existing, make it into cakes, and dry it by exposure to the sun. These cakes, we are informed by the French missionaries, have no disagreeable smell, and form a common article of commerce in the Empire.' Actually this was not quite correct. Liebig pointed out Daubeny's error. 'In spite of the ubiquitous stench,' he wrote, 'the Chinese do not disinfect this manure, but they are perfectly aware that it loses part of its fertilizing power by the action of the air; and they therefore take great care to guard against evaporation.'[1]

Daubeny's last published address was to the Devonshire Association for the Advancement of Science, Literature and Art at its meeting in 1865, where, as befitted the occasion, he gave a broad survey of the scientific problems of the day but had no further progress to report in agricultural science. His interest in the Association arose from the circumstance that for some years past for reasons of health he had wintered at Torquay.

He died in December, 1867, in his seventy-third year. He was one of the most highly cultured of the men who have adorned the ranks of British agriculturists: he had a wide knowledge of the sciences as they stood in his time, and was well read in English literature and the classics. His lectures on Roman agriculture were much esteemed by his contemporaries. 'Firm and gentle, prudent and generous, cheerful and sympathetic' are among the attributes assigned to him by his biographer. A likeable man evidently, free from the pugnacity that characterized many of the Victorians, and always ready to seek

[1] *Letters on Modern Agriculture*, pp. 248–9.

a way of reconciling conflicting opinions in controversial matters.

The period 1857 and 1867 was a sad one for British agricultural science for during that short time three of the most brilliant of its followers were lost: Johnston, Way and Daubeny.

CHAPTER V

ROTHAMSTED'S GOLDEN AGE AND TEMPORARY DECLINE

1850 – 1900

UNHASTING, unresting, with no fuss or advertisement, Lawes and Gilbert were quietly feeling their way to an expanded programme of work.

Before long, however, troubles began; the superphosphate business was clearly very profitable and others began to embark upon it. Early in 1848 Lawes discovered considerable infringements by the London Manure Company and others, and with characteristic energy he proceeded to take legal action against them. Actually there were two weak points in his patent. The preparation of superphosphate by treating calcium phosphate with sulphuric acid had long been well known to chemists: indeed the quantities of acid and mineral phosphate specified in the patent are practically the same as those in D. B. Reid's *Elements of Chemistry* (3rd Edition, 1838),[1] Lawes copy of which is now in the Rothamsted library.

At the outset Lawes disclaimed the use of bones and bone ash, Liebig having already in his book recommended their treatment with sulphuric acid for use as manure nearly two years before the date of the patent. Parts of the second and third clauses, dealing with mixed fertilizers and silicates, were also disclaimed. On the strength of this, in the ensuing trial, Lawes v. Purser & Others, he was able to retain the title to his patent. His competitors were now at liberty to use bones and bone ash. This, however, did not help long, as they became more and more scarce, and far dearer than the abundant and increasing supplies

---

[1] The date of the patent was 1842.

of mineral phosphate of which Lawes still had the monopoly. There was also much illicit making of superphosphate from mineral phosphate by unscrupulous manufacturers and by farmers who could get access to mineral phosphate and were not afraid to treat it with sulphuric acid.[1] It was a very unsatisfactory position of which some of the manufacturers hoped to take advantage. So in March 1852, the Purser group of manufacturers met at the Green Dragon, Bishopsgate St., London, and after presenting a piece of silver plate to Mr Purser for his spirited but unsuccessful action they resolved to make a further attempt to break Lawes' monopoly.

This new trial, Lawes v. Batchelor, came on in November, 1853. It was a big affair, and Lawes' counsel advised a heavy array of scientific evidence, which was duly secured. Much time was spent in arguing whether apatite and phosphorite were or were not fossil bones: if they were, the patent would fail, as also it would have done had there been an apatite that would not yield superphosphate. There was argument also as to whether coprolites, which were discovered after the patent was granted, and which Lawes had been using, could be covered by the clause 'any other substance containing phosphoric acid'. The fundamental weakness of the patent, that the reaction was well known and was to be found in all the standard books on chemistry, was pointed out by the Attorney General: 'if the patent is valid it leads to the extraordinary consequence that a person may manufacture superphosphate of lime for one particular purpose but cannot manufacture and use it for agriculture'. It was in fact already used for the manufacture of phosphorus. Lawes' claim was really for the use of mineral phosphate as manure. As the validity of the patent had already been upheld in the earlier trial, however, it could not now be called in question. A final appeal by Lawes' counsel, Sir F. Kelly, settled the matter: Lawes, he argued, had spent some £10,000 from first to last on agricultural experiments, and was now spending £1,500 a year on them; the results were freely published for all farmers to use. Counsel expressed the hope that

---

[1] In a paper in Royal Agricultural Society's *Journal* in 1851, J. T. Way, the Society's Consulting Chemist, stated that he had found it impossible to make anything like a correct estimate of the quantity made annually but from the number of persons known to be engaged in its manufacture the total production must be very high.

Mr Lawes would not be 'deprived of his Patent by the application of any hypercritical construction of language . . . or especially upon any claptrap pretence of promoting the public Advantage by putting an end to a temporary monopoly fairly granted in his favour, but yet a very inadequate compensation for the large amount of time and labour and money he had expended'.

The verdict was given for Lawes on ten out of fourteen pleas and against him on four; it was a complicated judgment which only a Patent Law expert could expound, but it established Lawes position with absolute security and stopped all further infringements. Others continued to manufacture superphosphate, but in so far as they used mineral phosphate (and in actual fact there was very little else they could use) they had to pay a royalty of 10s per ton to Lawes.

Agriculture continued to prosper and with it Lawes' business. Ample funds were now available for carrying on the Rothamsted experiments, and Lawes was so good an organizer that the factory claimed only part of his time and he was able to spend some days each week at home and on the farm. He maintained a close connection with the factory till he sold it in 1872 to the Lawes Manure Company for £300,000. This gave him more time for the experiments but it did not relieve him of all London business liabilities, for he had acquired a tartaric and citric acid factory at Barking as a bad debt and put in a young chemist, Robert Warington, junior, to help in its reconstruction. This he continued to hold.

It is impossible to say what would have happened to the Rothamsted experiments had the verdict gone against him. This was clearly felt at the time and the verdict was very popular among farmers. On December 24, 1853, just after it was given, a meeting of Hertfordshire farmers was held at St Albans to organize the presentation of a testimonial to Mr Lawes in recognition, as the circular states, of his 'scientific and disinterested investigations for the improvement of agriculture generally, which have been carried out to an extent, with an attention to accuracy and detail, and at a cost, never before undertaken by any individual, or even by any public institution'. The movement soon became nation wide, and some £1160 were collected.

Lawes decided that the money should be spent on a new laboratory where more and better work could be done. The architect was Gilbert's brother Charles. No worse choice could have been made. Unfortunately Charles completely lacked Henry's competence: design, estimates, and materials were all bad. The building was begun in November 1854 but one of the walls soon collapsed and there was much drastic comment. Henry expostulated with Charles: copies of the letters still survive at Rothamsted; their tone becomes progressively more caustic as time goes on. But the building was completed, and was formally opened on July 19, 1855, the Earl of Chichester presiding. It was a wretched piece of work; later it had to be buttressed up and tied with rods, but it lasted till 1912. In the end it collapsed, all contents and workers had, however, been evacuated.

Unfortunately after the new laboratory was erected the old one was pulled down. This was a quite unnecessary act of vandalism, but like many eminent Victorians Lawes had no feeling for historic places, and so we lost what would have been a priceless relic of the early days of agricultural science in this country. Only two old photographs and a few reminiscences, chiefly E. Grey's, still survive.[1]

Lawes had apparently anticipated a favourable verdict and had already planned a great expansion of the field experiments. The original experiments of 1843 had required part of two fields only; the new plan required four fields, and a fifth was soon added for grassland experiments. The total number of plots was considerable and the best of the farm workers were organized as a special experimental group. Lawes had, in short, provided a solution to the problem raised both by Daubeny and Johnston: how can the field experiments necessary for the development of agricultural science be carried out? Lawes decided that they should be done at Rothamsted.

THE 1852 REORGANIZATION:
THE FIELD EXPERIMENTS TAKE FINAL FORM

In 1852 the field experiments were set out in their final form.

[1] Edwin Grey, *Rothamsted Experimental Station: Reminiscences, Tales and Anecdotes, 1872–1922*. Privately printed (1922).

The crops were wheat, barley, roots, clover. In 1856 grass for hay was added. The treatments invariably included:—

No manure; nitrogen only; minerals[1] only; nitrogen and minerals; farmyard manure.

The nitrogen was supplied as sulphate and muriate of ammonia, equal parts mixed, and later, also as nitrate of soda; usually there were two doses, and in the case of wheat and grass three; for the wheat experiments the minerals were tested separately as well as mixed so as to show their individual effects; for the other crops, however, they were mixed. The design of the experiments was very simple; they were in long strips each receiving a specified treatment for its full length, in some cases these were crossed with strips each also receiving specified treatment.

To eliminate the effect of seasons and to minimize the inequalities due to previous treatment the same crop was grown year after year, and the same manurial treatments were given. This practice has been continued without a break since 1852 on most of the arable plots, but since 1843 on some of the wheat plots, and although in recent years some of the plots have been split to allow of new treatments a significant number remain under the original treatments, only the implements and plant varieties having perforce been changed. Nowhere in the world is there such a striking demonstration of the long continued effects of fertilizers on the soil and on the growth of crops, or such a wealth of material for investigation. One weakness of the design is that information about the effect of phosphate is incomplete: the series include N, NP, NPK but not NK, so that while it is possible to work out the mutual interactions of N, K, and farmyard manure, this cannot be done for P.

Farmers always insist on the importance of soil and climate in determining crop yields and there were various suggestions that the experiments should be repeated elsewhere to ascertain how far the results would generally hold true. Lawes arranged for a repetition of some of the Broadbalk wheat experiments on the famous Holkham Park Farm in Norfolk (1850–1854), and for five years on a farm at Rodmersham, Kent (1856–1861). The results were reported in the Society's *Journals* for 1856 and 1862:

[1] The name used by Lawes and Gilbert for the mixture of the sulphates of potassium, sodium and magnesium and superphosphate.

they were in general agreement with those obtained at Rothamsted.

It would be impossible in the space available to give any
adequate account of the results of the Rothamsted field experiments, nor is it necessary, as it was the first duty A. D. Hall
set himself when he followed Gilbert as Director in 1902.[1] The
long continued classical experiments which are still going on
after well over 100 years—and it is to be hoped that they will
be kept on indefinitely, for nowhere else in the world can
anything similar be seen—include wheat, barley, mangolds,
meadow grass. Clover could not be grown continuously, being
wiped out by disease after a few years; a small garden plot was,
however, and still is, kept going. These have provided material
for investigating the effect of fertilizers on the milling and
baking qualities of wheat, the malting and brewing qualities of
barley, the sugar content of mangolds, resistance to diseases of
all the crops, and their reactions to different weather
conditions.

Shorter term experiments were made with oats (10 years),
turnips (4 years), swedes (4, 5 and 10 years); these had to be
abandoned as the soil got into bad condition. Potatoes were
grown for 26 years continuously (1876–1901) but the varieties
then available gave very low yields—only four tons per acre
on the plot receiving 14 tons per acre of farmyard manure
annually and 96 cwt. per acre with a heavy dressing of artificial
fertilizers. Ten or 12 tons per acre are expected on the farm
today. On two occasions there were experiments on sugar beet.
The first was a five-year series (1871–5), the second was started
in 1898 but stopped in 1901. They are now chiefly of interest as
showing the great changes in the crop since those days effected
by breeding and management. The percentages of sugar in the
roots in the 1870's were about 10 to 13: on the farm today they
are about 17 or 18; the yield of sugar per acre ranged up to
50 cwt. per acre and is now about 62 cwt. per acre. The yield
of roots has gone down, which means that they are smaller than
they were, but richer.

[1] Published as *An account of the Rothamsted Experiments*, A. D. Hall, John
Murray, 1905.

THE PARK GRASS EXPERIMENTS

The grassland experiments did not begin till 1856, four years after the arable experiments had been reorganized, and they were on different lines. Their aim was not only to determine the weight of the produce but also its character. They occupied some seven acres in the park which had not been broken up for centuries so that the various species in the herbage had reached their climax equilibrium. The grass was cut for hay each year; this was carted off; there was no grazing except of the aftermath in the first few years, but not later. The different manuring acted differently on the different species, favouring some more than others: the favoured ones flourished, crowding out the unfavoured so that the flora became simpler but its quantity greater. The unmanured plot, however, became progressively poorer, the plants smaller. There were numerous small empty spaces, competition diminished, and any seeds blown on to the land had a chance of germination and life. There was little crowding out of neighbours. The herbage was therefore the richest in number of species, but the poorest in quantity of vegetation.

Lawes and Gilbert decided to follow the course of this competition and arranged for periodical complete botanical analyses of the herbage on all the plots, and in the intervening years when this was not possible there were partial separations into gramineous, leguminous and miscellaneous species.

The botanical analysis of the herbage was an elaborate operation requiring the supervision of a professional botanist, and M. T. Masters was appointed for this purpose. The main work was done by the group of village boys trained to do the monotonous routine work needed for the Rothamsted investigations to which reference has already been made (p. 104). A quantity of hay from a particular plot was placed on the table round which the boys were sitting with the supervisor at the head; every single leaf and stem was picked up, identified and placed on to its proper heap. These were checked by the supervisor, then weighed and packed up for ashing, which was done in large platinum trays by a village man who had grown up with the work. The ashes were bottled and set aside for analysis.

The results of the botanical analysis gave a clear quantitative expression of the remarkable changes produced by the continued use of the different fertilizers on the flora of a meadow which at the outset had been fairly uniform. It was a newly discovered property of fertilizers, and the results aroused such widespread interest that they were exhibited for many years in the South Kensington Museum in a large glass-fronted case later returned to Rothamsted.

The data relating to the grass experiments were so voluminous that they had to be published in three sections. The agricultural results appeared in 1880, the botanical in 1882 and the chemical in 1900,[1] the delay being due to the large number of ash analyses made. For these and other ash analyses a skilled German chemist, R. Richter, was brought over to Rothamsted in 1862 and stayed for a few years. On returning to Germany he worked at the Charlottenburg laboratory and samples were sent to him. In all, he analysed some 900 samples: many of the data have not yet been published. The analytical data faithfully represent the sample but this may not with equal fidelity represent the herbage: there is always the possibility, not realized at the time, that some of the potassium and sulphur may have been lost by volatilization during the ashing process. The error may, however, come within the error of sampling.

From the early days farmers came from far and near to see the field experiments. The simplicity of the design made them easy to follow; Lawes himself was frequently the demonstrator, and as in those days the journey had often been arduous, a marquee on the lawn contained cold beef, cheese, bread and beer for the visitors' refreshment.

Broadbalk[2] has always been the most popular of all the Rothamsted fields: no matter how short the visit, it has usually had to be included: it is the most famous wheat field in the world. Lawes and Gilbert wanted to do more than record the weights of wheat given by the different fertilizers: they wanted also to know how fertilizers and seasonal variations affected the

[1] The respective references are: *Phil. Trans. Roy. Soc.* Vol. 171, p. 289, 1880. Vol. 173, p. 1181, 1882, and Vol. 192, p. 139, 1900. A paper in *Journ. Roy. Agric. Soc.*, Vol. 24, 131 and 504, 1863, deals with the effects of different manures on the mixed herbage of grassland. There had been earlier papers in Vols. 19 and 20, 1858, p. 552. and 1859, pp. 228 and 398.

[2] See p. 105.

quality of the grain—particularly its composition and its baking quality. They also wanted to examine a number of varieties. The scheme proved too ambitious, and in any case human physiology and biochemistry were not sufficiently advanced to make a proper investigation possible. For several seasons they determined the dry matter, ash, nitrogen and phosphoric acid in the grain from several of the plots, and in 1857 they published the results of experimental millings of grain from three plots: unmanured, sulphate of ammonia only, and complete artificials.[1] Nothing of interest emerged from this, however. There had long been advocates of the whole meal of the entire grain as against ordinary white flour on the grounds that the bran is richer both in nitrogen and in mineral matter than the flour. Gilbert in a letter to the *Journal of the Royal Society of Arts* pointed out in 1881 that the greater peristaltic action of the bran was an advantage for the overfed and sedentary, but a disadvantage for the poorer fed manual workers. Moreover, the nutritive value of bread was not determined solely by its ash and nitrogen content; digestibility and other factors had to be taken into account, and when this was done he considered that white bread would be found to have higher nutritive value than wholemeal. No investigations were made at Rothamsted but the subject was taken up in the United States and Gilbert's view was vindicated.

THE ROTHAMSTED FEEDING EXPERIMENTS, 1848–1862

Lawes had always been interested in the feeding of farm animals, and some of his earliest papers had dealt with the feeding and fattening of sheep and pigs. Liebig, unlike Davy, had brought animal nutrition into the ambit of agricultural chemistry and had raised various points with which Lawes could not agree. Whether this influenced Lawes is not clear: the fact remains that when the field experiments were well under way a long series was begun on the feeding of farm animals; these ran from 1848 to 1862.

The first experiments were done with sheep at Rothamsted and dealt with the relation between food consumed and the resulting weight increase. The previous investigations—all

[1] *Journ. Chem. Soc.*, Vol. 10, p. 1, 1857.

Continental—had indicated that the nitrogenous constituents of the foods played a highly important part: the Rothamsted results showed the non-nitrogenous constituents were even more important.

The scope of the investigation widened; pigs and cattle were brought in. The Rothamsted farm was not large enough for the cattle experiments, but the Duke of Bedford allowed them to be done on his Woburn Park Farm. They had to be done on the practical farming scale, laboratory techniques not yet having been evolved. In all about 600 sheep were used, 160 pigs and 200 cattle.[1] The results were:—

Dry matter in food consumed, lb.		lb. dry matter consumed in production of 1 lb. live weight increase.			Dry matter excreted[2] per 1000 lb. live weight lb. per week
Per head per week	Per 1000 lb. live weight per week	Lawes and Gilbert.	Modern data. High energy diet slaugh- tered at 12 months	Conven- tional diet slaugh- tered at 18 months	
Oxen 146¼	121	13·0	4·4	9·0	50
Sheep 20½	159	9·2	5·4	10·0	54
Pigs 48	270	4·8	2·6	3·5	63

Pigs were the most economical food producers, and cattle the most extravagant.

Modern food requirements are less than these because modern high energy concentrated rations speed the rate of growth and enable the animals to reach slaughter condition weeks or even months earlier than before, thus saving cost of food and attention. Modern science has lengthened the expectation of human life, but shortened that of farm animals.

The experimental records were very complete. The foods

[1] The results with sheep were published in six reports, the first being in *Jour. Roy. Agric. Soc.*, Vol. 10, 1849, the last in Vol. 23, 1862. The cattle results at Woburn are in Vol. 22, 1861 and those giving the composition of the bodies are in *Phil. Trans.* Vol. 149, 1859 and Vol. 174, 1883. An account for farmers is given in *Jour. Roy. Agric. Soc.*, Vol. 21, 1860.

[2] In solid excretions and in urine.

were not only weighed, but their content of dry matter, fat, nitrogen and mineral matter was determined; for some of the animals the urine and faeces were analysed for dry matter, nitrogen and mineral matter. Finally—and in this the experiments differed from practically all others before or since—some of the animals were slaughtered and their bodies dissected, the carcase and different parts thereof were weighed, and the proportions of water, fat, nitrogen and mineral constituents in each determined. The animals used were a fat calf, a half-fat and a fat ox; a fat lamb, a store sheep, a half-fat, a fat and a very fat one; a store pig and a fat one: ten in all. The composition of the farm animals at different stages of growth could thus be studied in relation to the food consumed.

Another investigation related to the source of fat in the animal's body. It had been widely believed that the fat in the body was entirely built up from the fat in the food. The analytical results soon showed that this could not be true: the amount in the food was quite inadequate to account for the amount in the body. The fat must therefore be formed in the body from non-fatty constituents of the food. For some time Lawes and Gilbert went no further as the question of its actual origin had not been raised. But in 1865 Voit deduced from his experiments on dogs that the fat was formed from protein, and he argued that this was true also for herbivorous animals. Liebig, who had at first regarded carbohydrates in the food as the main source of fat in the body, now became more doubtful and attributed considerable importance to the proteins. It was the supreme value of the thoroughness of Lawes and Gilbert's work that from their masses of carefully obtained data they were able to test this view. In the case of cattle and sheep the quantities of food required to produce a given live weight increase had been so large that it might all be attributed to the fat and protein in the food; but in the case of the pig the quantities were much smaller, and the fat and protein supplied were quite inadequate to account for the quantity of fat found in the body. As Liebig had at first supposed much of it could only have come from the carbohydrates.

Another investigation dealt with the relation of nitrogen in the food to the work done. Here as on various other matters, they disagreed with Liebig. He had put forward the view that work done by the animal involved the metamorphosis of muscular tissue with elimination of nitrogen which appeared in the urine: the quantity found there would measure the amount of work done. Lawes and Gilbert showed that this was not so; pigs at rest voided in their urine quantities of nitrogen proportional to the amount contained in their food: the amount present in the urine could not, therefore, be taken as a measure of the amount of work done but only of the amount of protein digested.

A great deal of useful and interesting information can be deduced from the vast array of data obtained in Lawes and Gilbert's feeding experiments. For every healthy farm animal, except the fast disappearing horse, fattening is the accustomed ending and the experimental data show the changes in percentage chemical composition of the animal's body as the process continues.

Percentage changes in chemical composition of the entire body as fattening proceeds

	Oxen			Sheep		Pigs	
	Half fat	Fat	Store	Fat	Fat lamb	Store	Fat
Water	51	45	57	35	48	55	41
Fat	19	30	19	46	28	23	42
Nitrogenous substances	17	15	15	11	12	14	11
Mineral substances (ash)	4·7	3·9	3·2	2·9	2·9	2·7	1·7
Total dry substance	40	48	37	60	44	40	55
Contents of stomach and intestines (moist state)	8	6	6	5	8	5	4

The pig is shown to be the quickest and most economical producer of flesh, and oxen the slowest and most extravagant. Per 1000 lb. live weight the food consumption (dry weight) and the live weight increases per week were:

	Oxen	Sheep	Pigs
Food consumption	120–150	150–160	260–280
Live weight increase	10	17–18	50–60

Other examples could be given. Remembering that the work was done mainly under ordinary farm conditions and before the days of respiration chambers, digestibility determinations etc. it is remarkable how much information the results contain. As A. D. Hall expressed it, they give 'a sound general idea of the broad principles of animal nutrition as they affect the farmer. They are noteworthy for the intuition with which correct opinions of the general processes were deduced ... from experiments carried out in the main under ordinary farming conditions, opinions which have in all cases been abundantly verified by later and more accurate research'.

Lawes and Gilbert attempted to round off the work by studying the relations of food and manure, a question of considerable practical importance as many farmers in arable regions kept cattle and sheep largely for the sake of the manure they produced. In particular it was desired to know whether nitrogen in the excretions plus the nitrogen retained in the body represented the whole of the nitrogen of the food consumed, or whether there was a loss of gaseous nitrogen during digestion. A loss was always recorded, but it diminished as the technique of collecting the excretions improved, and Lawes and Gilbert did not feel justified in supposing that any evolution of gaseous nitrogen took place. Modern more refined experiments confirm this view. In the Society's *Journal* for 1895 Lawes and Gilbert summarized their views on the feeding of animals for the production of meat, milk and manure, and for the exercise of force.[1] While these experiments were going on Lawes and Gilbert took advantage of a long stay (1857 to 1859) at Rothamsted of a young American scientist, Dr Evan Pugh,[2] to revert to the question of the source of nitrogen for growing plants. Could they assimilate it from the air? Earlier studies by the distinguished French agriculturist J. B. Boussingault had shown that the experiment would be very difficult because it would be almost impossible to exclude small quantities of ammonia, nitrate and other nitrogen compounds, from the air, water, etc., over the long period required for the growth of plants. Yet Lawes and Gilbert succeeded in accomplishing this. The experi-

[1] Vol. 56, p. 47, 1895.

[2] Besides working on this problem he introduced many new methods into the routine of the laboratory. He returned to America in 1859, became President of the Agricultural College, Pennsylvania, and held this position till his death in 1864.

ments ran over the two years 1857 and 1858, the plants used were wheat, barley, oats, buckwheat, peas, beans and clover; they were grown under glass shades sealed with mercury lutes, and constantly supplied with air well washed with sulphuric acid and potash; then carbon dioxide was added. Some plants had no manure, others had a small dressing of sulphate of ammonia to give them a vigorous start, but in no case was any nitrogen fixed.[1] It was a superb example of meticulous care, clean manipulation and high class experimental technique.

The results with the non-leguminous plants agreed with those of the field experiments, but the results with the leguminous did not. In field experiments the plants not only obtained all the nitrogen needed for full growth, but actually left the soil richer in nitrogen than at the outset. Lawes and Gilbert were greatly puzzled: they felt certain the nitrogen could not have come from the air nor from the surface soil: the only possibility seemed that it came from the subsoil, being extracted by some of the deep roots which the leguminous plants possessed and other did not. Much time was spent in investigating this possibility but without result. It was long an unsolved mystery of soil science.

Nearly thirty years later, in 1886, Gilbert attended a meeting of the Naturforscher-Versammlung (corresponding to our British Association) at Halle when Hellriegel and Wilfarth described their experiments proving that gaseous nitrogen was in fact fixed from the air during the growth of leguminous plants, not, however, by the plants themselves, but by microorganisms living in the nodules that formed on their roots when growing in natural soil. Lawes, Gilbert and Pugh were thus perfectly correct in their demonstration that the plants had no power of nitrogen assimilation, but it was the rigour of their experimental procedure that destroyed the organisms in the soil, and prevented their reintroduction from the air thus removing all possibility of nitrogen fixation. Had they been less careful some of the organisms would almost certainly have leaked in and the result would have been different. But they could not have solved the problem; this was possible only after the science of bacteriology had sufficiently developed. To Gilbert's credit it must be recorded that although nearly 70,

[1] *Phil. Trans.*, Vol. 151, pp. 431–577, 1861.

on returning to Rothamsted he repeated Hellriegel and Wilfarth's experiments and confirmed the results.

Lawes had always been interested in the water requirements of crops and as early as 1850 he showed that wheat, barley, clover, beans and peas used about 200 to 270 lb. of water for each pound of dry matter produced, figures which were broadly confirmed by later workers in Western Europe. In 1870, however, a much more elaborate investigation was made on some of the Park grass plots. The spring had been very dry, only 2·8 inches of rain having fallen in the three months April, May and June—much less than half the average for this period. The yields of hay differed widely on the plots, being very low on those receiving inadequate manuring, but the amounts of water taken from the soil were remarkably uniform. Yields and water consumption were in fact quite unrelated: the unmanured crop used about 6 inches of water—3 from the rain and 3 from the soil—to produce $5\frac{1}{2}$ cwt. per acre of hay, while a crop ten times this size (56 cwt. hay per acre) resulting from a dressing of nitrate of soda required only 7 inches of water, 4 being from the soil. Unfortunately Lawes and Gilbert did not follow up this interesting line of work: had they done so they would have laid the foundations of the important branch of soil physics dealing with the relationships of soil, water and plants, and soil physics might have originated in England instead of Germany.

In 1870 Lawes and Gilbert entered upon the last of their continuous experiments. Their main purpose was to discover what became of the rain water falling on the ground: how much percolated as drainage water, and how much evaporated. Incidentally they gave Gilbert the opportunity of having another fling at Liebig by providing continuous samples of rain water which showed more conclusively than before that while rain water almost invariably contained ammonia the total amount reaching the ground in the course of a whole year was quite inadequate for the nutrition of plants.

Three square blocks of undisturbed soil on Barnfield, each 1/1000 acre in area and 20, 40, and 60 inches respectively in depth, were made into drain gauges and a rain gauge of the same area was constructed alongside them. Daily readings were taken of all four gauges, and ammonia and nitrate were determined in bulked samples of the water periodically at first, but regularly and systematically by N. H. J. Miller from 1888 till 1916 when they were discontinued as serving no further useful purpose. The quantities of ammonia and nitrate present in a year's rainfall contained only about 4 lb. of nitrogen per acre—a result in accord with earlier determinations at various intervals from 1853 onwards. A disappointing series of records of ammonia and nitrate in the drainage water from certain experimental plots of Broadbalk field was discontinued at the same time because of the difficulty of knowing exactly what the samples represented. The most interesting of these had been a set by Augustus Voelcker taken between 1866 and 1869 from the plots receiving respectively no manure, farmyard manure, and complete artificial fertilizers; the analytical data included a wider range of mineral substances than others of the time.[1]

The great value of the drain gauges was the information they afforded about the fate of the rain water in different seasonal conditions. Following their usual custom Lawes and Gilbert published little for a long time. In 1891 Gilbert dealt with the rainfall, percolation and evaporation data for the first twenty years, and ten years later R. H. Scott gave the data for 30 years.[2] The average percolation through the 20 and 40 inches gauges was approximately the same and amounted over the whole period to 48·4 per cent of the rainfall: in other words about half the rainfall soaked into the soil and half evaporated.

The average quantities of the substances determined in the rain were in lb. per acre:—

Annual rainfall inches	Nitrogen as Nitrite and nitrate	Ammonia	Total lb. per acre	Sulphuric Acid (H_2SO_4)	Chlorides as Chlorine (Cl)
27·6	1·2	2·8	4·0	21·5	15·4

Lawes and Gilbert did not confine their activities to Rothamsted. The Government had but few facilities for dealing with scientific problems and remitted to Rothamsted those involving agricultural factors such as bread reform, and the question

---

[1] *Trans. Chem. Soc.*, Vol. 24, pp. 276–297, 1871 and *Journ. Roy. Agric. Soc.* Vol. 35, p. 132, 1874.
[2] *Proc. Inst. Civil Engineers*, Vol. 105, part III, 1891 and *Quart. Journ. Roy. Met. Soc.*, Vol. 26, p. 139, 1900 (Scott).

whether the nutritional value of barley was improved by malting, while on his own initiative Lawes undertook investigations of practical importance like the making of silage.

The most important of these subjects was the disposal of sewage which occupied the attention of Lawes and Gilbert during some eleven years. Way had in 1854 published an important paper in the *Journal of the Royal Agricultural Society* on the use of town sewage as manure and giving many analyses of London sewage. He could see no way of making a manure sufficiently concentrated to bear carriage to any area beyond that served by town stable manures. Irrigation of grassland seemed the only way of utilizing the sewage. The alternative was simply to pour it into the nearest river. In the following year (1855) Lawes had also discussed London's difficult sewage problem, and two years later (1857) he and Way were both appointed members of the Royal Commission 'to inquire into the best mode of distributing the sewage of towns, and applying it to beneficial and profitable purposes'. Lawes and Way were constituted a sub-committee to experiment during 1861-4 at Rugby with the effect of sewage irrigation on grass and the value of such grass as food for stock. They concluded that this was the best way of dealing with sewage: the best results were obtained with large quantities of sewage—as much as 9,000 tons per acre in the course of a year: a depth of about 7 feet. The herbage changed rapidly: the leguminosae and most of the plants other than grasses disappeared as did the weaker grasses. But the more vigorous rough-stalked meadow grass, couch grass, cocksfoot, rye grass, and Yorkshire fog flourished and constituted almost the entire flora. The best returns were obtained by feeding the grass to dairy cows; a three or four fold increase in the milk yield was obtained. Lawes' last paper with Way was in the Third Report of the Commission (1865): Lawes and Gilbert ceased publication on sewage in 1866.

THE END OF AN EPOCH: 1876–1903

Although he was now more than 60 years of age, Lawes could hardly have failed to see that research at Rothamsted had begun to stagnate. The laboratory work was simply a continuation of the old determinations of nitrogen and ash in some of the Broadbalk wheats, and of ammonia and nitrate in the rain and the drainage waters of the drain gauges and of some of the Broadbalk plots. The nitrogen and ash determinations had been reduced to a skilled routine within the compass of the village workers whom Gilbert had trained from their boyhood. He designed an elaborate system of checks on all their work and it was hardly possible for any errors to escape detection: Gilbert was a martinet but just. The only part he personally played was to standardize the acid and alkali used in the titrations. The analyses of rain and drainage water were made by his assistant, Dr N. H. J. Miller, who was kept at this task long after it had ceased to serve any useful purpose; he was allowed no part in the planning or discussion of the experiments. Unfortunately Gilbert with all his good points was completely intolerant of any other scientific worker at Rothamsted.

Lawes, however, wanted to break new ground and in 1876 he invited a young chemist to come and study the carbon and nitrogen changes in the soils by methods more refined than those hitherto used—a subject that had appealed to him in his early youth.

This new worker was Robert Warington, son of a distinguished consulting chemist, also Robert, who had helped Lawes in his lawsuit and in dealing with some of the factory problems. Robert junior played so important a part in subsequent events at Rothamsted that it is necessary to give some account of him. He was born in 1838 in the parish of Spitalfields, London, but being of delicate health never attended an ordinary school nor later did he go to any college or university: instead he was brought up at Apothecaries Hall. He studied chemistry in his father's laboratory and attended lectures by Faraday, Brande, and Hofmann. On account of his poor health he sought work in the country and in 1859 at the age of twenty-one he spent a year at Rothamsted as Lawes' unpaid assistant helping with the analysis of the ash of wheat and of grass. It was a very interesting period at Rothamsted, as both Dr Pugh and Prof Th. Segelcke were doing research there. In 1860 he returned to London and worked for a time as research assistant to Edward Frankland at South Kensington.

In 1862 he went as 'teaching chemical assistant' to the Royal Agricultural College, Cirencester, where he remained for four

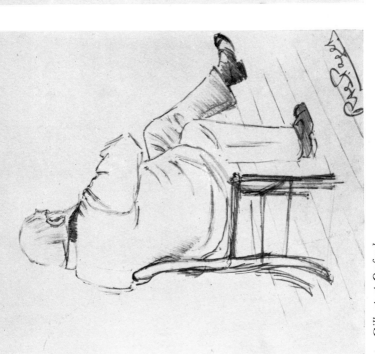

Gilbert's lecture

4. Gilbert at Oxford

5. *Sir John Bennet Lawes*

and a half years, at first doing analyses under Augustus Voelcker and when he left in 1863 transferred to his successor, Prof Church, who kept him mainly occupied with teaching. Here he published his first paper: it was on the quantitative determination of phosphoric acid, and was followed by an important paper on the part played by ferric oxide and alumina in decomposing soluble phosphates and other salts and retaining them in the soil.[1] Starting from Voelcker's observation that hydrated oxides of iron and aluminium can decompose monocalcic phosphate in solution with formation of tricalcic phosphate, he showed that the reaction was general: these oxides had a notable power of taking up phosphoric acid from a solution of any of its salts. They could also, but to a much smaller extent, absorb bases from solutions of chlorides or nitrates, apparently forming highly basic double salts with acids absorbed either previously or at the same time. He regarded the absorption as a chemical action. Liebig, however, did not agree: he asserted that the action was physical. 'All the component parts of arable soil', he wrote in *The Natural Laws of Husbandry*,[2] 'have a share in these properties, but only when they possess a certain mechanical condition like wood or animal charcoal, . . . this power of absorption depends, as with charcoal, upon a surface attraction, which is termed a physical attraction because the attracted particles enter into no combination, but retain their chemical properties.'

Warington was obviously very industrious. In addition to his teaching duties and his own research work, he also offered to assist Lawes with the large number of analyses of ash associated with the animal nutrition experiments (pp. 151–155). He periodically lectured on the Rothamsted experiments and began, but apparently never finished, a book on them with Lawes' (but not Gilbert's) consent. He also tried to trace relationships between the yield of hay on the Rothamsted Park grass plots and the weekly rainfall and temperature data: Glaisher of the Meteorological Office provided the data for the 16 years 1852 to 1868. Gilbert, however, refused to give him figures for the dry matter of the hay, and as the moisture content was variable this meant that the investigation had to be abandoned. Warington left it on record that Gilbert was

[1] *Journ. Chem. Soc.*, Vol. 21, 1868. [2] Pp. 67–69.

F

highly displeased at the request: 'You are trying to get known out of my hard work', he said.

From Cirencester Warington went in 1867 to the Lawes tartaric and citric acid factory, where he rendered very useful service. Here he had some leisure for writing: among other activities he dealt with various agricultural subjects in *Watts' Dictionary of Chemistry*, which was then being prepared. This seems to have strengthened an innate desire to write, for a few years later from 1878 onwards he wrote *The Chemistry of the Farm*, one of the most successful books ever issued on the subject. It was one of a series projected by a great promoter of agricultural education, J. Chalmers Morton, for use in schools, to be issued at 2s 6d each. Nine other volumes were actually issued: one on soil by Professor Scott and J. C. Morton passed through five editions, the others were less successful. But Warington's book published in 1881 far and away surpassed them all: within twenty years it had passed through fourteen editions[1] and four revisions—further evidence of the avidity with which good agricultural text books were taken up in those days.

By this time he had left the factory. He was still not very robust and was anxious to get back to the country, so Lawes invited him to work in the Rothamsted laboratory. He went in 1876 to work on soils, especially the changes affecting carbon and nitrogen therein.

Gilbert unfortunately had not been consulted and was furious at the intrusion, regarding it as an infringement of his rights. Mediation by arbitration was attempted, but the arbitrators (Prof. A. W. Williamson, first with Augustus Voelcker and then with Sir John Lubbock) gave such vague judgments that they furnished no solution; finally Lawes cut the knot by appointing Warington as his personal assistant. This Gilbert had to accept, but the breach with Warington was never healed. Both men were of strong but incompatible character, unyielding in what they regarded as matters of principle, and agreeing on few if any other points.

Warington began by studying methods of water and gas analysis in Edward Frankland's laboratory, and improved the methods of nitrate, chloride and carbon determination. Then

---

[1] The size of the edition, however, is not known.

at Rothamsted he used these improved methods to determine chloride and nitrate in rain, drainage and well waters, and carbon, nitrogen and nitrates in soils of known history. Hardly had this soil work started when two French chemists, Th. Schloesing and A. Müntz, following up Pasteur's wonderful discoveries of micro-organisms and their work, showed that nitrate formation during the purification of sewage was the work of micro-organisms: it ceased in presence of antiseptics, and began again when the antiseptic was removed and a little of the original material was added to re-start the process. (1877). They were, however, unable to isolate the organism concerned. Warington immediately tried the experiment with soil, and obtained the same results: antiseptics stopped the formation of nitrate, but once they were removed, seeding with a little untreated soil started the process once more. This rounded off the work of Way, who had already demonstrated the formation of nitrates in soil, but he could never get further because there was as yet no science of microbiology.

Warington tried to isolate the organism by culture methods. He picked out a white organism, a mycoderm, as he supposed; when inoculated into a solution of ammonium salts, it produced nitrate or sometimes nitrite. By 1879 he had prepared liquid cultures that would oxidise ammonia to nitrite but not to nitrate, and two years later he had cultures that would oxidise nitrite to nitrate but would not oxidise ammonia. He did not at the time realize that they were separate organisms: he regarded them as different conditions of the same organism, due to difference of age or virulence. He wanted, however, to isolate the organism. In order to prepare himself he went in 1886 to the Brown Institution in London to study bacteriology under Dr E. Klein, and he learned Koch's new technique of culture of bacteria on gelatine plates. Returning to Rothamsted and applying this method he picked out a large number of organisms from the soil and studied their chemical behaviour: many of them could decompose nitrate but none could produce it. It was a very disappointing ending to so much careful, tedious work.[1] The results were published in 1888.

In 1890 Percy Frankland made a long series of successive

[1] Its value was recognized, however, and he was elected a Fellow of the Royal Society in 1886.

cultures in an inorganic ammoniacal solution thereby reducing the number of species present, then continued by the dilution method till he obtained a culture apparently containing only the nitrite producer. This was its first isolation. Quite independently by using a better technique Winogradsky also isolated the nitrite producing organism. A little later Warington returned to the subject and obtained a culture that would oxidise nitrite to nitrate but it was not pure; he found also that his white mycoderm was not the active organism. He read his paper before the Chemical Society in 1891. A few days later, however, Sergei Winogradsky presented to the Academy of Sciences in Paris his paper on the formation and oxidation of nitrites, thus completing his investigations and clearing up the whole complex subject of nitrification. It was a dramatic and wholly unexpected ending to a long and arduous search.

Winogradsky had succeeded because he brought in a new idea derived from studies entirely remote from agricultural science: that some organisms can obtain their carbon from carbon dioxide using as source of energy the oxidation of an inorganic substance. He had studied a group of organisms oxidising sulphur, and another that oxidised iron compounds, and it seemed to him that the nitrifying organisms behaved in a similar way. For such organisms organic matter was unnecessary, and could be harmful—as indeed in this case it was. He had therefore broken away from gelatine plates and other organic media and used instead plates of silica gel and inorganic media, and was rewarded by obtaining colonies of the long-sought organisms.

It was of course a profound disappointment to Warington after all those years of good work to have been so near and yet in the end to have missed complete success because his technique, though the best available at the time, had not been suitable. He had varied his approach to the problem but throughout had used an organic medium on which to grow the organism. He did not know, and it is difficult to see how he could have known, that organic matter was something the organism could not tolerate, as it never appeared on his plates. It was Winogradsky's researches on autotrophism—a subject far remote from agriculture—that solved this very important practical problem.

In spite of the impossibility of infusing new life into the Rothamsted investigations Lawes retained his faith in their future. In February, 1889, he set up the Lawes Agricultural Trust, and endowed it with £100,000 and a hundred year lease of the laboratory and experimental fields so that the work should be continued in perpetuity. The management thereupon passed out of Lawes' hands into those of the Trust Committee, who, however, made only one change during the lifetime of Lawes or Gilbert. But that, though quite unavoidable, was a very sad one.

Warington's disappointment had been made all the more bitter by the worsening of his quarrel with Gilbert, and in 1890 the Lawes Agricultural Committee decided that he must leave. The blow was softened in various ways. In August, 1891, he was sent to Washington to deliver under a clause of the Trust Deed six lectures on his work before the Association of American Agricultural Experiment Stations; they were published by the United States Department of Agriculture[1] and give an excellent picture of the bacteriology of soil nitrogen as then understood. In 1894 he was appointed Sibthorpian Professor of Agriculture at Oxford for three years: he chose as his main subject the physical properties of soil and later recorded the material in his *Lectures on some of the Physical Properties of Soil* (1900), the first book on the subject to be published in Great Britain.

But he never got over his disappointment at missing the main object of his fourteen-year search, and when I met him for the first and only time in 1906 he seemed to have lost all interest in agricultural science: I could get nothing out of him. His indifferent health had necessitated austerity and his interests lay in the direction of educational and religious work, especially, in his later years, in Church Day Schools.

He died in 1907 at the age of sixty-nine.

But his name lived on. His daughter Katherine joined the staff as botanist in 1921 (I had already selected her while she was still a child) and remained for thirty-six years making valuable contributions to agricultural botany as will be shown later. She is the third generation of her family to add to the laurels of Rothamsted and their aggregate association with the place extends well over 100 years.

[1] *Bulletin No. 8, 1892.*

His work was not wasted. During his long search he had isolated a number of micro-organisms from the soil and studied their chemical behaviour: his note books had been preserved. His work was so painstaking and accurate and so thoughtful that it was full of suggestions for further research and one could only wish that he could have had fuller opportunities of developing it.

It is impossible for us now to recapture the feelings of wonder and amazement with which agriculturists learned that the production of nitrates in the soil—that vital process on which the lives of plants and therefore of animals and of ourselves depended—was brought about by living organisms so small that they could be seen only with a powerful microscope, and with such unimaginably strange modes of existence. A little book by Percy Frankland and his wife, *Our secret Friends and Foes* (1893), explained in popular language the significance of this new science of bacteriology.

The fiftieth anniversary of the founding of the station was celebrated on July 29, 1893, and as commemoration a great Shap boulder suitably inscribed was set up in front of the laboratory: somehow it contrived to get lost on the way down, but fortunately it arrived in time.[1] A fortnight after the proceedings Gilbert was knighted: Lawes had already been created a baronet in 1882, the original title awarded to his ancestor, John Wittewronge, having become extinct.

It was never Lawes' intention that the results of the Rothamsted experiments should simply lie undisturbed in volumes accumulating dust on the shelves of a library. He rarely appeared at scientific meetings, but spent his spare time on the farm or in country pursuits. Gilbert, on the other hand, regularly attended scientific meetings and delivered many lectures on the Rothamsted experiments. His attendances at the British Association meetings began in 1842 and during many years he scarcely missed any of them: on various occasions he read a paper dealing with some of the Rothamsted results. In 1880 he was President of the chemistry section and gave an interest-

---

[1] It was later transferred to the grounds of the Manor House along with the wonderfully accurate sundial that Vernon Boys had made for the hundredth anniversary and which he himself had with very great care set up in front of the laboratory.

ing address 'A sketch of the Progress of Agricultural Chemistry'. In 1882 he was elected President of the Chemical Society. In 1884 he was appointed Sibthorpian Professor of Agriculture at Oxford University, a post offering exiguous emoluments but no responsibilities beyond the delivery of twelve lectures a year. This he held for six years, the limit imposed by statute. In 1884 he was appointed Honorary Professor at the Royal Agricultural College, Cirencester; one lecture a year was required. A volume of his lectures was published; they make very heavy reading and even the tolerant audiences of eighty years ago, inured to dull discourses, must have found them rather dreary. Many years ago an old Oxford tutor told me that on one occasion, fearing that the audience might be very small, he required one of his pupils to attend. After the lecture, being curious to know what had happened, he called for the man's notebook. It contained no notes but only two sketches, both excellent; one of Gilbert, a fine head and splendid Victorian beard; the other was labelled '1/6th of the audience', an elderly man with shoulders hunched up; a perfect representation of utter boredom. The tutor very properly reprimanded his pupil for wasting an exceptional opportunity, and with a great show of indignation confiscated the notebook, recognizing the merit of the sketches. He showed them to me and allowed me to photograph them. He had forgotten the pupil's name.

I had lantern slides made of the sketches, and on one occasion I showed them in a lecture in a remote little town in New Zealand and mentioned that the artist was unknown. At the conclusion of my lecture one of the audience came up to me and said: 'I was one of the six, I knew the artist', and told me his name. But if Gilbert was a dull lecturer he was a forceful personality, and unforgettably impressed those with whom he came in contact.

During his last years Gilbert was busily occupied in summarizing the results of the field experiments; he did not, however, deal with all the accumulated analytical results nor has anyone since done this. He collected the published papers and had them bound; they filled ten large volumes. In 1890 Lawes generously presented sets to the chief libraries, Agricultural Colleges and Experiment Stations both at home and abroad. This collecting and binding of the important papers still continues: Vol. 38 was issued in 1962, but free distribution is no longer possible.

Lawes, however, wanted to ensure continuing wide publicity for the results of the Rothamsted experiments, and accordingly he had inserted in the trust deed a provision that a lecturer should be sent to the United States every two years to give an account of the work. Warington was the first to go in 1891 and his lectures, as already mentioned, described his work on nitrification.[1] Then in 1893 Gilbert went. He summarized the results of the 50 years' experiments on crops and of those on the feeding of animals. Owing to its importance a somewhat expanded version was published in the *Journal of the Highland and Agricultural Society*;[2] this is by far the best summary Lawes and Gilbert ever issued.

The next series of lectures was given by H. E. Armstrong, but these were not published, nor does any text survive; then came a gap as no suitable lecturer could be found till 1902 when Bernard Dyer presented an account of numerous determinations of various constituents of the soils of the field plots, especially nitrogen, phosphoric acid and potash, also loss on ignition—which, however, had been drastically scrutinized by Gilbert. After that there were no more Trust lectures, at first through dearth of lecturers, later because the funds could not meet the increasing costs of the journey. The visits were occasionally resumed, but the invitations came from the United States.

For many years the results of the Rothamsted experiments had remained in the separate journals in which they had been published. In 1888, however, William Freed published an extremely interesting account of the experiments on wheat, barley and grassland with discussions of the significance of the analytical and other data recorded. It is so readable that one wishes he had completed the account and included the feeding experiments and the rest of those on crops. Later came Gilbert's ponderous summary of the results of the first fifty years of work. The best is the masterly description by A. D. Hall: *the Book of the Rothamsted Experiments*, 1905. The centenary came

---

[1] See p. 165.
[2] The two versions were *U.S.D.A. Bull.*, 22, 1895, and *Trans. High. Agric. Soc.*, 1895, Series V, Vol. 7, pp. 1–354.

during the second World War and neither then nor later was it found possible to prepare an adequate history.

Lawes died in 1900 and Gilbert in 1901.[1] But the faithful band of workers taken on as boys from the village school and trained with meticulous care under Gilbert carried on their duties so honestly and well that when the next Director took up his duties he found not a single gap or faulty entry in the records.

Fortunately for Rothamsted that noble spirit still animates both the assistant and scientific staff.

THE WOBURN EXPERIMENT STATION 1876–1936

The Woburn Experiment Station was founded in 1876 by the Duke of Bedford and the Royal Agricultural Society to deal with certain problems which had arisen and which Lawes was not prepared to investigate at Rothamsted. The immediate question was this: how long would a dressing of farmyard manure continue to benefit the soil? Farmyard manure was by far the commonest agent for maintaining and increasing soil productiveness, and many farmers kept cattle in sheltered yards largely for the purpose of making it. The manure could be enriched, as the Rothamsted feeding experiments had shown, by giving the animals grain, oil cakes, etc. and similar high value foodstuffs. A common dressing was about ten tons per acre and marked effects could be seen for four or even five years. Also some other manures and fertilizers, especially phosphates, potash and lime, were effective for several years after application. All these soil-enriching agents cost money. If the farmer or his family remained in possession, well and good; but if he had to quit the holding equity seemed to require that he should receive some compensation for the enrichment of the land which he had effected but not enjoyed.

That view, however, was not universally accepted, and there was no ruling in the mid-nineteenth century that compensation must be paid in those circumstances. The soil, it was held, be-

---

[1] The Royal Society's biographical memoir of Lawes appeared in the *Proceedings of the Royal Society*, Vol. 75, pp. 228–36, 1905, and Gilbert's in the same volume, pp. 237–242, both written by Warington with no indication whatever of the feud with Gilbert.

F*

longed to the landlord, and the tenant had presumably benefited by any steps he had taken to improve it. In practice, however, the hardship of losing what he could ill afford was mitigated by various 'customs', and the outgoing tenant was paid something based on the amount of his bills for purchased feedingstuffs during the last few years. Compensation was made compulsory in Ireland in 1870 in Mr Gladstone's Irish Land Act, but, as Lawes pointed out, though this was very explicit in all that related to the legal machinery for trying the claims, it did not say how the compensation was to be assessed. In one of the early cases the tenant claimed £4,000 but pressed only for £1,170: the landlord offered £123.

Lawes was a witness and recorded his impressions: 'During the trial', he wrote, 'I had ample opportunity of observing how great were the difficulties with which both the judge and the opposing counsel had to contend.' Lawes saw clearly that the basis of the claim for compensation should have been the amount of fertilizing material, nitrogen, phosphate and potash in the manure which could be attributed to the purchased feedingstuffs, and he showed how this could be determined. Knowing the quantities of these substances present in the food, and the amounts retained in the animal's body during growth,[1] he found by subtraction the amounts in the manure.

The nitrogen, however, was very liable to get lost: not indeed in the animal, but by volatilization as ammonia after it had been voided in the excreta: he estimated that in practice 50 per cent would be lost during the making and storing of the manure. It is typical of the Lawes' shrewdness that this figure still remains the best we have. Appropriate assumptions were made for potash and phosphate, and a Table was drawn up showing what compensation should be paid to an outgoing tenant for the manurial value of the food supplied to his animals during the final period of his tenancy. He discussed this question in a paper at the Farmers' Club in 1870.[2]

Farmers in general are unwilling to accept results obtained by deduction so long as there is the possibility of direct trial, and moreover it was objected that the values were too high.

[1] See p. 155.
[2] *Journ. Farmers Club*, 1870. *Roth. Mem.*, Vol. 3. No. 9. See also No. 14. He had already drawn up a Table in 1860 but no copy of it can be traced.

A proper farm investigation was obviously needed to see how far they really were valid.

The matter became urgent when the Agricultural Holdings Act of 1875 gave farm tenants quitting their holdings in Great Britain the right to compensation for the value of their improvements, including the enhancement of fertility due to the feeding of cake and corn. Following on this Lawes published in the *Journal of the Royal Agricultural Society*[1] a second paper on the valuation of unexhausted manures showing the estimated money values of the manure obtained by the consumption of 1 ton of each of the commoner farm foods.

The Royal Agricultural Society decided to make the necessary investigation and the then Duke of Bedford (Hastings Russell) offered the use of land at Woburn, and funds to pay the cost of the experiments[2] provided the Society would undertake their entire direction and management. This very generous offer was accepted and in 1876 the Woburn Experiment Station came into being with Augustus Voelcker as Director; its main purpose was to study the effect produced on the composition and manurial value of farmyard manure by feeding cake or corn to the animal. Lawes and Voelcker were asked to draw up the programme of investigation, and supervise the first year's experiments. They did this and signed the first Report, after which Lawes withdrew and Voelcker carried on alone.

Two lots of manure were made; for one the animals were given decorticated cotton cake, containing 6·6 per cent of nitrogen; for the other they had maize meal containing 1·7 per cent only. The quantities used supplied respectively 96 lb. and 21 lb. of nitrogen per acre: the compensations that would have been payable according to Lawes' and Gilbert's Table were respectively £6 10s and £1 11s per ton fed to the animals. The dung was applied to the roots and its effects on them and on the succeeding barley, seeds, and wheat crops were recorded.

Greatly to everyone's astonishment the two lots of dung behaved alike; throughout two rotations the dung from the cake-fed animals gave no higher yield than the much poorer

[1] Series 2, Vol. 2. p. 1. 1875.
[2] The gift of funds ceased in 1910 when the Development Commission was set up. *Vide infra*, p. 268.

material from the animals receiving only maize meal. Scientists and farmers alike knew perfectly well that the result was wrong, but no one could impugn the accuracy of the work: some factor was clearly operating which made the conditions different from those of ordinary farm practice. Lawes left no record of his views on the result of the experiment, although he had taken part in designing it. Voelcker thought there might be something in the nature and action of the nitrogen returned to the land which militated against its becoming available to crops. Alternatively the explanation might simply be that as the soil is a light sand the additional nitrate formed on the cake-fed plot was washed away before the crop could take it up. Later workers preferred this view. A lysimeter experiment would have tested this possibility, but it was not made.

Another puzzling result, also at variance with well established practical experience, was that a leguminous crop, vetches, was no better as green manure than a non-leguminous crop, mustard. This also has not been explained: it is probably a variant of the preceding problem.

The Station was not restricted to this one investigation; it was also used to provide information on current problems that could be obtained only by an experimental study. In the *Journals* for 1880, 1881 and 1882 are records of comparisons of soluble and insoluble phosphates: superphosphates and mineral phosphate in this case—a hardy annual that never seems to lose interest.[1] Then in 1883 Augustus Voelcker published in the Society's *Journal*[2] an important paper—his last—on the chemistry of ensilage, studies started by him and continued by his oldest son, John Augustus, to discover the conditions under which it could be used as a substitute for hay-making in wet seasons. A series of experiments on sheep feeding was carried on for several years, and the Consulting Botanist, William Carruthers, experimented there on different species of clover and their manuring.

On the death of Augustus Voelcker in 1884 his son John Augustus succeeded to the official posts held by his father and

---

[1] *Experimental Husbandry*, No. 8, 1963, records the first seven years of a fifteen year experiment at six centres comparing superphosphate, mineral phosphate, basic slag and dicalcium phosphate, which promises to provide more complete information than has ever been obtained before.

[2] Vol. 19, Ser. 2.

to the Directorship of the Woburn Experiment Station; while he and his brother William continued the consulting practice. For the next fifty years he played a great part in applying chemistry to the solution of agricultural problems and he rendered great service to the farming community.

He was born on June 24, 1854, at Cirencester where his father was Professor of Chemistry, and he spent his first years there. From his earliest youth he lived in an atmosphere of agricultural chemistry and easily absorbed the tradition of careful analytical work characteristic of his father's activities. He was educated at University College School and afterwards at University College, London, and obtained both the B.A. and B. Sc. degrees of London University. He early decided to follow his father's profession and proceeded to his father's University, Giessen, for the necessary specialization in agricultural chemistry.

His contributions to practical agriculture include his Reports published in the Society's *Journal*, and a valuable series of Notes issued periodically dealing with problems of current importance, especially valuation of new or adulterated products. He was a shrewd and competent analyst, painstaking and very reliable, and he became highly expert in using the microscope for detecting foreign material in feeding cakes. One case involving castor seed, brought before the Courts, became almost a *cause célèbre*. His analytical figures were so trusted that a large part of the sulphate of ammonia handled in this country was at one time sold on his reports. He was in due course elected President of the Society of Public Analysts.

It had been decided at the outset to repeat at Woburn the Rothamsted wheat and barley experiments on a modified scale, and they were duly laid out on Stackyard field. In the Society's *Journal* for 1888 Lawes gave a very interesting account of the results obtained in the first ten years. They were generally similar to those at Rothamsted; the differences were mainly of emphasis. Farmyard manure gave the best results; rape dust in quantities containing only half as much nitrogen was nearly as good. Nitrate of soda increased the liability of wheat to rust and gave poorer grain with a higher proportion of tail corn than sulphate of ammonia. Voelcker had, however, a very different account to give when he wrote up the results for the first twenty years.[1] By now the soil of the nitrate of soda plots had begun to take on a dark colour after rain and developed a slimy, sticky surface that held up water and prevented it from soaking into the lower depths. After sixteen years (in 1892) the yields on the barley plots receiving sulphate of ammonia had begun to fall and they rapidly became worse till finally the failure became almost complete: actually the plants were there, and they produced seed, but they were very much dwarfed. Tests showed that the soil had become acid. A similar failure and acidifying effect had been observed a year earlier (1891) by H. J. Wheeler at the Rhode Island Experiment Station, and fortunately he was able to follow the matter up. A brave attempt to do so was made at Woburn in 1903, but the Station had neither staff nor facilities for this purposes, and so the connection with Way's studies of the interaction of ammonium sulphate with soil was missed. Some forty years later the question was taken up at Rothamsted.

The results of the Stackyard field experiments after fifty years are set out in a book prepared by E. John Russell and J. A. Voelcker[2] which gives the field data and also the results of examination by A. Margaret Webster (later Russell) and by W. G. Cochran using modern statistical methods. Many interesting details were brought out and differences from the Rothamsted results arising from the difference between a sand and a clay soil were discussed.

Up to 1897 the Station had no laboratory facilities, all work of that nature being done in London in the Voelcker laboratory. In that year, however, Mr E. H. Hills left the Royal Agricultural Society a legacy of £10,000 for the study of the less commonly occurring constituents of plants and soils. With the income from this a laboratory was built and also a Pot Culture Station modelled on one or two in Germany that Voelcker had seen, the first of its kind to be set up in this country. The work was carried on for 24 years, but nothing of special interest emerged. The fund was then transferred to the School of Agriculture at Cambridge where the only positive result was an indication of a beneficial effect of lithium salts in conferring some degree of resistance to rust on wheat. By one of those tragedies from

---

[1] *Journ. Roy. Agric. Soc.*, 1897, Vol. 58, p. 258.
[2] E. John Russell and J. A. Voelcker, *Fifty years of field experiments at the Woburn Experiment Station*, London, 1936.

which agricultural science has periodically suffered the investigators did not realize the importance of a high degree of purification of the materials used, and so they missed the fascinating subject, as yet unborn, of the effects of the trace elements later studied at the Long Ashton Research Station.

The Royal Agricultural Society carried on the Station till October 1921, then as an economy measure gave it up. Dr Voelcker was keenly interested in its work, and was desperately anxious that it should be continued. Rather than see the Station closed he took it over with the aid of a small grant from the Development Commission, bearing all the remaining costs himself. He had continued his father's useful policy of investigating at Woburn matters of practical importance about which existing information was inadequate. In 1923 he published an account of the work of the Station from its inception in 1876 to the year 1921.[1]

In 1936, however, with the consent of the Duke of Bedford, he handed the Station over to Rothamsted and it has since served the very valuable purpose of providing a sandy soil on which field experiments can be carried out. This had long been needed: the soil at Rothamsted is a clay, and repetitions on a light soil have often been difficult to arrange.

[1] 'Woburn and its Work', 1876—1921; *Journ. Royal Agric. Soc.*, Vol. 84, 1923.

CHAPTER VI

THE YEARS OF DEPRESSION
1875 – 1900

THE year 1877 had been the last with a high price for wheat; it had then averaged 56s 9d per Imperial Quarter in England and Wales. Ten years later in 1886 the price was down to 31s, and by 1894 it had fallen to 22s 10d. This was the lowest point reached, but from then on until the time of the 1914 war the price only three times rose above 32s per quarter.[1] In the old days low prices had often been balanced by high yields, but this was so no longer; the fall was attributed to the growing imports from North America due to the rapid opening up of the virgin lands and the completion of the chain of transport from the prairies to the British markets. In the old days also it had often happened that the return from beef rose in years of low corn prices and *vice versa*: 'Down horn, up corn; down corn, up horn' was a common saying. But that also was no longer true: live cattle were shipped here from North America in large numbers and at low prices, tinned meat also; refrigerator steamers were carrying beef from the Argentine and mutton and lamb from Australia and New Zealand. Grain, meat, butter, cheese, were all put on to our markets at prices with which our farmers could not possibly compete; many became bankrupt or gave up in order to avoid bankruptcy.

In the long period of depression there were two specially bad periods: from 1875 to 1884, and from 1891 to 1899. During each of these periods a Commission of Enquiry had been appointed: one which sat from 1879 to 1882—the Duke of Richmond's Commission—and the other, a Royal Commission,

---

[1] Lord Ernle, *English Farming Past and Present*, 3rd. ed., 1922, p. 441.

set up in 1893; their reports are extremely gloomy.[1] The first period was bad enough and was long remembered because of the disastrous harvest of 1879, but the second was worse, for in the interval the value of farm produce had fallen by nearly one half, while the cost of production had if anything risen. Large areas of grain-growing land had gone out of cultivation and neither owners nor tenants could afford to restore it or to adapt it to other farm use; farmers' reserves by now were utterly exhausted, and rents had been so reduced that landlords had nothing for spending even on maintenance.

This second period, 1891 onwards, was one of the saddest in the history of the English countryside. Farmers had made pathetic efforts to struggle against the terrible collapse of prices. Some, like John Jeseph Mecchi of Tiptree Hall, Essex, had tried intensifying their methods and increasing their output: they mostly went bankrupt. Lawes more sagaciously argued that high farming was no remedy for low prices, and advised farmers not to spend a shilling more than they could possibly avoid. The large farmers growing corn in the eastern counties were very badly hit, especially those on the difficult heavy or very light soils. Maintenance costs had to be cut; buildings, fences, ditches and hedges went untended, farm workers had to be turned off. Farmers grieved for themselves but still more for their land, for they had been brought up in the tradition that at all costs the fertility of the soil must be maintained and the village kept going.

During the good years much of the profits had been put back into the land, the farm buildings, the house and cottages, and the church; and although one often wishes the restoration of the church had been less drastic it is impossible to quarrel with the sentiment that inspired all this activity. At the beginning of the depression the land had been in a state of high productivity and the buildings and equipment in sound condition, but, as the years of depression continued, sons inheriting a farm in good condition saw it go to pieces and they were helpless. They felt deeply the rack and ruin going on around them: fields of strong soil once carrying heavy crops of wheat now abandoned to weeds and thorn bushes; the light lands, once famous for

[1] A vivid picture of the countryside and of the farm labourer's way of life was given by Richard Jefferies in *Hodge and his Masters* (1879).

barley and sheep, becoming game preserves for wealthy city people. 'If my old father could see this he would turn in his grave' was often said to me in the 1890's. It was all embittered by the recollection of the better days: 'A sorrow's crown of sorrow is remembering happier things'.

There was, of course, another side to the picture. Food was abundant in the shops and extremely cheap: meat was usually 7d to 10d per lb., eggs commonly one penny each, butter 1s per lb. or less. As ordinary butchers rarely had refrigerators of their own they had to sell all their stock of meat before closing down on Saturday evening: prices in Hulme, Manchester, in the 1890's would regularly fall to 4d per lb. for Argentine beef; I have myself bought it at that price and had it cooked, it was perfectly sound and was much appreciated by the poorer people. In the country prices sometimes fell very low: as a student in Carmarthen in 1892 I have bought eggs in the market at 6d per dozen and butter at 9d per lb. though the more usual price was 9d per dozen eggs, and 10d to 1s per lb. for butter.

These low prices of food made low wages possible in industry, and lowered costs of production so that considerable expansion took place. Demand for labour increased and the strong healthy farmworker had little difficulty in finding employment if he sought it in the town. Still more important, emigration agents were busy pointing out to him that he could have a farm for nothing if he emigrated to Canada, and he could be sure of land or well paid work in New Zealand or Australia. So many men left the land that agricultural wages did not fall; though as it was usually the best men that went there was some deterioration in quality. However, the old ones still remained, keeping alive the memory of the old crafts and of the old days when the land had been really productive. And they were always happy to find someone who would listen to their tales of those days.

It could not be said that the townspeople of the 1890's troubled much about the agricultural depression; they were content with the system that gave them cheap and abundant food. Advanced politicians began to hint that the land of Britain would be better used for recreation of an industrial people than for producing food that could always be imported so abundantly and cheaply. Looking back on those years they stand out as a period of almost incredible faith in the strength of the country to assure long continuance of Peace and Plenty, the great watchwords of the time. There seemed no reason why the flood of cheap food should ever cease.

There were however, some thinking people who realised that a decaying countryside was a source of weakness, and as a boy I often heard Goldsmith's lines quoted:

'Ill fares the land to hast'ning ills a prey
Where wealth accumulates and men decay,'

indeed one of my school tasks had been to learn by heart the first hundred lines of *The Deserted Village*.

There were, however, already signs of a way out. The grass farmers of the west, mostly small men producing meat and milk, suffered much less than the large grain growing farmers of the east and south. The young farmers from Scotland and the west of England who had come to Essex to take up farms abandoned by their previous owners would not admit to prosperity, but they were doing sufficiently well to induce others to follow them. They had introduced an entirely new set of products: milk and potatoes; and a new system of farming entirely different from those of their predecessors. Growers of fruit, vegetables and hops suffered, but not so badly as some of the farmers. Looking back one can see that the solution of the problem would have lain in a complete change of system: accepting cheap corn as inevitable, and welcoming it as cheap raw material for the production of commodities for which absolute freshness was essential, like milk, new laid eggs, green vegetables and high quality meat. Cold storage was as yet in its infancy.

Even if this solution had been universally recognized, however, neither farmers nor landowners any longer possessed the money to make the necessary extensive changes in equipment. Instead farmers called out for protection, but this was completely against the national free trade and *laissez faire* policy of the time. They were, however, offered technical education, from two different quarters: the Government and the Royal Agricultural Society.

It was widely believed in the towns that country people in general were woefully ignorant. In the pages of *Punch* the farmer, and especially the farm worker, was regularly a figure of fun. The Government regarded technical education as the remedy for the current agricultural distress and sought means of providing it. In 1875 at the outset of the depression the Government took steps to train teachers who could spread the necessary knowledge far and wide. Numbers of Mechanics Institutes and similar bodies were giving inexpensive evening courses of lectures in various scientific and technical subjects and the Government Department of Science at South Kensington held examinations each May at three levels, elementary, advanced and honours, awarding to the successful candidates certificates stating the result achieved and to the Institute a grant for each success. These certificates were very helpful in getting posts and many men collected a number of them.

As a contribution to the problem of disseminating knowledge of agriculture and agricultural science the Department included it among the subjects for the May examinations and appointed Henry Tanner, of the Royal Agricultural College, Cirencester, as examiner, a post he was still holding in 1890. In 1882 the further step was taken of establishing a lectureship in agricultural science at the Normal School of Science, South Kensington, the first in this country to be established at an institution of university standing. Tanner held this for four years and was then in 1886 succeeded by John Wrightson, Head of Downton Agricultural College. The course consisted of forty lectures and the fee was £4. The lectures were never popular, however: the numbers attending in 1886 and 1887 were nine and eight respectively, and in 1891 six only. This did not prevent Wrightson from declaring in 1887 that 'there never was a time when greater interest was shown in agricultural education because of the bad times through which we have been passing'.

Some of the examination papers survive. In the elementary stage of the 1889 examinations the questions dealt mainly with crops and soils: the reasons for the 'richness of clay soils' and the poverty of sandy and peaty soils; why Tull could grow wheat year after year provided he thoroughly tilled the soil, and on what kinds of soil could such results be obtained. Another question was: why is a corn crop more exhausting than a root crop? Questions in the advanced stage asked for proof that different crops require different supplies of plant food; or that soils are always fertile if they contain all necessary elements of plant food; what principles should regulate the use of lime as a fertilizer. Animal husbandry had an important place and some difficult questions were set: such as: how does regularity in the supply of proper food influence the meat produced by its use? The honours papers had the special interest of including new ideas and subjects deemed most important at the time, such as the calculation of the albuminoid ratio in particular foodstuffs or rations. Other topics included better cropping systems on clay land so as to produce large quantities of wheat and oats.

Tanner was clearly a good coach; he wrote two little books, models of compactness, which would have guided students through the examinations. There is nothing to show that either agriculture or agricultural science benefited much from the South Kensington efforts. London is apparently not a suitable home for a chair in agriculture; its significance was as a tangible demonstration of the Government's interest in agricultural education, and its determination to keep the subject alive through a period when it was in real danger of falling into oblivion.[1]

Little help to agricultural science came from the scientific societies. The Chemical Society helped to sustain interest by giving space in its *Journal* for abstracts of papers on Agricultural Chemistry that had appeared elsewhere. But the ordinary science colleges were mostly too busy developing subjects with an assured future to concern themselves with one so uncertain as agricultural science; in any case young scientists much preferred the rapidly developing sciences of chemistry, physics and the various branches of biology. Agricultural science was at a low ebb, and by 1890 its future looked very gloomy.

The Royal Agricultural Society was more successful. Its Council recognized that greater farming efficiency was needed and they suggested the preparation of a small text book on

---

[1] I am indebted to Mr H. E. M. Icely, late of the Oxford University Dept. of Education for kindly supplying information about this period. The main sources are: Tanner's contribution to the second Report of the Royal Commission on Technical Education (1884); and Annual Reports of the Science and Art Department for years 1886—1891 inclusive.

Tanner's books were: *The Abbot's Farm, or Practice with Science*, 1880; *Elementary Lessons in the Science of Agricultural Practice*, 1881; *First Principles of Agriculture*, 1890.

improved methods to be issued at half-a-crown so as to ensure wide distribution. The Council commissioned William Fream, Lecturer in Agriculture at the Downton Agricultural College near Salisbury[1], to write 'an elementary work on Agriculture adapted for use in rural and other schools and classes' and to be sold at 2s 6d.

Fream was born at Gloucester in 1854 of what were then called 'humble parents'. He left school early to work for a firm of seed and corn merchants, but in 1872 at the age of eighteen he won an exhibition at the Royal College of Science, Dublin, which kept him there for three years. Two years later (1877) he obtained the London B.Sc. with honours in chemistry, and was appointed Professor of Natural History at the Royal Agricultural College, Cirencester. He gained a reputation as an enthusiastic teacher, but stayed only two years. For a short period in 1879 he was a demonstrator at Guy's Hospital, and then joined Wrightson at Downton. Here he lectured on natural science, including therein the first course in England on entomology. In 1888, as already mentioned, he had published a useful small book on the Rothamsted experiments which, as Hall wrote, 'though dealing only with wheat, barley, and grass, has formed for so many readers their introduction and guide to the Rothamsted investigations'.

His entomological course attracted the attention of Eleanor Ormerod, one of the leading entomologists of the time, and through her good offices he was appointed in 1890 the first Steven lecturer at the University of Edinburgh. In 1890 also he became editor of the *Journal of the Royal Agricultural Society*, and he was asked by the Board of Agriculture to prepare a report on agricultural education in Scotland: he also made three visits to Canada to report on farming conditions there.

This background, combined with an easy and interesting style of writing, promised well for the success of the book. But its astonishing reception when it appeared in January 1892 exceeded all expectations. In the expectation that they would last some time, 1250 copies had been printed: all were sold on the day of publication. Another 5,000 copies were quickly run

---

[1] Downton was a break-away college from Cirencester under John Wrightson, who had been Professor of Agriculture there, and who with a few colleagues left because of irreconcilable differences with the college authorities.

off and sold by the end of the month. A second impression of 5,000 went during February; by the end of the year the fourth edition was out, completely revised and with new illustrations. During its first ten years seven editions were prepared by Fream and the sales amounted to 30,000.

Fream died in 1906 at the early age of fifty-two, a great loss to agricultural writing. But the book lives on: its present editor (1965) is D. H. Robinson, who is also editor of the Society's *Journal*. He reports that the total sales now exceed 125,000 copies and the demand is greater than ever.

During all these unhappy years the best advice available was given in the Society's *Journal* to help farmers over their practical difficulties. Increasing efforts were made to protect crops against diseases and pests, but once an outbreak occurred little could be done to control or palliate it. The great advance so far had been in the study of fertilizer action.

Scotland also suffered, as shown by the fact that men like Middleton and Gilchrist had left their farms, but the distress was probably less than in England, because during the years of depression there was a larger element of local consumption and less dependence on open markets for the disposal of the farm produce. The Highland and Agricultural Society's *Journal* gives little indication of distress among the farmers, but the Society vigorously continued its efforts to improve Scottish agriculture. It did not adopt the method of the English society but intensified its experimental programme.

In 1877 Dr A. P. Aitken was appointed chemist to the Society.[1] It was a singularly happy choice, and for the next twenty years he rendered great service to Scottish agriculture, and added much to the factual basis of agricultural science. His first duty was to draw up programmes of research on the two experimental centres.[2] Both were old arable fields 10 acres in size, apparently uniform, but Pumpherston had the higher rainfall. Forty plots each a quarter acre were marked out and put under a four course rotation; turnips, barley, grass, oats; and the effects of nitrogenous, phosphatic and potassic fertilizers were tested. The superphosphates were of different degrees of water solubility. Many of the experiments were repeated on microplots of 1/112 acre to provide information for a con-

[1] At a salary of £300 a year.　　　[2] See p. 135.

troversy then going on about the size of field plots. In order to eliminate the variations due to inequalities of the soil Aitken had the upper layer removed from the entire plot and thoroughly mixed up, the subsoil was dressed and the surface soil replaced. But it was no use; the experiments were still liable to be spoiled by local soil irregularities and accidents of growth. In 1883 he therefore abandoned microplots in favour of plots of 1/10 acre.

Aitken was a keen field experimenter and tried to get farmers to do more of them, establishing Field Experimental Clubs for the purpose. At first he had only limited success. In 1884 he had designed an interesting set of experiments including mineral phosphate: a hundred farmers were approached but only nine agreed to undertake them. But he persisted, and by 1892 they were being made at 45 centres by farmers clubs, associations and experimental clubs, and the Board of Agriculture gave £150 towards the cost: by 1894 this had been raised to £200 in consequence of further expansion in 1893.[1]

In 1886 two four-year rotations on the Experimental Fields had been completed, and Aitken wrote his report thereon. He gave so full an account of the fertilizers applied—they included all in common use—that the report could almost serve as a text book on the subject. But that was typical of Aitken's thoroughness. At Longniddry the responses to the fertilizers had been so small owing to the richness of the soil that the experiment was discontinued and the field given up. At Pumpherston the cropping and manuring were discontinued, the field was sown with grass and the residual effects of the fertilizers on its yield and botanical composition were periodically recorded. In 1891 he published the third year observations on the abundance of grass and of clover, and the extent to which stock had grazed down the plot. In 1892 observations of the fourth year were published, also chemical analyses of the herbage, and botanical analyses showing the changes as the pasture had aged. The 1894 paper records the position after six years. This was the only experiment of its kind in Britain.

This 1894 paper also includes an interesting discussion on the question whether chemical analysis gives reliable indications of

[1] In 1889, Vol. 1, Series V, of the *Journal* he summarized the results of a large number of these outside experiments.

the feeding quality of a pasture. This is shown to be a complex matter, involving analyses of soil, subsoil and crop, also a knowledge of productivity and of what the animal actually eats—which is difficult to discover. Aitken's fertilizer experiments covered a wide variety of crops and provided much useful information. He also did helpful work on silage around 1885. As in England, much wet weather in summer made hay-making difficult and wasteful: farmers wanted to know whether ensiling might not be better. In 1891 and 1892 he reported on cattle feeding experiments at the outside centres, giving analyses of the food consumed and of the manure produced.

More attention was now being paid to the grassland. In 1899 David Wilson, jun., published a mass of data on the chemical composition of various species of grasses and clovers at different stages of growth.

One of the most striking figures in Scottish agriculture during this period was Thomas Jamieson of Aberdeen, an agricultural chemist and the City Analyst, also appointed Fordyce Lecturer in Agriculture at the University in 1879.[1] He was a remarkable character, outstanding even in that city of sturdy individualists. He was a keen experimenter and vigorous advocate of agricultural science. In 1879 he founded the Aberdeenshire Agricultural Association, which received much support among farmers and carried out many field trials in various parts of Scotland to investigate the effects of phosphatic and nitrogenous manures on the turnip crop. He also secured the help of some of the University staff in organizing courses on agricultural science for teachers. These he gave from 1877 onwards, grants being obtained from the Privy Council; students of the Aberdeen Training Colleges for Teachers could include these lectures in their courses. Apparently these lectures to teachers were immediately successful; all the grants offered in 1878 for agricultural instruction in schools in Scotland went to those in the north-eastern counties, mainly in Aberdeenshire.

Many of the field experiments seem to have been made on acid soils, and finely ground mineral phosphate gave as good or almost as good results as superphosphate. This led Jamieson

[1] His predecessor, Thomas F. Jamieson, was an entirely different person: a well known farmer and breeder of Shorthorns and a geologist.

to suppose that treatment of the mineral with sulphuric acid was an unnecessary extravagance, and farmers could save much on their manure bills by using the mineral in place of super-phosphate. He vigorously proclaimed that his procedure would cause a revolution in fertilizer manufacture and insisted that it should be tried on the large scale. Jamieson was a very successful publicist and Aitken felt that the matter must be taken up. Accordingly he included mineral phosphate in his next set of field experiments. It was effective, but basic slag, which had also been included, was at least as good, beside being cheaper. Soil acidity had been but little studied; as more and more soils were neutralized the superiority of superphosphate was more widely recognized.

Later on, about 1905, Jamieson thought he had obtained evidence that nettles could assimilate gaseous nitrogen from the atmosphere. The hairs on the leaves he regarded as antennae sticking up to facilitate the collection of the gas. He read a paper on the subject at the York meeting of the British Association in 1906 and made the sectional meeting where he presented it memorable by defying the Chairman's instructions to keep to the timetable in order that a later paper could also be heard. He regarded his own paper as much the more important, however, and flatly ignored the Chairman's repeated calls to order. His successor remained disconsolate and unheard.

The Government offer of technical education already mentioned (p. 180) was not at first well received, but in the end it brought about great developments. In 1888 a departmental committee under Sir Richard Paget recommended state aid for establishing local centres of agricultural education; the county councils established in the same year were also empowered to provide it out of their own funds. In the session 1888–9 the Agricultural Department of the Privy Council expended in educational grants £1,630 in England and Wales and £1,300 in Scotland. In 1889 the Board of Agriculture was set up, one of its duties being the development of higher agricultural education; in its first session it made grants for this purpose of £4,585, of which £2,425 went to Scotland and £2,160 to thirteen local bodies in England and Wales. Hitherto agricultural education had been provided only at the old institutions already mentioned, the Royal Agricultural College at Cirencester and Edinburgh University, and at two more recently established agricultural schools or colleges: Aspatria, (Cumberland) founded by Dr Webb in 1874, and Downton, started by John Wrightson in 1880; both were privately owned personal ventures. By 1890, however, two University Colleges had started Agricultural Departments: Bangor in 1889 and Aberystwyth in 1890. With some exceptions farmers had not been sufficiently impressed with the products of these institutions to press for more of them, and there was little enthusiasm in the counties for agricultural education.

There might have been little progress but for one of those curious accidents that have not infrequently led to important developments in British agriculture. It had long been felt that public houses were far too numerous in the towns and that the numbers ought to be reduced. This would involve the surrender of licences, for which in fairness some compensation should be payable. In the budget for 1890 a special tax had been put on alcoholic liquor with the purpose of providing the necessary funds, but later, when authority was sought for payment to the licence owners (who were mainly brewers), there was such a public outcry that it was refused. The Government therefore found itself in possession of an income of several hundred thousand pounds a year for which no specific purpose any longer existed. 'In a lethargic and half-empty House', wrote H. E. Dale,[1] 'Arthur H. D. Acland suggested that the money should be allocated to technical education and it was so agreed.' The money—commonly called 'whisky money'—was made available to the county councils: it could be spent on technical education, or if they preferred, on relief of the rates. For many of the counties technical education meant agricultural education.

Independently of all this a beginning had already been made. For some years the university colleges had undertaken in certain towns educational work outside their own precincts. At first the old universities, Oxford and Cambridge, took no part in this, but by 1885 two Oxford men, Dr Percival, then President of Trinity College and later Bishop of Hereford, and Michael Sadler vigorously promoted these extra-mural activi-

[1] H. E. Dale, *Daniel Hall, Pioneer in Scientific Agriculture*, John Murray, 1956. The author had access to all relevant papers and gives a full and accurate account of this curious episode.

ties, and widespread University Extension lecture courses were inaugurated. A number of Oxford's able graduates accepted posts as lecturers and they gave systematic courses at various centres, large and small. Among these was a remarkable young man, Alfred Daniel Hall, who afterwards played so great a part in the development of agricultural science and education in this country that it is necessary to give some account of him.

Alfred Daniel Hall was born on June 22, 1864, in Rochdale. Both his father and his grandfather were small flannel manufacturers, but the earlier generations had been small farmers on the edge of the moorlands near Bury. His mother was from Lincolnshire, of yeoman stock. He was fortunate in his home: one of his sisters records that 'we were encouraged to read widely and to realize the beauty in books, music and paintings, and in all things fine and good. Our home life was happy and free—we went long walks with our father at the week-ends, spent Sunday at home with attendance at Church and Sunday School: seated round the fire on Sunday evenings before bedtime with a little Bible reading, ending with the singing of hymns standing round our mother at the piano'. It was a kind of upbringing not uncommon in those days, and it produced many famous men.

Moreover, there was at that time much intellectual curiosity among the Rochdale working men. Hall described one little group to whose meetings he was admitted. One man, a cotton spinner, had added several mosses to the British flora; another had made a detailed study of the calcareous shale brought up from a coal pit and had prepared numerous sections of the fossil vegetation which he passed on to Professor Williamson at the Owen's College, Manchester, for use in his paleobotanical studies. There were also the fanciers: working men in their little gardens were growing tulips, dahlias, carnations, gooseberries and other plants for exhibition at a series of Shows— commonly held in public houses. This intellectual curiosity was widespread in the mid- and latter part of the nineteenth century: it had been fostered by the popular lectures and writings of men like T. H. Huxley, John Tyndall, H. E. Roscoe and others, and had expressed itself in the formation and expansion of a wide range of societies: Scientific and Philosophical Societies for the higher professional and business people, Mutual Improvement Societies in the Chapels, and Mechanics Institutes for the 'labouring classes'. Some of these latter, e.g. Liverpool and Sheffield, developed and ultimately became Universities.[1]

Hall fitted well into this atmosphere, he was a vigorous healthy boy, fond of country walks and keen on the birds, the plants and fishes: the fringe of Rochdale was, as he said, 'still untarnished'. He collected fossils from the quarries and glacial drift beds, helped by the borough surveyor, for he had the gift of making friends with interesting adults. But he was also in the school football team and joined in any fun that was going.

He began his education at a good private school in Rochdale, and at the age of thirteen was transferred to the Manchester Grammar School, whither he travelled daily by train, doing his homework *en route*. Here he was not at first specially interested in his school work till he joined a voluntary chemistry class, and then, as he afterwards wrote: 'I found something of vital interest, something worth working at. In a spare room at home I improvized a laboratory of sorts, and all my pocket money, and indeed some of my lunch money as well, was spent on chemicals and apparatus.' Here among other things he prepared some of the metal tungsten, then a great rarity, and showed it to one of the boys who showed it to the science master; he, incredulous at first, tested the metal and found it really was tungsten. 'Then,' Hall wrote, 'things began to happen. I was hauled before the head science master and cross examined; my father was asked to see the High Master, and I suddenly found myself translated into the Science Fifth. Henceforward I began to enjoy school.' And well he might, for he was under Francis Jones, one of the best science masters of the day. When only seventeen years of age he gained a Brackenbury Scholarship at Balliol College, Oxford, and entered in October, 1881, taking chemistry as his subject.

The renowned Jowett was then Master, and his tutors were H. B. Dixon, the chemist, an old Westminster boy, and R. L.

[1] In Wales both the Aberystwyth and the Bangor University Colleges had been built largely out of donations by small farmers and workpeople. For Bangor over £1250 was provided by men of the Penrhyn and Dinorwic Quarries, who contributed each payday a fixed sum out of their earnings (D. Emrys Evans, *The University of Wales*, Cardiff, University of Wales Press, 1954).

Nettleship, the philosopher, who at that time was the strongest intellectual influence in the college. Both were men of wide culture: Dixon had been brought up on the classics and to the end could quote Horace aptly. Chemistry, however, was not at that time in much repute in Oxford.[1] At the end of three years Hall got his First and went up for a fourth year. At that time Oxford gave no Ph.D. degree and he was not drawn to specialization; he did little or no chemistry, but spent his last year, as was not uncommon in those days, in widening his cultural background. He had gone up, as H. E. Dale, his biographer, states,[2] 'a rather raw provincial boy, entirely ignorant of great regions of knowledge and delight; he went down in 1885, a young man of high scholastic and athletic distinction, confirmed in his attachment to his boyhood's interests, science and the countryside, but with interests enlarged far outside these limits and with the capacity of moving among men of widely different origins and pursuits'.

Events proved the wisdom of this course.

At the end of his four years (1885) Dixon did not advise him to take up chemistry as an academic career, so he did not follow the course customary for budding chemical professors, which was to proceed to Germany for a year's research and a Ph.D. Instead he became a schoolmaster, first at Blair Lodge School, Scotland, then at the Hulme Grammar School, Manchester, and finally in 1888 at King Edward VI High School for boys in Birmingham, where he became Senior Science Master. Among his pupils was E. W. Barnes, afterwards Bishop of Birmingham, whom he greatly impressed. 'Hall,' wrote Barnes, 'made chemistry a subject of enthralling interest. Experiments at school had to be repeated at home, and I became such a nuisance at the scullery sink that my father had a shed built to contain my enthusiasm.' Hall was very happy at Birmingham. He spent much time in the home of an old college friend, Francis Brooks, one of a large attractive family living

---

[1] Dixon was fond of quoting a rhyme current in those days: the lament of an undergraduate who showed no signs of passing in anything:

'I thought to pass some time ago, but here, alas! I am,
Having managed to be plucked in every classical exam.,
I cannot get up Plato, so my reverend tutor thinks
I had better take up Chemistry, which is commonly called "Stinks".'

[2] H. E. Dale. *Daniel Hall, Pioneer in Scientific Agriculture*, John Murray, 1956.

in a comfortable roomy house in Edgbaston with a delightful garden. Hall became engaged to the eldest daughter and married her in 1892. Francis Brooks became Professor of Classics at Bristol.

Hall did not, however, remain for long in Birmingham or even in the schoolmastering profession. In common with a number but not all of the counties, Surrey had decided that its share of the 'whisky money' should be used for extending education, and had appealed to Oxford University for help under the University Extension scheme: there was a call for lecturers which Hall in 1891 accepted. Chemistry was his subject; it was very popular at the time and Hall's courses obviously gave great satisfaction. He tried also agricultural chemistry, but here he was less successful; the intellectual curiosity which had been so marked a characteristic of the working men of the north was not shared by the farmers of the south. They were in the trough of the depression and had been for ten years; they saw no way out and were unwilling to believe that these young men from the universities could help them.

The main courses, however, were going well: Hall could have continued at extension work, quietly dropping the agricultural efforts. But he was a born pioneer and rather lost interest in an activity after it had got over its initial troubles and was sailing in smooth waters. He wanted to 'carry science to the farmers', to borrow a phrase of the time. Clearly the University Extension method was unsuitable: he realized that the only way would be to set up a college staffed by men well trained in science which they were prepared to apply to the solution of the farm problems. Much of Surrey was still agricultural, though of only mediocre quality; it was, however, rapidly becoming suburbanized. In Kent, on the other hand, agriculture was not only more important, but it was on a far higher level; and it had special branches, the growing of hops and fruit and the breeding of pedigree sheep. All this had produced a highly skilled and very intelligent body of farmers.

Hall realized that the college must be placed in Kent. He knew what kind of a college he wanted and proceeded to take the necessary steps for its foundation.

A NEW PROFESSION:
THE CONSULTING AGRICULTURAL CHEMIST

As already stated Augustus Voelcker had in 1863 retired from the Chair of Chemistry at the Royal Agricultural College, Cirencester and set up as consultant in London. It was a bold venture, for the profession was new, but it had arisen because farmers were becoming alive to the fact that they needed more specific advice about the use of fertilizer and feeding stuffs than their own knowledge could supply, and also there were certain quantities of both these essential materials on the market which were grossly over-valued by the vendors or unsuitable for the farmer's purposes. Agricultural science had reached the stage when general statements were no longer sufficient: much more quantitative expression was required, but this was not possible till accurate analytical methods had been devised.

Bernard Dyer was one of the first to improve the method of soil analysis. He was born in London in February 1856 the son of John A. Dyer, then News Editor of the *Daily News*. After some preliminary instruction he went in January 1871 to the City of London School, then in Milk Street, which was already distinguished for its science teaching. Among his school contemporaries were F. Gowland Hopkins and W. H. Perkin jun., whose distinguished father had earlier studied there. Dyer stayed, however, only two years and left in December 1872 having already decided to take up agricultural chemistry as a career. Accordingly he became pupil-assistant to Augustus Voelcker, and worked for three years in his laboratory in Salisbury Square, Fleet Street. Here the training must have been excellent, for although the number of student assistants was not large, four of them became Presidents of the Society of Public Analysts.

After four years, in 1877, at the age of 21, he took his courage in his hands and set up quite independently as analyst at 17 Great Tower Street, where he remained till the place was destroyed in the great air raid of May, 1941. He struck out on very broad lines. In addition to his laboratory work he wrote articles on rural water supply, a great variety of agricultural subjects including crop manuring, cattle condiments, home brewing, disposal of rural sewage, and a long series of

Sir Joseph Henry Gilbert

7.
Sir A. Daniel Hall
Professor T. B. Wood

geological sketches. Like others of his generation Dyer lacked neither courage nor self-confidence, and was not at all abashed at attempting so wide a range. He soon became favourably known and acquired a large agricultural connection. He became Lecturer in Agriculture at the City of London College and gave courses there during the next eight years. He was appointed consulting chemist to the agricultural societies of Essex and Leicestershire, and other smaller agricultural organizations.

He carried out numerous field experiments many of which were of more interest than was recognized at the time. His first recorded experiments were on turnips in 1882 and 1883 and gave the unexpected result that coprolites gave better response than superphosphate—the insoluble superior to the soluble— which seemed absurd till Dyer found that the soil was acid and the coprolites would help to neutralize it. This was fourteen years before acidity was noticed at Woburn. Also farmyard manure in spite of its low content of phosphorus proved to be an adequate source of phosphate for the turnip crop, and nothing was gained by adding superphosphate. This also was fully confirmed many years later by Scott Robertson in Northern Ireland and by others.

In 1886 he started a five-year course of experiments in Essex where dairy farming was being developed, necessitating large quantities of mangolds as winter food for the cattle. The Rothamsted experiments, then in their tenth year, had shown the striking effect of nitrogenous manuring and the superiority of nitrate of soda over sulphate of ammonia. The Essex farmers wanted to know if this would be true for their soils, but, more important: were the heavy crops of mangolds given by artificial fertilizers obtained at the expense of the soil condition, as many farmers then believed, and would they be followed by poor crops of oats? The Rothamsted experiments threw no light on this. Dyer showed that these fears were unjustified; the heaviest crops of mangolds were followed by the heaviest crop of oats; indeed heavy dressings of nitrate of soda benefited the succeeding oat crops, probably, as he surmised, because they produced a large weight of leaves, which being ploughed in, constituted a valuable green manure. Still later (1894) he began with F. W. E. Shrivell of Golden Green, Hadlow, Kent, an extensive

G

series of experiments on the manuring of market garden crops, aided by the Chilean Nitrate Committee; these were the first of their kind and the published Report (1904) gave much new information on this important subject.

He recorded no fertilizer experiments with grassland, though he recognized their necessity. 'There is, perhaps, no crop more amenable to good treatment than grass' he wrote, 'and none more apt to be neglected'.

Dyer's field experiments were all made to answer definite questions put to him by farmers. They were simple in design and could be easily apprehended; they were carefully carried out and the results described in clear concise language that all could understand. He gave also a financial summary of the results with shrewd business-like comments. The field experiments were not only useful to farmers: they yielded new information about the effects of fertilizers on growing crops; unfortunately for Dyer the time was not yet ripe for devising hypotheses that would link facts together and explain them.

The experiments, however, furnished Dyer with a fruitful subject for investigation. He had analysed the soils by the method Voelcker had taught him, based on Davy's as modified by Way: the soil was heated with concentrated hydrochloric acid under specified conditions and the amounts of phosphoric acid, potash, and other constituents extracted were determined. He set out the analytical data in his reports on the fertilizer trials, but significantly enough did not discuss them, and indeed it is difficult to know what he could have said, for they had little or no relation with the field results. Soils showing a high phosphate content might respond well to phosphatic fertilizers, and conversely those of low content might give little response. So with potash.

Dyer realized that the solvent was unsuitable, and in 1884 he began studying the actions of various solvents on the soil. Unfortunately he does not seem to have seen Daubeny's paper on 'active' and 'dormant' nutrients in the soil: the distinction, however, had passed into the pool of common knowledge under the names of 'available' and 'unavailable', while Daubeny himself was forgotten—a not unusual fate for a scientist. Daubeny had in fact suggested that solution of carbon dioxide (carbonic acid) should be used to estimate the quantity of 'active' material, but no practical method of doing this had been devised. Liebig had suggested acetic acid but this had not proved acceptable here. Dyer turned to some of the solvents coming into use on the Continent for evaluating the new phosphatic fertilizers free from water-soluble phosphate which were coming to use in the early 1880's. Ammonium citrate was one of these: it had answered for some fertilizers but not for others. A German chemist, Tollens, had suggested a one per cent solution of citric acid, and this proved satisfactory for the fertilizers.

Dyer now tried a different approach. His problem was to distinguish the available fraction of the phosphate from the total. He tried various strengths of citric acid and ammonium citrate and found no constancy in the amount of P_2O_5 extracted: this varied with the solvent and its concentration.

He therefore changed his attack. He started with the assumption, then widely accepted by plant physiologists including Sachs, their great leader, that as Dyer put it, 'plants help themselves to a part of their mineral food by means of the solvent action of their acid root sap on the particles of soil with which the rootlets come into contact'. He collected a hundred plants of twenty different natural orders, separated their fine rootlets, estimated their moisture content, crushed them and boiled them in water, estimated the acidity of the extract in terms of hydrogen by titration with phenolphthalein as indicator, and then calculated the results back on the moisture content, so arriving at the acidity of the root sap. He frankly admitted that the value of the results depended on the efficacy of the extraction process, which he therefore described in considerable detail. The values ranged from 0·003 to 0·014 per cent in terms of hydrogen: he adopted 0·013.

He then had to decide what acid to use. He chose citric acid for several reasons. It was 'an organic acid, and in that sense kindred to other root sap acids'. It was also the acid generally used by those who have attempted to determine available phosphoric acid in manures', and moreover 'it is at hand in every agricultural laboratory in a state of purity, and therefore a convenient acid'. An acid value of 0·013 in terms of hydrogen became 0·91 per cent in terms of citric acid: for convenience he rounded this off to 1 per cent, no doubt influenced by the fact that this was the concentration adopted by the German chemists, then at the height of their prestige in Europe.

Dyer claimed no scientific basis for the choice of citric acid as solvent: it was purely empirical. In order to give it a thorough test he obtained permission from Lawes and Gilbert to take samples of soil from the Hoosfield barley plots. Values for phosphate and potash determined by his method accorded with the agricultural history of the plots; those by the older 'total' method were meaningless. Lawes and Gilbert were so impressed that they invited Dyer similarly to survey Broadbalk which he did with equally satisfactory results.

The method proved so helpful that it remained in general use in Britain for some fifty years with minor modifications to make it quicker and easier in operation. It was much used in advisory work, in chemical sections of soil surveys, and in studying the relations of soil and plant growth.[1]

Like John Augustus Voelcker at the Royal Agricultural Society, Dyer fearlessly exposed fraud whenever he detected it. He was made a member of the Government Advisory Committee in connection with the first Fertilizer and Feeding Stuffs Act of 1893 and was consulted in the framing of the more comprehensive Act of 1906.

Dyer had in a high degree all the personal qualities needed for success in his profession. He was a lively sociable person who appreciated good fellowship and good living; he had a striking and unforgettable appearance, an air of competence that inspired respect, a good voice and an excellent speaking and lecturing manner. Farmers and Courts alike trusted him, impressed by his wide knowledge and shrewd judgment combined with obvious sincerity and intellectual honesty. He was one of the early members of the Society of Public Analysts, and he was held in such high esteem that a Memorial Lecture had been founded to be delivered biennally.[2] He died in 1948 at the age of 92

[1] Dyer used the work as a D.Sc. Thesis (University of London) in 1892 and published it in 1894 in *Trans. Chem. Soc.*, Vol. 65, pp. 115–67. The testing of the method on the Rothamsted soils gave such interesting results that the paper was published in *Phil. Trans.*, 194 B, 235–90, 1902. He discussed the question of the analysis of soil as a guide to its fertility in *Trans. Highland and Agric. Soc.*, Series V, Vol. 10, p. 26, 1898.

[2] The first was given in March 1950 by the author and was published in *The Analyst*, May 1950, Vol. 75, pp. 240–51.

having retained his vigour and interest in life almost to the end. Much useful analytical work was done by the Voelcker family: the father, Augustus, the founder of this branch of agricultural science, his sons, John Augustus and E. W., and Eric of a later generation; by Alfred Smetham, F. J. Lloyd, H. Droop Richmond and other able analysts in improving methods of analysis and gaining fuller knowledge of the materials with which both farmers and scientists had to deal.

CHAPTER VII

THE RENAISSANCE (1)

1890 – 1910

CAMBRIDGE SCHOOL OF AGRICULTURE

AFTER the passing of the Whisky Money Act of 1890 it
was expected that a considerable demand for agricultural
education would arise in the counties, necessitating the appointment of a number of teachers who did not yet exist. Viscount
Chaplin, President of the newly established Board of Agriculture, wrote on July twenty-fifth, 1890, to the Chancellor of
Cambridge University suggesting the establishment of a
Department of Agriculture where they could be trained. The
suggestion was referred to a syndicate which, after two years
deliberation, recommended that it be adopted. The University,
however, rejected the recommendation, pleading lack of funds.
Meanwhile G. D. Liveing, the Professor of Chemistry and a
member of the syndicate, recognizing the urgency of the matter
organized a voluntary class in agricultural chemistry for senior
students during the long vacation of 1891 with Henry Robinson,
his assistant, in charge. It was very successful, and at least four
of the students later did much for the promotion of agricultural
science: John Percival, Cecil Warburton, R. H. Adie and
Thomas Barlow Wood.

Undeterred by the cool reception accorded to the syndicate's
recommendation, Liveing and one of his colleagues, Professor
McKenny Hughes, started negotiations with representatives of
the neighbouring county councils which led to the formation of
the Cambridge and Counties Agricultural Education Committee.
This body received grants from the constituent counties and
the Board of Agriculture, and in January 1893 it sponsored a
course on agricultural science in rooms lent by Liveing in the
basement of the chemical laboratory, while the committee itself

maintained a reading room and library in St Mary's Passage. Later in November, 1893, the syndicate made a second report, this time recommending the institution of a Diploma in Agriculture: the report was adopted and the first examination was held in July 1894.[1] The emphasis was on the basic sciences, chemistry, botany, zoology etc. treated in a very elementary manner with some reference to agriculture: knowledge of agriculture was supposed to come from practical experience obtained later. T. B. Wood and R. H. Adie combined to write a suitable text book for their part of the course.[2] It is one of the most interesting books ever written on the subject, combining pure chemistry and agricultural chemistry, teaching each without assuming prior knowledge of either.

Its interest here is that it shows the level of agricultural science just before the renaissance that was now beginning. The technique of field experiments and the properties of fertilizers remained much as Augustus Voelcker had left them, except that bacterial decomposition of nitrate was known to occur in presence of organic matter, and students were advised not to apply fertilizers in the same season as dung. Way's double silicates still held the field as agents for the retention of ammonia by soil; other factors, however, contributed: Davy's physical absorption in the pores of the spongy humus; combination with humic acid to form insoluble 'double humates'; and an unexplained combination with 'hydrated oxide of iron'. Potash was retained as Way had indicated by turning out lime, soda or magnesia from the double silicates of the clay.

The new feature was the movement of water in the soil. It was supposed to rise by capillarity from the ground water to the surface, quickly but to no great height through a sandy soil; to a great height but only slowly through a clay; and both quickly and to a great height through a humus soil. These movements, however, were possible only in compacted soil; they ceased altogether in loose soil, indeed a layer of loose soil made a good protection against drying out of the underlying compact mass of damp soil. These ideas had recently come from

---

[1] F. L. Engledow, Address at the Jubilee Celebrations, July 1949.
[2] *Agricultural Chemistry*, R. H. Adie and T. B. Wood (Secretary and Lecturer in Agricultural Chemistry to Cambridge and Counties Agricultural Education Scheme), 2 vols., 1897.

America and were accepted for some twenty-five years when they were found to need modification. Acidity of soil is mentioned as sometimes due to soluble organic acids: it could be remedied by drainage after which 'application of chalk or limestone is beneficial'. Two most important advances had been made, quite unspectacular and lacking entirely in dramatic quality— Kjeldahl's method of determining nitrogen; and the ammonium molybdate method of determining phosphate. Had these been available to Davy his account of plant nutrition would have been very different.

Of the students who attended Robinson's long vacation course in 1891, T. B. Wood played the most distinguished part in the subsequent development of agricultural science and education at Cambridge. He was born at Habberly, Shropshire, in 1869, the son of E. D. Wood, a farmer at Field Dalling, Holt, Norfolk; he was educated at the High School, Newcastle-under-Lyme, and in 1887 entered Gonville and Caius College, Cambridge; in 1889 he obtained a first class in the Natural Science Tripos. After the 1891 course he was sent to Devon by the University Extension syndicate to lecture on soils and manures but remained only a few months; in January, 1892, he returned to Norfolk to develop agricultural instruction there. He had an extremely strenuous life. During the week he taught science in the County School; on Saturdays he gave some lectures on agricultural science to elementary school teachers; during the winter he lectured to farmers at various country towns; all the time he was conducting field experiments on manuring and other subjects at various centres for the Norfolk Chamber of Agriculture. The considerable amount of travelling involved was done by train if available, otherwise by open trap or dog cart; the so-called 'safety bicycle', the clumsy prototype of the modern machine, was not yet in common use and the old high bicycle was unsuitable. It was a hard apprenticeship, but it gave him a knowledge of farming and an insight into the farmer's character that stood him in good stead in his later life.

He remained only two years; then in January, 1894, Liveing invited him to return to Cambridge to help with the first lot of diploma students in place of Robinson who had died. His duties were varied: besides teaching agricultural chemistry to the diploma students he was secretary to the Agricultural

Education Committee, and he supervised manurial experiments in the contributing counties. The published reports of these experiments are very interesting; they are scarce, but sets are preserved in the library at Rothamsted.

As at Wye, there were financial troubles, and in 1897 the question of closing down the whole enterprise was seriously considered. Fortunately the Cambridge County Council came to the rescue: their Secretary of Education, Austin Keen, had taken great interest in the work, and the difficulties were overcome.

Up to this point the scheme had been run by the County Council; the University had had no part in it, a lectureship in the history and economics of agriculture founded by Sir Walter Gilbey being their only agricultural activity. In 1898, however, the Drapers Company offered to endow a professorship of agriculture for ten years on condition that the University founded and maintained a department of agriculture and recognized agriculture or agricultural science as a subject for a degree. At the same time the Board of Agriculture offered to increase its grant. These offers were accepted though with some misgivings: considerable fear is recorded that 'however harmless it may be to try an experiment in this direction, the question whether "bread studies" are really things that a University should touch is a very open one'. However, the step was taken: the University duly established the Department in 1899, and work began in October of that year. It was still housed in the basement of the chemical laboratories, thanks to Prof. Liveing's continued interest;[1] but in addition a small room in the Botany School was lent by Prof. Marshall Ward.

Much to his disappointment Wood was not elected to the Chair. The prevailing view was that a professor of agriculture should be a technical man, not a trained scientist, and accordingly the choice fell on William Somerville, one of Robert Wallace's students at Edinburgh University, and at the time Professor of Agriculture at Armstrong College, Newcastle-upon-Tyne. His chief claim to distinction was that he had in

---

[1] Agricultural science owes a great debt to Prof. Liveing. He became also a Governor of Wye College where he was very helpful. Fortunately he lived to see the emergence of Cambridge and of Wye out of their early troubles: he was over ninety when he died.

G*

1897 established an experimental farm on the poor boulder clay at Cockle Park and made experiments on the effect of basic slag on its very poor pasture, using the live weight increase of sheep grazed thereon as the measure of the improvement. Remarkable increases were obtained, and Somerville's experiments on 'manuring for mutton' attracted much attention and made his reputation.

Wood was appointed Lecturer in Chemistry and R. H. Biffen Lecturer in Botany. In 1900 the Department was given the ten year lease of Burgoyne's Farm of 140 acres near the church at Impington. Somerville had an attractive personality and considerable social value, which did much to make the new department accepted in the University though he was not particularly interested in science. He did not remain long in Cambridge, however, but resigned the professorship in 1902 and went to London to the Board of Agriculture.

He was succeeded by Thomas Hudson Middleton, who, like Somerville, was a Scottish agriculturist, but of completely different character. He was a man of prodigious industry, wholeheartedly devoted to his work, meticulously attentive to detail, austere in his way of life and entirely lacking in the smoking-room graces. But he was kindly and helpful to younger men and quickly won their abiding and affectionate respect. He continued to develop the farm and the practical side, and he was also very interested in agricultural science and sympathetic to those who were trying to expand it. Wood was naturally disappointed at being again passed over, but he loyally accepted the situation and Middleton, seeing perhaps more clearly than those in higher authority, gave him all the help he could. Middleton though not himself a scientist had sound scientific instincts, and he did so much for the development of agricultural science in Great Britain that it is necessary to give some account of him.

Thomas Hudson Middleton came of a long line of farmers. His father's family had for some generations farmed in Northumberland but at the end of the eighteenth century migrated to Ross-shire at the invitation of George Ross, known as the 'Scotch Agent', who wished to improve the local agriculture. His mother was the daughter of the Rev. D. Walter Ross Taylor of Thursoe. The family lived at Rosefarm, Easter Ross;

here he was born on August 31, 1863. His father in accordance
with family tradition was an excellent farmer: 'I never yet heard
of a Middleton', wrote R. C. Munro-Ferguson, 'whose farming
was not celebrated'.

Both his parents had a keen sense of duty to their locality
and in particular to their staff. His father was a J.P.; a member
of the Parish Council and of the School Board, an active
supporter of the Cottage Hospital, an elder of the Free Church
and a delegate to the General Assembly, but he had no public
ambitions and confined his activities to the parish. He was a
fine, bearded gentleman; he loved his children and greatly
enjoyed a game with them. His mother was dignified, kindly
and gracious, a worthy representative of the stately Victorian
ladies; she ruled her household firmly and also kept the farm
accounts beautifully and clearly written. Each Sunday she
held a Sunday School in the kitchen for the farm workers'
children.

In the morning and evening of each day the whole household,
some fifteen in all, collected for prayers, the singing of a psalm
in the metrical version—the tune being 'raised' by the father—
and the reading of the Bible. Each one present had to read a
verse: the reading was done systematically, beginning with the
first chapter of Genesis and going steadily on. With all its
strictness, however, the home was a very happy place as
indeed was the whole farm; the workers stayed long: on one
occasion it was calculated that ten of them had aggregated 439
years of service.

This upbringing naturally developed in Middleton marked
integrity of character and a high sense of responsibility: it
was these, combined with his deeply ingrained knowledge of
good farming, that enabled him to achieve so much in later life.

He was educated at Merchiston School, Edinburgh, which he
left in 1880 at the age of seventeen. Normally he would have
started farming, but signs of the impending depression were
already appearing and in family council it was deemed better
that he should take up engineering. So he went to Glasgow
University, took his B.Sc. (Engineering) in 1883, and spent
some months with a Glasgow firm. His father's health broke
down as the result of overwork and he had to return home to
manage the farm; he went reluctantly, but being there, threw

himself whole-heartedly into the work, experimented with new methods and new materials, introduced labour saving devices into the buildings, made drainage schemes and improved the bookkeeping. He became so interested that he decided to give up engineering and follow agriculture instead. When in 1886 his father, being fully recovered, returned to take charge, he went to Edinburgh University to take the agricultural course under Prof. Wallace, and gained his B.Sc. (Agriculture) in 1889.

He was now twenty-six; he had become engaged to Lydia Miller Davidson, daughter of Prof. Davidson of Adelaide and grand-daughter of Hugh Miller the geologist; he wished to get married. The farm could not then afford him an adequate livelihood; he therefore accepted a chair in the Agricultural College of the small State of Baroda in India. Here he was fully occupied with teaching, though he also studied the diets of his students and recognized their deficiency in protein. In 1896 the University College of Wales, Aberystwyth lost its lecturer in agriculture, James Wilson, who returned to Aberdeen: Mrs Middleton, a very gracious lady, was in England and heard of the vacancy, she applied on her husband's behalf and he was appointed. He took up his duties as soon as he could get back from India. Besides his college teaching he had to frame the courses for the degree in agriculture then being instituted in the newly established University of Wales. He also organized short courses for farmers' sons; these were so successful that similar courses were soon arranged elsewhere: there were as yet no Farm Institutes.

After three years—in 1899—he left Aberystwyth for King's College, Newcastle (then called the Durham College of Science), to occupy the Chair of Agriculture vacated by William Somerville who had transferred to Cambridge. Here in addition to his college work he devoted much time to lectures and advisory work for farmers in the surrounding region, and he encouraged scientific work on the troublesome sheep diseases, braxy and louping-ill; he set up a laboratory in the affected area and put it under the control of the Professor of Pathology of Aberdeen University. He remained at Newcastle only three years.

In October 1902 he went to Cambridge, again following

Somerville. Here he developed the field experiments already begun by Somerville to show the advantages of sowing mixtures of recognized agricultural grasses and clovers instead of leaving the land to cover itself with any wild vegetation that sprang up—a not uncommon practice in those days of depression —and he encouraged S. F. Armstrong to work out methods of botanical analysis of the herbage, adequate but simpler than those used by Lawes and Gilbert. Very detailed lists of instructions about observations to be made on these grassland experiments were given to his staff. He tried to introduce ley farming into the eastern counties but did not succeed: farmers preferred the one year clover ley. Also, and with more permanent effect, he made numbers of trials with potatoes, not then very widely grown in the eastern counties. He completely gained the confidence of the farmers.

In Cambridge besides developing the farm classes he fundamentally altered the teaching of science to the agricultural students. Up to that time they had attended the ordinary courses in botany, geology, and to some extent chemistry and physics. In the main they had not been interested, and he thought it would be much better to have these sciences taught from the agricultural standpoint. The pure scientists did not like the idea, but Middleton's quiet diplomacy gradually prevailed, and Wood, Biffen, and Cecil Warburton the entomologist were encouraged to develop their special courses. The School of Agriculture grew so vigorously that proper buildings became necessary: the then Duke of Devonshire was interested and helped to raise the money needed and the present dignified building was begun.

In 1906 Middleton left Cambridge for the Board of Agriculture, again following Somerville who had been appointed to the newly resuscitated Chair of Rural Economy at Oxford University. There he remained till the exigencies of the First World War called him to much more onerous duties.

Hitherto, in spite of much useful work by the Staff, the School in its early days was not held in very high repute in the University. For the first nine years no degree could be obtained in agriculture but only a diploma, and the course of instruction was disrespectfully labelled 'dung special' by ribald undergraduates in the more respectable conventional sciences. After

Middleton left Wood was promoted to the Chair of Agriculture, to the great satisfaction of all who knew him. He was devoted to the School, and had stuck to it through good times and bad; he was thoroughly well equipped to direct it. Moreover it was now realized that the supposed necessity of appointing a practical agriculturist as head of a university Department of Agriculture was fallacious. What was wanted as its Head was a scientist acceptable on an equal footing with other members of the scientific staff, who had acquired a sufficient knowledge of agriculture to be able to play an important part in the development of agricultural science. This Wood could do and did.

Wood's immediate purpose was to obtain a more definite picture of the chemical composition of some of the more important crops. He began with mangolds. Dairying was on the increase: it was one of the few branches in agriculture that afforded some profit, and mangolds were vitally important as winter food. They were very responsive to manuring and management, and the yields might vary from twenty to eighty tons per acre. In conjunction with a young colleague, R. H. Berry, Wood determined the percentage of dry matter in roots grown under different conditions, but he broke new ground by working on large numbers of single roots, weighing and making the determinations on each individually, thus accumulating a mass of data that enabled him to study the variability in composition of the roots and opening the way also to improvement by selection. He and Berry did not confine themselves to determinations on the root as a whole; they sampled its different layers and so were able to make a map of the root showing how its composition varied in its different segments.

A parallel investigation on the variation in chemical composition of the swede was made by S. H. Collins at the Armstrong College, Newcastle-on-Tyne. He expressed the values by a simple mathematical formula; a summation of a constant for the crop and factors for soil, variety and farm. It was interesting, but, far more important, it evoked a criticism from A. D. Hall to the effect that in any such attempt it was necessary to attach to the various experimental data an estimate of the magnitude of their error. It was a new idea to agricultural experimenters and it at once attracted attention. Fortunately, among Wood's friends at Caius College was the astronomer F. J. M. Stratton, who of course was familiar with the methods for estimating the error of a measurement. In an important investigation he and Wood in 1910 showed how the magnitude of the error of a feeding trial and of a field experiment could be ascertained. Two of Wood's pupils, G. T. Spinks and F. R. Pethybridge, had divided a field of mangolds into 900 plots, and weighed the roots on each. The methods of least squares was then applied to the data and the magnitude of the errors estimated when the plots were considered singly or in certain groupings. This paper is of great importance in agricultural science in Great Britain as it showed how the subject could be put on a quantitative basis instead of being as in the past mainly qualitative.

Hall made a somewhat similar study at Rothamsted with the assistance of W. B. Mercer. An acre of mangolds was harvested in 200 plots of equal size, and an acre of wheat in 500 equal plots, grain and straw being weighed separately. The investigation involved an enormous amount of work most conscientiously carried out by Mercer, but it supplied data of impeccable quality which still serve a useful purpose. Hall and Mercer concluded that plots need not exceed 1/50 acre, and that with a five-fold replication distributed regularly over the experimental area the experimental error could be as low as 1 or 2 per cent.[1] These recommendations held the field till the whole subject was recast by R. A. Fisher, as will be shown later.

Wood also initiated some soil studies which though not developed at Cambridge were continued elsewhere. L. F. Newman surveyed the soils of Norfolk, F. W. Foreman those of Cambridgeshire and T. H. Rigg those of the market garden areas of Bedfordshire. G. W. Robinson had helped with these surveys and later developed an important school of soil studies at Bangor University College, and Rigg later did valuable work on the soils of South Island, New Zealand.

Wood also made important pioneering studies on the chemistry of wheat, working in close consultation with Biffen, Hall and A. E. Humphries, the well known miller of Coxe's Lock, Weybridge, Surrey. All four were impressed by the fact that English wheat, while useful enough for making biscuits,

[1] *Jour. Agric. Sci.*, 1911, Vol. 4, pp. 107–32.

did not make the well-risen beautifully piled-up cottage loaf then favoured by British housewives, consequently it commanded a lower price per bushel than Canadian prairie wheat, which was of excellent baking quality. Much of the English wheat, in fact, was used as chicken food, but in any case the price was so low that farmers hesitated to grow it. Replacement of the standard English varieties by Canadian Red Fife or Marquis was no solution as the yields were too low—only about half those of the standard varieties. Attempts were made to discover whether English wheat could be raised to the same level of baking quality as Canadian. Hall showed that this could not be done by any manurial or cultivation treatment: he thereupon dropped out of the team. Wood studied the proteins of English and Canadian wheats and observed physical differences which he investigated along with W. B. Hardy, also of Caius College; the results are published in an important paper in the Royal Society's *Proceedings*, but they did not help in the 'strengthening' of English wheat. The problem was solved by Biffen, who showed that baking quality was a varietal character which could be somewhat enhanced or considerably impaired by cultural treatment but could not be created thereby; it was, however, heritable, and he proceeded to breed wheats combining English yielding power with some degree of Canadian strength. The problem still persists: in the 1960's only about twenty per cent of English-grown wheat was going into bread, and about half into household flour.

Rowland Harry Biffen was born on May 28, 1874, at Cheltenham, where his father, Henry John Biffen, was Headmaster of the Christchurch Higher Grade School. At the age of nine he went to the Cheltenham Grammar School where he remained for ten years. The only science taught then was chemistry, and the method appears to have been somewhat on the heuristic lines advocated by H. E. Armstrong, then a dominant figure in the chemical world: the boys were left largely to teach themselves with encouragement from the teacher. Given the right conditions the method produced some good results; it developed habits of close observation and independence of thought, but it proved unsuitable for mass instruction. Biffen's spare time was spent in the Cotswolds collecting plants, flint implements, fossils, in which activities he resembled Hall. He also made sketches for which he had great talent.

In 1893 he entered Emmanuel College, Cambridge, as Exhibitioner, took a first in both parts of the Natural Science Tripos, and did so well in Part II in 1896 that he was awarded the Frank Smart Studentship in Botany at Caius College and began investigating the life history of certain fungi under Prof. H. Marshall Ward. The scholarship did not require continuous residence in Cambridge and he was able to join a small expedition to Brazil, Mexico and the West Indies for several months in 1897 and 1898 to study the sources of rubber which, although not in much demand at the time, looked as if it would shortly be needed in large quantities. Motor cars and 'safety' bicycles had recently been invented; they were not yet in general use but obviously had great possibilities of future developments if sufficient rubber could be obtained. The wild trees of the Amazon were then the chief sources of supply: the plantations of West Africa, Ceylon, Malaya and Indonesia had not yet been started.

The journey was the turning point in Biffen's career. He was impressed by the immensity of the natural resources of the tropics, and the complete absence of any scientific direction in their exploitation. He decided therefore to make Economic Botany his main work. Cambridge could offer no such post, but on his return in 1898 he was given a demonstratorship in Botany and he continued his studies of the general biology and the life histories of various fungi. He remained in this post only a year: in 1899 when the University Department of Agriculture was inaugurated he accepted the lectureship in botany there and so accomplished his desired purpose of devoting himself to economic botany. Probably influenced by Wood he began with studies of the wheat crop, making a number of crosses indiscriminately, 'trusting that some few might give improvements in the required direction'—for at that time John Lindley's dictum of 1844 still held true, that it was a 'game of chance played between man and plants', to which Biffen soon added that 'the chances seemed in favour of the plants'. But a movement was going on in Cambridge the importance of which Biffen had the instinct to recognize and it determined the course of his whole life's work.

William Bateson, a zoologist of St John's College, Cambridge, and somewhat of an intellectual rebel, had had the temerity to dispute the long-cherished idea that evolution was brought about by the action of natural selection on a continuously varying material. He had the naturalist's eye and from an immense amount of material he became convinced that variation was frequently discontinuous and could be brought about by hybridisation. His book, *Materials for the Study of Variation*, published in 1894, aroused a vigorous, even embittered controversy which went on for years, headed by W. F. R. Weldon, Linacre Professor at Oxford. A particularly lively turn was given to it in 1900 when, on his way to London by train to deliver a lecture before the Royal Horticultural Society, Bateson read an account of Mendel's paper on heredity which had lain unknown in an obscure journal since 1865 and had just been discovered. He at once grasped its fundamental significance, recast his lecture *en route* and made the first announcement in England of Mendel's laws.

Returning to Cambridge he straightway began to repeat Mendel's experiments, with the aid of a few volunteers, some of them women. It was all so revolutionary, however, that neither *Biometrica* nor *Nature* was prepared to publish their papers. Bateson set out his position in a small book, *A defence of Mendel's Principles of Heredity* (1902), but the orthodox scientists still looked askance at him and his team. It is related that a don of the old strict school reduced his hostess to tears and completely upset her tea party by publicly upbraiding one of the women guests for her impropriety in engaging in the indelicate and unladylike occupation of crossbreeding small animals. But some of the younger biologists were attracted by the subject and rallied round Bateson. The controversy reached a high pitch of excitement at the meeting of the British Association at Cambridge in 1904 when Bateson was President of the Zoology Section and he and his workers presented their results in detail, sparing no one and nothing in the sturdiness of their attack. At a crowded meeting Weldon responded with vigour: the proceedings were lively and Karl Pearson proposed a three-year truce. The chairman, the bland and genial Rev. T. R. Stebbing, in his concluding remarks began by deploring the high feeling that had been aroused: 'My profession' he said, 'is one of peace, you have all heard what Professor Pearson has suggested'—then after a pause and in a louder voice went on: 'But what I say is, let them fight it out'.[1]

Of all people Biffen was one of the most peaceful—though firm as a rock on matters of principle—and it speaks volumes for his clear scientific vision and complete freedom from domination by preconceived ideas that he recognized at once the significance of Bateson's work; like many of his fellow workers he believed that it could transform plant breeding from 'a game of chance' to an exact science. He accordingly began assembling wheats and barleys from many parts of the world for the study of variation and hybridization. He announced his object in a short paper published in 1903 in the *Proceedings of the Cambridge Philosophical Society*;[2] 'raising improved varieties from the point of view of the farmer and miller, and also to ascertain to what extent Mendel's Laws of inheritance hold for the distinctive characteristics of wheat'. With shrewd scientific insight he included in his studies not only certain morphological characters, but also some 'constitutional' characters, length of growing season, and susceptibility to rust.

His manipulative skill was so great that even in this first paper he felt he could announce that 'from the preliminary experiments it appears that immunity from rust is a definite recessive character'. In his first big paper, *Mendel's laws of inheritance and wheat breeding*,[3] he showed that morphology of ear, leaf and stem, grain colour, size of loaf and baking quality were all Mendelian 'characters', showing the phenomena of dominance or recessiveness and independent segregation. In another set of investigations he showed that sterility in barley—in the form of suppression of female or male or both reproductive organs in certain florets—was also heritable. The achievement to which both Bateson and Engledow attached the greatest importance was his proof that susceptibility to yellow

[1] A lively description of those early days is given in a characteristically interesting paper by R. C. Punnett in *Heredity*, 1950, Vol. 4, pp. 1–10. The full story is given in Mrs Bateson's *Life of William Bateson*. The Cambridge incident recalls the historic fight between Huxley and Bishop Wilberforce at the Oxford meeting in 1860.

[2] *Proc. Camb. Phil. Soc.*, 1903, Vol. 12, pp. 279–82. Also a note in *Nature*, 1903, Vol. 69, 92–3.

[3] *J. Agric. Sci.*, 1905, Vol. 1, pp. 4–48.

rust (*Puccinia glumarum*) was a simple, single-factor Mendelian dominant.[1] Biffen thus united plant genetics and plant pathology, the subjects of his two great masters, Bateson and Marshall Ward, and opened the way to the avoidance of the great losses farmers had long suffered through the attacks of diseases: he showed the possibility of conferring resistance on desirable but susceptible varieties. This method is now widely practised for all crops.

As almost invariably happens, later work has shown that disease resistance is genetically very complex, there being a number of physiological races of the pathogens and resistance to one does not necessarily mean resistance to all. Further, new forms may arise. But this does not detract from the value of Biffen's demonstration that the Mendelian conception is valid not only for morphological and growing-period characteristics of plants, but for others as well.

Genetics developed rapidly as a science, becoming highly intricate and even mathematical, with a copious new vocabulary of its own. Biffen's interest, however, was not in theoretical genetics but in the production of new varieties of plants. He was a florist, managing his roses, alpines and other choice plants in his garden with consummate skill, and he set about breeding new wheats on these lines to suit the changed conditions of British agriculture. The Mendelian principles swept aside some of the old vague ideas such as 'prepotency', 'reversion', 'breaking of type', and others, and substituted for them definitely established scientific principles. 'Orderly synthesis' writes Engledow, 'replaced mysticism and guess work'. Biffen's supreme qualification for the work was that he had a clear conception of the kind of plant he wished to produce, and the artist's eye for recognizing the desired qualities at an early stage in the investigation. Looking back it is astonishing that he was able to achieve so much with such slender resources. He had neither staff, space nor statistical apparatus; but his sound florist's instinct enabled him to make the right decision in rejecting unsuitable segregates, and his gift of improvizing got

[1] W. Bateson, *Principles of Heredity* 1909; F. L. Engledow R. H. Biffen, *Obituary Notices, Royal Soc.*, 1950, No. 19, pp. 9–26. An admirable summary of R. H. Biffen's work to which I am indebted for much help in preparing this section.

him over difficulties which to a lesser man would have been insuperable.[1]

By 1910 his first triumph, Little Joss, was on the market—ten years only after his first tentative crosses had begun, as against the twelve to fifteen years normally required—it was a cross between a sub-variety of the old-established Squarehead's Master and Ghirka, a rust-resistant strain selected by him from an imported bulk of Russian wheat. It was immediately successful; it yielded well, it was notably resistant to yellow rust, its grain though not superior in baking quality to Squarehead's Master had special value for biscuit making, and its straw was so resilient that it stood up well against wind and storm: incidentally also it was excellent for thatching, for paper making, and for the packing of pottery. It was recommended at first for light soils of moderate fertility, but it proved to be admirably suited to the fertile Black Fen soils of East Anglia. It aroused wide interest as being one of the first fruits of the application of a new science to agriculture, and it proved so valuable that for the next forty years it was one of the most widely grown of British wheats.

Biffen's work was widely recognized: he was elected into the Royal Society in 1914 and knighted in 1925. He continued his plant breeding on the same lines, combining artistic perception with scientific acumen till 1936 when he retired to enjoy more fully the pleasures of his garden. He died on July 12, 1949.

In order to complete the group of workers at the School of Agriculture it was decided to invite F. H. A. Marshall to join them. He came from Edinburgh University where he had been working with Cossar Ewart on problems of animal physiology. Great developments followed which will be described in a later chapter. Under Wood's guidance the status of the school in the University rose. In 1908 the restriction of awards to diplomas was abolished and degrees were granted on exactly the same footing as other non-tripos subjects. The restricted courses in chemistry and biology were also abolished and agricultural students now had to take Part I of the Natural Science Tripos before turning over to agriculture. This completely removed

---

[1] Improvising was not uncommon in Cambridge in those days. J. J. Thomson of the Cavendish laboratory was a master of the art.

any suggestion of inferiority and Wood retained some of his best students to build up a good research team.

THE FOUNDING AND EARLY DAYS OF WYE COLLEGE, 1894–1906

In his modest and self-suppressing account of Wye College published by the Agricultural Education Association,[1] Hall attributed the conception of an agricultural college to Hugh Macan, Secretary for Technical Education in Surrey, and a very able administrator. But he was also an old friend of Hall's at Oxford, they having taken the chemistry course together, and it is more than likely that the idea would spring from one of the many conversations they must have had on agricultural education.

Hall also states that having decided on Kent 'someone' suggested the 'royal and ancient vil' of Wye as the most suitable location for the College. As he gives the names of the persons concerned in other developments and never mentions his own name it seems safe to assume that Hall himself was the 'someone'. It is exactly the place he would have chosen. Wye is beautifully situated on the river Stour—then a good fishing stream, a recommendation with Hall—where it breaks through the North Downs; happily the district has remained untouched by nineteenth century industrialism. It was conveniently placed for access to the great fruit and hop growing districts and to the famous Romney and Thames-side marshes. But its great attraction was that it already possessed the buildings of an old college which would make a suitable nucleus for a new one. This had been founded by John Kempe, a native of the town who had become Cardinal Archbishop, and who endowed it in 1447 as a College of Secular Clergy, with twelve poor priests to pray for the souls of his parents and to teach the children of the place the art of grammar. The building retained some good fifteenth and sixteenth-century work, an attractive quadrangle and a beautiful refectory; it had escaped the nineteenth-century restorers. It was still used as a school, which however, was decaying, and the Charity Commissioners were prepared to hand it over if a new school were provided.

[1] 'In the beginning' Series of *Agricultural Progress*, 1937.

E. J. Halsey, a City financial magnate, and Chairman of the Surrey County Council, wholeheartedly supported the project, and he and Macan persuaded the Kent & Surrey County Councils to combine for the purchase of the buildings and the establishment of the College therein, with Hall as Principal. The governing body was appointed by the two Councils, and the Universities of Oxford, Cambridge and London were invited to appoint representatives. Halsey was Chairman. A farm also was needed: there were two possibilities, and the Governors chose the poorer in accordance with a view widely held at the time: 'If the Professors can make that pay they will have something to teach us'. Of its 270 acres about half was thin sheep pasture and only about forty acres had reasonably good soil. It was rightly called 'Coldharbour'. 'It was hungry', wrote Hall, 'and out of condition, and in the droughty seasons that prevailed during the last years of the nineteenth century it hung like a millstone round the necks of the College'. The Governors clearly had little confidence in the 'Professors' to do anything about the farm, for they kept control of it themselves and appointed the bailiff who remained their employee and was not on the college staff. 'The Professors were to teach, the Farm Committee would demonstrate the practice'. There was no need for a Professor of Agriculture and none was appointed. The Governors were not united as to what should be taught. 'What we want' said one of the most respected of them, 'is a place where we can get a really good ploughman or shepherd'. Some were surprised and angry when they found they were committed to the development of a college of higher education.

In practice of course the training had to be such that the students could get desirable jobs when they left. At that time the qualification most useful for getting a post was the diploma of the Royal Agricultural Society and for the first few years this was what the students aimed at. Hall was scathing about the syllabus: the necessity it imposed on students for 'acquiring parcels of miscellaneous knowledge in which they can be examined, forgetting or unaware that the essence of education consists in learning how to use your tools'. The teaching had to include some chemistry, botany, zoology, physics, geology, veterinary medicine, bookkeeping, building construction, surveying, engineering and a little law. 'The greatest sinner' wrote

Hall, 'in piling up subjects to represent agriculture was the examination of the Royal Agricultural Society, for it then exercised pontifical authority'. However, the College very soon established its own diploma which adequately served the needs of the students.

The appointment of staff was done simply by transferring to the College the lecturers who, like Hall, had been working in the counties. In spite of its unconventionality the system answered admirably: looking back one feels that a better choice could hardly have been made. Halsey had the greatest confidence in Hall: 'You go ahead', Halsey would say, 'make the College as you think it ought to be and I will see you through'. He was a wonderful chairman with a great gift of diplomatically getting his own way, and he supported Hall so thoroughly that Hall regarded him as the real founder of the College.

The College opened on November 29, 1894, with thirteen students and a staff of five. One of Hall's first acts was to appoint F. B. Smith of Downing College, Cambridge, the son of an East Anglian farmer, as Lecturer in Agriculture, He proved so capable that he was soon given charge of the farm and the bailiff, who thereupon was transferred to the college Staff. He was an ideal choice: able, modest, an attractive personality and very good company, well versed in his subject, familiar with the practices in different parts of the country and with the problems that needed solution. He had great respect for science and the capacity for getting on well with scientific workers and enlisting their interest in agricultural problems.

The botanist, John Percival, later achieved wide reputation. Like Hall, he came of north country yeoman stock: he was born at Carperly in Wensleydale on April 3, 1863, being thus nearly fifteen months older than Hall. Like Hall he had no direct connection with farming; on leaving the village school he had gone to work at Spence's Glassworks in York. But he remained the ardent field naturalist and collector he always had been, and he attracted the attention of Miss Spence (later Mrs Cotton) who enabled him in 1884 to go to St John's College, Cambridge; there he had a brilliant career, and took Part II of the Natural Science Tripos in 1888. In that year he also published an account of the flora of Wensleydale, listing

653 species and varieties, all but ten of which he had himself seen.

From Cambridge he went to London and worked on a voluntary basis in the botanical laboratory of the British Museum on diseases of plants and other subjects, spending much time also reading widely in the London libraries. After three years— in 1891—he returned to Cambridge as Junior Demonstrator in the chemical laboratories but he did not remain long; he was soon caught up in the University Extension activities and was assigned to Surrey and Sussex where his courses included botany, chemistry and diseases of plants. Hall met him there and quickly appreciated his good qualities. He was wiry, active, with keen, piercing eyes, an extraordinarily quick and accurate observer of every living thing in field or wood. He and I have walked over meadows where he knew that plovers were nesting, and although I could see nothing he would simply dart from one nest to another, laughing at me for my inability to know where they were likely to be. On one occasion we heard that a nightjar had come to settle in a wood. We went to look for it, but at first in vain; then suddenly he whispered to me to stop, pointed to a bush, told me to tip-toe round to the other side of it and at a signal from him to clap my hands and shout: this we both did: and sure enough, up from the bush rose the nightjar.

As chemist Hall chose Herbert Henry Cousins, the youngest of the team and of altogether different history. He was the son of the Rev. W. E. Cousins, was born in 1869, educated at Merton College, Oxford, where he was a postmaster, took a First in 1889 and then, as usual for young chemists at the time, proceeded to Germany where he studied at Heidelberg. He returned to Oxford as demonstrator in the chemical laboratories but was soon brought into the University Extension scheme, met Hall and was invited to join the staff at Wye.

The fifth member of this band of pioneers was Frederic Vincent Theobald, a man of private means who lived at Wye Court, an attractive Georgian house set in pleasant meadows by the riverside. He was born in 1868 at Kingston-on-Thames and educated at St. John's College, Cambridge. All his life he was interested in insects, and he became an economic entomologist of distinction with a thorough knowledge of farm insects.

He was an attractive personality, very sociable and hospitable, and like F. B. Smith, a batchelor to the end of his days.

All five were men of marked personality and outstanding ability, but the four recognized Hall as the undoubted leader, and they worked together in the greatest harmony and confidence. Each was well grounded in his fundamental science: Hall knew well that while they could and indeed must learn some agriculture at Wye no weakness in their scientific equipment could be corrected there. Three of them, Hall, Percival and Cousins, became keen gardeners and their success brought them much esteem from the local residents who, themselves skilled in the arts of gardening, recognized the craftsman's spirit in the newcomers. Hall was particularly successful with roses, sweet peas, tulips, and fruit. For the study of ordinary agriculture there was the farm of 270 acres under the kindly and patient F. B. Smith; on this Hall set up a fruit section and an experimental hop garden. East Kent has always been fortunate in its large farmers, and some of them speedily recognized the quality of the Wye group and were ready to work with them.

The courses for the students had to be developed, for there was at the outset little guidance: the spate of text books that was to come later had not yet begun. Agricultural chemistry at that time covered a very wide range: soils, fertilizers, plant nutrition, feeding stuffs, animal nutrition, dairy chemistry, insecticides, fungicides and various other things; it had no obvious relation with chemistry as taught in schools and colleges. There was only one student's book of any consequence on the subject: Warington's *Chemistry of the Farm*, already mentioned—small, but solidly packed with information and first published in 1881. On animal nutrition there was nothing suitable in English, but Cousins made a good and smooth translation of Kellner's excellent text book.

Agricultural botany was not so well off: Percival literally had to build up the subject as he went along. He was an inspiring teacher, bursting with energy and having the gift of conveying his own enthusiasm to his pupils. In going round the laboratory class a clear well-cut section would cause him literally to dance for joy: 'Good night! man!' he would exclaim, 'that's a wonderful section!' and forthwith the class would be invited to come and see it while Percival expounded its beauties, the producer meanwhile standing self-consciously by, more than half aware that the result had been achieved by accident and was unlikely to be repeated. He worked out simple schemes for identifying grasses, weeds and twigs of the common trees in winter. Another activity, aided greatly by his collector's instinct, was the assembling of species and varieties of wheats which he obtained from various countries and grew near his house: they were unprotected in the open air and being isolated were liable when the grain had formed to suffer heavily from the depredations of birds. Percival, however, was up at dawn scaring away intruders with his gun. The collection grew; he worked at it for some thirty years, distributing many sets to colleges and museums.

Theobald had on the whole a fairly easy task, agricultural entomology having been well studied. John Curtis had published his classical book, *Farm Insects*, in 1860, described by L. O. Howard as 'far ahead of any written up to that time in any language'.[1] Eleanor A. Ormerod's large *Manual of Injurious Insects* had appeared in 1881, and a second edition in 1891. Theobald put life into his teaching by using much local material, studying the insect pests of fruit, hops, and the ordinary farm crops.

Besides building up systematic courses on their subjects for the students the staff also had to lecture to farmers in the county and to advise on farm and garden problems, while the chemist had in addition to supervise much analytical work for farmers. Neither the fertilizer nor the feeding stuff industries were as yet well organized, and unscrupulous dealers still as of old put low quality materials on the market at excessive prices, relying on seductive advertisements to ensure sales.[2] Samples of well water were frequently sent, for piped water supplies were rarely available in the villages, and it was quite usual for the household well to be near the household cess pit,

[1] L. O. Howard, *A History of Applied Entomology*, Smithsonian Misc. Collections, 1930, Vol. 84. (entire volume).

[2] The opponents of fertilizers made capital out of this. An agricultural colleague soon after my arrival at Wye gave me a categorical warning: "Have nothing to do with fertilizer people: they are all rogues' which I soon learned was a gross exaggeration. Some of them became good friends of mine and helped me greatly with technical information.

thereby on sandy or gravel soils closing the water circuit. Soils also were analysed.

This was all very valuable: personal links were established with numbers of highly competent farmers, fruit growers and hop growers, while the analytical work furnished a wide knowledge of the soils of the counties and of the materials supplied by the dealers. These services were accepted by the counties as a partial set-off to their grants. The professional analysts objected at first, as they feared this rate-aided competition would cause loss of practice; but Hall agreed to stipulate that the analytical data should be for the farmers' information only, and must not be used in legal proceedings or disputes with the merchants. This met the analysts' difficulties and cordial relations grew up between them and the college.

The farmers' lectures, however, were very strenuous. There were no motor cars, and Wye was not well served with trains: long drives in an open trap or a dog cart were usually involved, often in the cold and the rain. The lectures were commonly given in the club room of the largest public house: some were on market day at the close of the business about 5 p.m. others were in the evening and involved staying the night on a farm, which was usually very agreeable, or going up to London to stay at a hotel which was much less pleasant as the travelling allowance was very meagre.[1] If one returned to Wye the same night (as might be necessary if there was a 9 a.m. lecture the next day) it was a case of reaching Ashford at midnight, and driving the four and a half miles to Wye in Ben Coulter's open trap, reaching home at 1 a.m.

The contribution to agricultural science made by the Wye College group thus fell into two divisions. Much systematizing of knowledge was done to produce first of all consecutive lecture courses and then books for the guidance of others. Cousins was the first to produce a book. He was an indefatigable gardener and in his large garden made many trials with fertilizers, usually obtaining good results. As a chemist he was naturally much influenced by Liebig's view that fertilizers could entirely replace farmyard manure—a view vigorously upheld at the time by Georges Ville, Professor of Vegetable

---

[1] 9s 6d per night for dinner, bed and breakfast in London; 5s in the country. The lecturer received a fee of 5s per lecture.

Physiology at the Jardin des Plantes, Paris, who made numerous trials (which have since been severely criticised) on the experimental field at Vincennes. Sir William Crookes thought so highly of this work that he translated two of Ville's books into English: one of them, *On Artificial manures, their chemical selection and scientific application to agriculture* (1879) had a considerable vogue here. Cousins recorded his experiences in a delightful little book, *Chemistry of the Garden*, in which he went out whole-heartedly for fertilizers as against farmyard manure. He was misled by the circumstances that his garden was an old one which had almost certainly received large dressings of farmyard manure for many years before he came into possession, and on which therefore fertilizers would be needed more than further additions of organic matter.

The book was very popular, especially with suburban gardeners who were then proliferating in Surrey; it was short, easy to read in the train, very lively, even spicy, and it showed simple ways of overcoming the shortage of farmyard manure, usually one of the gardener's greatest troubles. Unfortunately many of Surrey's best building sites were on light chalk or sandy soils where organic manure was indispensable, and where Cousins' recommendations failed.

Notwithstanding this a number of fertilizer salesmen, feeling that they had scientific support, were pushing this same idea that fertilizers could entirely replace farmyard manure. So the old controversy was revived, and was active for some years: when I started lecturing to farmers in 1902, it was generally assumed that I should begin by denouncing farmyard manure as wasteful and unnecessary and that I should then proclaim the superiority of fertilizers. The local funny man had usually prepared some quips on this assumption, and commonly let them off, but they fell flat as I began by emphasizing the need for both. My garden was on poorer soil than Cousins' and I had learned the need for organic manure. But controversy is always an effective way of rousing interest and Cousins certainly succeeded in doing that: he thoroughly enjoyed a fight; he was small in stature but full of courage.

Meanwhile Percival was steadily developing his subject and in 1900 brought out his *Agricultural Botany; theoretical and practical*, the first English text book on the subject. It was

immediately successful and had a long life; in the course o
forty years it ran into eight editions and was translated intc
several languages: as his distinguished successor at Reading
W. B. Brierley, wrote: 'Its several editions largely shaped the
pattern of the subject as it developed in University College
teaching'. As his collection of wheats expanded (he had finally
2000 different sorts) he prepared a monograph, *The Whea*
Plant, published in 1921 and described by Brierley as 'probably the finest monograph in the world's agricultural literature'.[1]

Theobald published his *Text book of agricultural Zoology* ir
1890 systematizing the subject, but his task was easier thar
Percival's as so much pioneering work had been done. Latei
on, when the relation between mosquitoes and malaria was discovered, Theobald was invited to study and classify the vas
number of specimens sent to the British Museum and he published the results in a series of volumes issued between 1898
and 1905: L. O. Howard described it as 'a most notable piece o
work, and of the very greatest use in medical entomology'. A
in most pioneering endeavours there have been subsequen
emendations, but that does not detract from the importance o
the work.

Hall always preferred a wide field for his activities: they
included soil, general agriculture and horticulture, hops, rose
and tulips, and he achieved marked success with all of them
He early began collecting material for a book on soil and wa
greatly helped by the works of Hilgard, King, the Unitec
States Bureau of Soils and by Déhérain's *Chimie Agricole*, latei
by Warington's *Physical Properties of Soil*, already mentioned
a painstaking summary of much American, French, and Germar
work on what was then a new subject in Great Britain. Hal
had the enviable gift of being able to assimilate great stores o
information, testing it by his wide knowledge of Nature gainee
by shrewd and remarkably accurate observation, and setting ou
the result in lucid and attractive English that gave the subjec
life. His first book finally appeared in 1903. It was called *Th*
Soil; it long remained the standard treatise and the early un-
revised editions are still among the most interesting. I

[1] W. B. Brierley, *Proc. Linnean Sc.*, 1949, Session 161, pt. II. An excellen
summary of Percival's work.

covered, however, only part of Hall's wide ranging lectures—
he always enjoyed a large canvas. A second volume appeared,
Fertilizers and Manures, in 1909; it was as successful as the
first. Then in 1911 he pulled the whole subject together in *The
Feeding of Crops and Stock* showing the interrelationships of
its various parts. As the years went by the subject expanded so
much that the second edition had to be broken up into three
volumes: I. The Plant, II. Soils and Fertilizers, III. The
Nutrition of Animals and Man.

These volumes by Hall, Percival and Theobald cover most
of agricultural science at the beginning of this century. Revisions
in successive editions kept them as the most authoritative texts
for the next twenty years. Their production had been greatly
helped by the building up of the lecture courses and the advisory
work for farmers, which had had the advantage of putting into
systematic order much scattered empirical knowledge about
soils and their relations to plant growth, and also of revealing
gaps and inconsistencies that needed correction. It was research
for use, not research for discovery, but it served a valuable
purpose in the development of the subject.

The other direction in which the college contributed to
agricultural science was in the solution of specific problems
raised by farmers; this of course followed no systematic lines
and might easily have had little permanent value: instead it was
so well done that it gave little islands of facts that the science as
it expanded had to assimilate.

The soil problems raised by farmers were still mainly
manurial, especially the role of fertilizers, and the perennial
question: were they stimulants or foods?—beef steaks or whisky?—
was still the favourite. Crop yields were well below present
levels, and cultivation on the good farms was so well done that
problems relating to soil crumbs or water relationships rarely
arose. Soil physics had hardly come even into the Rothamsted
purview, and in those early days had only academic interest for
Wye College. No questions connected therewith were raised
by the farmers.

Hall decided to go straight for some of the problems of the
big men; they were on the whole more willing to cooperate
than the smaller ones: hops, fruit, and some important agricultural crops were studied. In the college hop garden he and

Monson made experiments on the manuring of hops and on
different systems of training them on string and wire, a method
then replacing the older one of growing on poles. Hall himself
attacked the very difficult problem of hop drying. This was done
in the oast, a round or square building with a conical roof sur-
mounted by a movable cowl. Part way up was fixed a perforated
floor on which the hops were placed: below it a fire was maintained and the hot air worked its way through the hops at a
speed determined by the setting of the cowl in relation to the
wind. The process was very delicate and required a fine dis-
crimination to keep in step the cowl, the fire, and the piling of
the hops on the floor. Overheating and underheating were
alike to be avoided. No thermometers were used, only the
thumb of the operator. Drying was—and still is—an extremely
skilled craft, handed down empirically; a good dryer can obtain
remarkably good results, while a poor workman can in a few
hours do hundreds of pounds worth of damage. Hall had the
greatest respect for a craftsman, but he wanted to reduce this
ancient art to more precise terms, and during the drying period
he would sit up night after night with the dryer, measuring
temperatures and taking such other observations as seemed
important so as to find out exactly what was happening. He
never rushed to conclusions and always avoided premature recommendations, but after a few seasons' work he had learned
where control thermometers should be placed and what the
draught should be: a beginning had been made with the laying
down of a standard procedure in place of the old rule of thumb
methods.

Cousins attacked the important problem of insecticidal and
fungicidal washes for fruit trees and hop plants on which large
sums of money were being spent. There were no recognized
principles underlying their preparation, and Cousins at once
saw that the infusion of some chemistry into the manufacture
would lead to considerable improvements. He studied one of
them in detail and devised a soundly-based formula which the
college patented under the name Paranapth to prevent exploitation.[1]

Cousins also attacked another problem. Hops were brought
by the factors largely on appearance and smell. Cousins sought

[1] *Journ. South Eastern Agric. Coll.*, 1895, No. 2, p. 18, and later issues.

a more objective basis and fixed on the resins as the most
promising constituent for study. The methods of organic
chemistry were then not far enough advanced to allow him to
make much progress, but he broke the ground, and opened up a
way that others could follow when a suitable technique became
available.

Meanwhile the diseases of hops and fruit were being studied.
Silver leaf disease was giving trouble in plums: Percival discovered that it was caused by the fungus *Stereum purpureum*
though he could find no remedy. It was often difficult to deal
with the farmers' problems because in general they were rather
ill defined. Some helpful experiments were made on the feeding
of sheep and the manuring of barley and swedes. The college
steadily rose in reputation and in 1900 it was accepted by the
University of London as its School of Agriculture.

In spite of much good work the college had passed through
some difficult times. Some members of the county councils
had objected to spending on education money that might have
been used for the reduction of the rates. There were some
internal troubles; the committee of management did not always
understand how a scientific staff of some distinction should be
treated. On one occasion in addition to some general overspend-
ing the farm had incurred a heavy financial loss through the
incompetence of a new farm manager whom they had themselves
appointed, and the whole staff were curtly informed that their
salaries would be docked to help make up the deficit: alternatively they could take three months notice. This rankled long,
but to the credit of the staff they did not allow it to affect their
work. Gradually their good work prevailed; the early financial
storms were weathered, thanks to the magnificent support
given by the Chairman, Mr Halsey, and the college became so
firmly established that it has never been seriously shaken
since.

The remarkable team that had done so much for Wye
College began to break up after about six years. Cousins was
the first to go: he left in the autumn of 1900 to become Agricultural Analyst to the Government of Jamaica and later its
Director of Agriculture. He spent the rest of his working life
there, and although he returned to England on retirement took
no further part in the development of agricultural science.

H

F. B. Smith left in the spring of 1902 to become Agricultural Adviser to the new Government of South Africa set up after the war of 1899–1902, and played an important part in the development of agriculture in the new conditions. Hall left shortly afterwards to take charge of Rothamsted, and Percival left still later in the year to become Director of the Agricultural Department at the forerunner of Reading University. 1902 was indeed a sad year for Wye College, for during its course three of the best men were lost and there were none of equal competence to replace them. Theobald only remained, and he stayed on till 1920 when he gave up his lectureship at Wye but continued as Advisory Entomologist for the South Eastern Province of England till his death in 1930.

Throughout all this period agriculture continued very depressed, and agricultural science remained in low repute in the universities: it was not good enough for their best men, nor big enough to absorb their lower grades. On personal grounds explained in my autobiography,[1] I wanted to learn agriculture and I resigned my demonstratorship in pure chemistry at the Manchester University and on January 1, 1901 took Cousins' place at Wye. My professor was against this: there was, he said, no career in agricultural science in this country. This view was widely held in the University Colleges and it explained why so little advance was made during the 1880's and 1890's. After the dispersal of the original staff, the only important research work at Wye was on hops by E. S. Salmon the mycologist. For a time there were some soil investigations, which however, were transferred to Rothamsted in 1907 and will be described later. Wye College became one of the chief teaching centres for agriculture in Great Britain and its pupils have long held high positions in many parts of the world.

Years later research work was resumed under R. L. Wain: It was widely and justly recognized as being of a high order of distinction.

---

[1] *The Land Called Me*, Allen & Unwin (1958). My idea was to found a Land Settlement for city misfits and unemployed. At Wye I soon saw the impracticability of the scheme and decided instead to help in developing a science that would overcome some of the difficulties against which farmers were struggling.

THE LONG ASHTON FRUIT RESEARCH STATION
THE FIRST STAGE

Next to Rothamsted and Woburn this is the oldest research station in the country. It has had a varied and interesting history. It started as a cider research institute and had it so remained it would not have come within the scope of this book, which does not deal with the products of the land once they have left the land. But in this case the work of the Station has involved much harking back to the relations of the growing plant to its natural environmental factors, and as it developed it caused the Station to deal with difficult problems of great agricultural importance. At some stage in its history it would be necessary in any case to include it with the other stations, and it is simpler to bring it in from the start, even though strictly speaking, its work at that time does not come within our purview.

From early days apples and cider have had a place in the West countryman's scheme of things similar to that held by barley and beer by the men of the other counties. Home brewing had been common in both instances but it survived much longer in the case of cider than of beer, and those who remember travelling in the Western counties in the 1890's cannot have forgotten the painful experiences of trying to slake thirst on a hot day when the only drink available might on successive samplings vary from a delicious apple-flavoured beverage to a harsh, stomach-turning acid fluid that only a hardened practitioner could tolerate.

In 1893 Mr R. Neville Grenville of Butleigh Court near Glastonbury, impressed by the utter lack of knowledge of the principles of cider making, and the crudeness of the methods then commonly used on farms, decided to seek remedies for these defects. He secured the help of F. J. Lloyd, the London consulting chemist[1] favourably known in the West for his work on cheese-making carried out for the Bath and West of England Agricultural Society, and provided accommodation for the investigations on the Home Farm at Butleigh Court; they were sponsored by the Bath and West Society and aided by small grants from the Board of Agriculture.

[1] See p. 197.

After ten years Lloyd reported on them to the Board. The results obtained were so important and so promising that considerable extension of the work was obviously needed, and he appealed to the Board for help. They suggested the establishment of a special institute. A conference was accordingly called at Bristol on October 15, 1902, which approved the suggestion and appointed a Committee to carry it out. A plan and estimates were prepared: an income of £1,100 a year would, it was anticipated, be required, towards which the Board promised £300; some of the western county councils participated as did the growers. Within a year the funds were assured, the site at Long Ashton was secured and the Institute was founded.

The question of organization arose, however, and its solution is interesting. Unlike Rothamsted at that time the new Institute was not a private affair financed by one individual, nor was it a school or a college; it was something new in English life. The promoters were advised that the most flexible form of organization would be a non-profit making limited liability company operating under licence from the Board of Trade in conformity with the provisions of the Companies Act of 1867. The licence was granted in October 1903, and the Association was registered at Somerset House under the name of the National Fruit and Cider Institute.[1] Among the declared purposes of the Institute were four that gave its distinctive character:

(1) to investigate and demonstrate the best methods of cultivation of all kinds of fruit and vegetables; their habits of growth and leading characteristics, the best and most suitable varieties for all purposes, and as regards fruit, with special reference to the manufacture of cider and perry.

(2) To investigate and demonstrate the best methods for the utilization of the above products, especially with reference to the manufacture of cider, perry and kindred liquors: to promote and carry on research into the causes which affect the manufacture of such products.

(3) To improve the present varieties of fruit and vegetables and to create and introduce new varieties.

[1] The evolution to this stage is described in the Journal of the Bath and West Society, 1903–4 by A. E. Brooke-Hunt, a Board of Agriculture Inspector who deserves to be remembered because of his genuine interest in the project.

(4) To disseminate by means of classes, lectures or any other method, such results of investigation and research as seem likely to be of use.

Lloyd remained in charge of the experiments for the first two years as non-resident Director—he had a large analytical and consulting practice in London—and B. T. P. Barker was appointed resident Assistant Director for the same term.

Barker came of an old Cambridge family who for nearly a century had manufactured soft drinks there. He had been educated at the Perse School, Cambridge and later at Caius College where he had had a brilliant career. Like Percival and Hall he began as a Chemist, but did so well in Botany in Part I of the Tripos that Marshall Ward persuaded him to turn to that subject which he did with his parents full consent. Examinations over he started research: the obvious subject in view of the family interests was the fermentation organisms, yeasts in particular, and he had the good fortune to discover sexuality in yeast—which gained for him the Walsingham Gold Medal. When Brooke-Hunt went to Cambridge in search of a young scientist with some experience of research with yeasts and fermentation his choice naturally fell on Barker. He started work at Long Ashton in July 1904.

The work expanded so rapidly that a resident Director became indispensable and Barker was promoted to this post. Like the constitution of the station this was a new procedure, for at that time it was generally held that the Head of an agricultural research institute should normally be a chemist: Lloyd was one, so were the heads at Rothamsted, Wye, Cambridge, and Woburn. However, the break with tradition was only partial since Barker, as we have seen, had started as a chemist. Events showed that the choice was abundantly justified.

He had the fortunate gift of being able to educate his palate to discriminate between the various grades of cider and so could form a subjective judgment on matters for which no objective test had yet been devised. He had also the personal qualities which enabled him though an outsider to gain the respect and the confidence of the West Country orchardists and cider makers.

He soon recognized that part of the trouble lay with the fruit. The orchards had long been neglected and the fruit was of little commercial value: £1 or less per ton was a current price in the early 1900's. There was no separating of the many varieties but all were mixed indiscriminately in the mill; little was known of the vintage value of the different sorts. There was a tendency for varieties to be localized so that ciders of different districts had distinctive flavours.

It was at first thought that the cider made from a particular variety of apple owed its characteristic flavour to one or more special yeasts associated with that variety. Barker showed, however, that this was not so; the yeast microflora of any juice consisted of a miscellaneous mixture of several different kinds and no two mixtures were alike. The predominant factor determining flavour was the fruit from which the cider was made. It was decided, therefore, to leave the fermentation to the adventitious yeasts and to concentrate attention on improving the general standard of the fruit and preventing disorders caused by the incursion of harmful bacteria. Improvements in the manufacturing and bottling technique were already being made in the factories and on the farms, and to encourage better standards the Institute in 1905 organized an annual Cider Day which justifiably became a great event in the West Country. The Institute also interested itself in the cider competitions at the agricultural shows. Barker reports that as early as 1904 'so high a standard had been attained by the more prominent exhibitors that, with few exceptions, the entries in present-day competitions would have found it difficult to obtain awards'. But these samples were outstanding; the great bulk of the cider produced was far inferior.

All sections of cider making came within the purview of the Institute. The studies of the actual process on the farm and in the factory are of advisory rather than scientific importance and will not be dealt with here. In the orchard it was first necessary to find which of the many varieties used by farmers had high vintage value; little was known about this and still less about the composition of their sap, though a beginning had been made at Butleigh by setting up groups based on acid and tannin content.

A few cider varieties of high repute and of good growth and cropping character were planted in a trial orchard in 1908; others were added from time to time, and they were propagated in the Institute's nursery so that similar trial orchards might be established throughout the cider-making areas. The vintage value was estimated by fermentation tests of the juice in the laboratory and where practicable by making actual cider by a standardized process; as first carried out this required about half a ton of fruit, later a miniature technique was worked out requiring only about 50 lb. or less. The resulting ciders were judged by experts on the cider tasting day. For a time from 1926 onwards the Institute undertook to test in this way samples of any variety of apples grown by farmers themselves. This proved useful in directing general attention to the varieties of most promise and was very popular; unfortunately its very success was its undoing, for the testing interfered so much with the other experimental work that this privilege had to be abandoned in 1939.

A selection of apple varieties of high vintage quality having been made, it was next necessary to test their orchard performance and cropping capacity. This was duly done and the final result was the preparation of a list of recommended varieties of apples of satisfactory orchard performance and capable of producing high quality cider. Many of the newer orchards were planted with these and laid out on an improved plan to facilitate working and ensure better pest control.

During this period the substances responsible for quality were not known with certainty; chemical investigations not having gone far enough to identify them completely, and the judgment of the expert taster was still final. It was known. however, that while vintage quality is mainly determined by variety, environmental factors also play their part.

Fermentation had always been brought about by the natural mixed flora of the juice which includes a wide range of yeasts and bacteria. It had been suggested that better and more consistent results would be obtained by sterilizing the juice and introducing a pure culture of some selected yeast. It was recognized that brewers generally use pure cultures of yeast, but it was also known that makers of wine rely on the naturally occurring groups of organisms even though some of these may be objectionable. While these problems were under investigation the first World War broke out and during its course all the energies of the Institute were devoted to food production.

CHAPTER VIII

THE RENAISSANCE (II)

1900 – 1920

REVIVAL OF ROTHAMSTED

AFTER Lawes' death in 1900 the Lawes Agricultural Trust Committee very wisely allowed Gilbert great latitude in the management of the Station. The field experiments and the meteorological observations were continued with the same meticulous care as before by Gilbert's trained staff, and the observations were fully recorded: there were no gaps. So far as any scientific work was concerned, however, the place was absolutely moribund. Gilbert had never been able to attract younger workers to Rothamsted, and there was no one on the spot able to take charge when he died on December 23, 1901, a year and four months after Lawes' death. J. A. Voelcker was put in charge temporarily and did some tidying up and burning of the great mass of papers Gilbert accumulated—more indeed than his successors liked. But there was a very serious lack of possible directors.

Fortunately one of the most forceful personalities on the Lawes Agricultural Trust Committee, H. E. Armstrong, knew Hall well and recognized in him the qualities needed to revive the place. Hall was invited to take charge and he accepted, although it meant a lower salary, and life in the rather formal and very modern residential Harpenden, while Wye had then more than a touch of Mrs Gaskell's delightful Cranford. But he was a born pioneer and thoroughly enjoyed the prospect of making a new Rothamsted to suit the new conditions of the time. So in February 1902 he left Wye and started on this arduous task.

Hall's going to Rothamsted was a turning point in the history of agricultural science in Great Britain. For a number of years British work on the subject had been directed almost entirely to the collection and systematic arrangement of the large amount of empirical knowledge gained by farmers and others, and to the solution of practical problems important at the time though often of only transient interest. Hall's purpose was to develop a science that would reveal the nature and properties of soils and their relations with living plants; this, he maintained, would be of permanent value to teachers, extension officers and farmers.

He has left a record of his first impressions[1] when he got to Rothamsted. 'I will confess', he says, 'that my heart sank when I came to take possession of the laboratory . . . it was much more like a museum than a laboratory', and he goes on to speak of the 'mellow dustiness that radiated from the vast stove occupying the centre of the room'. There was a little room 'that would be recognized as a laboratory', in which determinations of nitrates in rain and drainage waters and of sugar in mangolds were made, and some nitrogen determinations were made in another room, but nothing more. The distinctive group of workers were the village boys trained by Gilbert each to do one job; now grown men, faithful devoted workers, thoroughly competent in the task allotted to them and some of them young enough to learn some of the new duties that Hall wished to entrust to them. They never failed him or his successor.

With this meagre staff, and equally meagre financial resources, Hall began work enthusiastically in three directions. Constant to his original purpose of carrying science to the farmer, and most anxious that the results of Lawes and Gilbert's sixty years of carefully conducted field experiments should not be lost, he summarized them in crisp, lucid English, giving for the first time an account that could be read with pleasure. John Murray published it worthily in 1905: it was called *The Book of the Rothamsted Experiments*. Hall modestly described himself simply as 'acting as an external demonstrator, describing from the outside, as it were, what seemed to be the chief lessons conveyed by the experiments', but he made the results live as they had not done for many years, and he showed their great value to the younger generations of farmers and

---

[1] *Records of the Rothamsted Staff*, No. 1, June 1929.

H*

students. His powers of close observation enabled him to give a much more vivid account than any merely statistical discussion could have done. He sought in the laboratory for explanations of various phenomena observed on the plots, including the effects of fertilizers on the chemical and physical properties of the soil.

His main purpose at Rothamsted, however, was to expand agricultural science. He saw clearly that it would be impossible to improve the teaching at the agricultural Colleges or the advice given to farmers until agricultural science was much more highly developed. Up to that time it had been regarded as a branch of chemistry—or rather as a very poor relation. Hall saw that this view was much too narrow; physical, biological, and microbiological sciences were equally involved, and they must be made to contribute. This could not be done single handed; more staff was needed and he wanted to bring in recruits from the departments of pure science in the universities. There were at that time no Government grants. An interview with Mr Hanbury, the President of the Board of Agriculture, (it was before the days of the Ministry) was fruitless. 'He told us severely,' Hall relates, 'that it was to Rothamsted the Board looked for scientific information for the needs of the industry, and that it was our duty to collect any money we required'.

So Hall had to begin a money-collecting crusade. He was well fitted for this, for he had great charm of manner and enviable social gifts. The country houses of England were then fully functioning: their squires interested in reviving the local agriculture, and their ladies wanting to improve the gardens. Hall could help both. And in the evening after dinner he could walk round the house, picking out and admiring any good pictures or good china, discreetly passing over poorer specimens so that his hostesses recognized him as being both knowledgeable and discriminating, or he could sit down and play an acceptable game of cards. But he was equally at home in a London club and was welcomed at the Savile—that friendly concourse of able and promising young men—or later at the Athenaeum to which he had the honour to be elected. He knew all the right people and the best ways of approach. Gradually the necessary funds came in.

In 1906 he was able to appoint as botanist an old Swanley student, Winifred Brenchley, who had gone from Swanley to University College, London, to specialize in botany under F. W. Oliver. She was the daughter of a very popular Clapham schoolmaster and was the first woman ever to work in the laboratories during their whole sixty years of existence, and it must be admitted was appointed because the funds available would not have attracted a suitable man. But she was retained for the whole of her working life because of the admirable qualities she possessed and which developed as the years went by: close observation, faithful recording, complete intellectual honesty and loyalty to the Station. No one in those days quite knew what to do with a woman worker in a laboratory; it was felt, however, that she must have tea, and so from the day of her arrival a tray with tea and a tin of Bath Oliver biscuits appeared each afternoon at four o'clock precisely; and the scientific staff, then numbering five, was invited to partake thereof. The custom has been kept up ever since—a source of abiding interest to many of the overseas visitors. Winifred Brenchley recorded her first impressions. 'During the first few months', she wrote, 'it was necessary to walk very warily in order that future women workers might be accepted as a matter of course. The position had its "inevitable difficulties" and much was owed to the kindliness of the laboratory assistants.'

Then came two big successes. First Mr James Mason of Eynsham Hall gave a sum of money to build a bacteriological laboratory and to provide for a term of years the income for a bacteriologist. H. B. Hutchinson (Henry Brougham, but always simply 'H.B.' to his colleagues) was appointed to this post. He had recently returned from Göttingen where he had studied bacteriology under Koch. He was a great acquisition to the staff, ingenious minded, a clean and accurate manipulator well acquainted with the best techniques of the time and possessing a sound knowledge of chemistry. Then the Gold-smiths' Company made a grant of £10,000, the income of which was to provide for a soil chemist, a post which came to me later in 1907. Around this small nucleus came accretions of young people fresh from the University, gradually forming a compact little group of keen industrious workers. Among the first comers was C. G. T. Morison, who did some interesting work on the flocculation of clay and later went to Oxford to start the first University School of Soil Science in Great Britain, where he became widely known for his interesting soil survey work in the Sudan. Another was R. D. Watt, who later proceeded first to South Africa and was then appointed to the chair of Agriculture at Sydney, where he rendered valuable service to the agricultural community acknowledged finally by a Knighthood. Later a small group of organic chemists was added: W. A. Davies and two juniors, A. J. Daish and G. C. Sawyer, all students of H. E. Armstrong: these were investigating the formation of sugar in the mangold.

Meanwhile a revolutionary hypothesis concerning the mode of action of fertilizers was being developed in the United States Department of Agriculture by Milton Whitney, its well-known Head: the series of papers had started in 1892 and continued for some twenty years. The plant, it was argued, draws its mineral nutrients from the soil solution. Most agricultural soils are ultimately derived from the same minerals, hence the soil solution must have approximately the same composition in all of them. Addition of fertilizers cannot alter this composition, since according to the current chemical theory any ions that might enter the solution would only force an equal number of the same ions out of solution. Fertilizers therefore cannot act by feeding the plant; where they are beneficial it must be for some other reason. Two were suggested: the fertilizers might change the physical nature of the soil for the better, among other actions facilitating the movement of the soil solution; and they might precipitate or otherwise put out of action soluble toxins produced during the decomposition of the soil organic matter or excreted by the plant roots. Whitney thought he saw indications of such toxins in certain poor soils. Oswald Schreiner and his colleagues thereupon undertook the most complete fractionation of soil organic matter attempted up to that time, and among the compounds isolated was dihydroxystearic acid which they regarded as a toxin: it was, however, thrown out of solution and rendered innocuous by various substances including fertilizers. Whitney thereupon regarded fertilizers as purifying agents removing toxins, and perhaps having other non-nutritive but beneficial effects.

The high authority of the Department, and the recognized

ability of the authors of the papers, compelled very serious consideration of this hypothesis. Hitherto agricultural chemists had worked on the assumption that fertilizers feed the plant, and their study must therefore link up with the work of plant physiologists to discover the most efficient nutrients and the conditions of optimum effectiveness. But if the action of fertilizers was to alter the physical properties of the soil or to precipitate toxins these ideas must obviously be completely re-oriented, the actions must be studied in detail, and substances sought that would produce the same effects more efficiently than the fertilizers.

In a well-planned investigation jointly with Winifred Brenchley and Lilian Underwood, Hall subjected this hypothesis to a searching criticism. They found that the composition of the soil solution on the different plots at Rothamsted was not constant, but varied from plot to plot according to the fertilizer treatment. Plants grown in the different soil solutions showed the same kind of differences as on the soil itself. The function of fertilizers was therefore nutritive, as the older workers had assumed—and agricultural chemists could continue their work on its accustomed lines.

But it must not be thought that the controversy had been in vain. Whitehead's dictum deserves to be posted up in every agricultural research laboratory: those ideas stand most in need of questioning that have longest remained unquestioned. Current ideas on fertilizer action were clarified and improved by Whitney's attack and Hall's defence.

Schreiner's work also has proved of lasting value. His isolations and identifications are still accepted and represent a great achievement in view of the undeveloped state of organic chemistry in those days. The only result that could not be confirmed is the supposed toxicity of dihydroxystearic acid. Search for organic toxins in our normal soils proved fruitless, as in Daubeny's time.

Hall's memoir is a model of clear thinking, constructive argument, and good manners in controversy: for Hall was always a most courteous antagonist—though he could hit hard enough if provoked. 'I counsel you', he once wrote to a young investigator, 'as a matter of principle to put the best face on other men's work, even to record their good intentions rather than their failures in performance. It is not so much a matter of sloppy good nature as of manners, but most of all it is a recognition that science grows by the accretions of knowledge (and the mistakes) of one generation after another. Each of us begins as an iconoclast and ends as an old fogey; in either manifestation let us avoid the incivilities characteristic of raw youth or hardened arteries'.

The idea of making soil surveys was already abroad; one was in progress in the United Sates—chiefly on physical lines— and C. M. Luxmoore had started one at Reading. While at Wye Hall had begun one covering the counties of Kent, Surrey and Sussex and assimilating into it many of the soil samples taken at the request of farmers seeking advice about the manuring of their crops. I had continued to collect material after Hall left Wye and when we joined at Rothamsted we decided to revise the survey completely and to finish it. There being no glacial drift the obvious basis was the solid geology of the area: in few parts of Great Britain are the soil and the underlying rock so closely related as here. The collection of the soil samples and farmer's information involved much travelling over the three counties on foot, on bicycle, or in a friendly farmer's dog cart—by far the best way of seeing the country till it was eliminated by the motor car: this was my task, as also was the assembling of historical accounts at the British Museum and elsewhere. Hall put the material together and worked it up into a brilliant description of the region, a great delight to read, and one that has never been bettered. It was submitted to the Board of Agriculture for publication, they having made a grant to cover the cost, but being completely unlike the usual official publications it aroused some misgivings. Hall received an unofficial letter from a high quarter asking if it really was necessary to quote a verse by Rudyard Kipling as well as some twenty lines from Mrs Marriott Watson's poem on the Downs. Such a thing, he was told, was not done. But he insisted: if these are cut out, he said, the Report will be withdrawn. The Board gave way and published the report as it stood: later, when a copy was sent to Rudyard Kipling, he acknowledged it in a charming letter as being unusually human for an official document.

We knew the agricultural behaviour of the soils sufficiently well to be able to assess the value of the analytical results as guidance to the farmer in organizing his fertilizer regime. But we soon saw that this could not have been done with certainty if we had known nothing about the soil: 'the significance of a given amount, for example 0·1 per cent of phosphoric acid in a soil of a given type', we wrote, 'cannot be laid down *a priori*, it must be ascertained from the results of field experiments upon the area in question. At its best, soil analysis only reveals one set of factors in plant production, and these have to be interpreted in the light of local conditions, such as climate, water supply and drainage'.[1] Without this local knowledge it was easy for analysts to go astray. Farmers and growers with a puckish sense of humour and a few guineas to spare would sometimes send samples of the same soil to half a dozen different analysts and would get back half a dozen different and sometimes conflicting reports. For some years we found it necessary to emphasize that an isolated soil analysis can prove very little: useful results can be assured only when a proper survey has mapped out the soil types, and field experiments have shown how crops on the different types normally react to fertilizers. If the soil in question appears on analysis to conform pretty closely to the type it may be expected to give the normal responses to fertilizers; if however it differs the analyst must try to suggest some suitable fertilizer scheme in accordance with the difference. Occasionally we were confronted with too exalted an idea of what soil analysis could do. It was supposed that chemistry had reduced the ancient art of manuring to a matter of simple arithmetic: a crop contained so many pounds of nitrogen, phosphate and potash: an acre of surface soil contained so many pounds: if these quantities were insufficient it needed only a subtraction sum to show how much more must be added as fertilizers. The best known exponent of this view was Cyril Hopkins of the University of Illinois.[2] He was a very shrewd observer and a great pioneer, with an intimate knowledge of his region and his farmers: in my early days I have driven many miles over the prairies with him in a 'buggy'

[1] A. D. Hall and E. J. Russell, *Jour. Ag. Sci.*, Vol. 4, 182–223, 1911.
[2] He had a wonderful capacity for getting his ideas over to his students and farmer friends. He wrote a novel in support of this particular thesis.

—the best way of getting to know them—and I saw the respect with which his advice was received by farmers. This simple arithmetical view was widely held for a time in Great Britain also, but not at Rothamsted.

The inadequacy of the methods then current of accounting for differences in soil productiveness was clearly brought out in our early investigations on the fattening pastures of Romney Marsh. It was well known that some pastures would fatten sheep while others, often adjacent, would not. The analytical methods of the time failed to give a satisfactory explanation: the fattening pastures certainly contained more phosphoric acid as also did the herbage, and the fattening soils had a higher power of nitrate and ammonia production than the non-fattening, but the differences seemed too small to account for the result. The botanical composition of the herbage was similar for both; the only difference was that the grasses on the fattening pastures were leafy while those on the non-fattening pastures were stemmy. We were not at the time acquainted with the idea of ecotypes, and for want of suitable methods no further progress could be made, as has so often happened in the history of agricultural science.[1]

Vegetation experiments necessarily have long vacant periods, and Hall set Winifred Brenchley three lines of work carefully chosen to make the most economical use of her time: detailed observations of the park grass plots; the distribution of weeds and the longevity of buried weed seeds; and the effects of small quantities of inorganic poisonous salts on the growth of plants in nutrient solutions (then called 'water cultures'): according to current ideas a stimulus was expected. Barley, peas and other plants were used, and the poisons tested included among others, copper, zinc and manganese sulphates and boric acid. With increasing dilution the harmful effects decreased, but at no stage, not even one part in ten million of water, was any stimulus observed. Small quantities of boric acid, however, increased the growth of peas, which 'raised the interesting question whether boron is in some way advantageous to the pea,

[1] A. D. Hall and E. J. Russell, *Journ. Agric. Sci.*, 1912, 4, 339–70. The position was clarified later on.

and therefore to be regarded as a nutrient'.[1] Unfortunately this observation could not be followed up at the time: some ten years later a similar effect was observed with beans and investigated with important results. Unfortunately another important point was missed. Minute quantities of both copper and zinc are now known to be essential to plant growth and the control plants which had received none should have failed to grow. Actually they made normal growth. The reason was that neither the nutrient salts nor the distilled water in which the plants were growing had been given the drastic purification needed to remove the last traces of zinc and copper.

It was a tragedy to have been so near and yet to have missed the discovery of trace element action, but pioneers always run that risk.

A third investigation was outdoor and ecological: it was to study the relations of weeds and the soils on which they grow: this continued for some years but was weakened by the circumstance that no measurements of soil reaction were taken, the idea of pH determinations not yet having reached Rothamsted.

Hall himself was interested in the question of the quality of crops, particularly the milling and baking quality of wheat. In this he was in association with the Cambridge group working on the same subject.[2] He passed on to Winifred Brenchley the morphological study of the development of the wheat grain— to which he later added barley.

While at Wye I had studied the rate of oxygen-absorption by soils, and finding that it was greatly reduced by sterilization attributed the major part to the activity of micro-organisms. When on one occasion the soil was by accident only partially sterilized the rate of oxidation instead of being reduced was greatly increased: it was inferred therefore that the action of the microorganisms had been increased by the partial sterilization. Unknown to me Hiltner and Störmer had already discovered this and shown that the numbers of bacteria rose considerably after partial sterilization, a result which they attributed to a stimulation of the organisms.

The subject was taken up at Rothamsted in conjunction with

[1] Report of Rothamsted Experiment Station, 1912, p. 10.   [2] See p. 207.

Hutchinson. Productiveness, rate of oxidation and bacterial numbers were all increased by partial sterilization, but no evidence of bacterial stimulation could be obtained. On the contrary the new flora was less efficient as a decomposition agent than the old; it owed its greater activity solely to its much larger numbers. The results indicated that the untreated soil contained some biological factor which kept down the numbers of bacteria and which was put out of action by partial sterilization. Search for possible organisms showed the presence of protozoa which, it was concluded, acted as predators, keeping down the numbers of bacteria, but they were killed on partial sterilization so that the numbers could rise to higher levels.

This conclusion led to a prolonged controversy. It was maintained especially in America that bacteria alone could live actively in soil: no larger organisms could survive the conditions. Any protozoa found were accidental only and in any case were not active but encysted and therefore entirely inert. Numerous investigations showed, however, that other organisms especially moulds and actinomycetes were active in the soil, also large numbers of free living nematodes, and a regular protozoan fauna. We had specifically mentioned ciliates, amoebae and monads: at first the emphasis was on the ciliates, notably *Colpoda cucullus* which dominated the cultures made by the usual technique.

Tom Goodey, a young microbiologist from Birmingham University, joined us at this stage and in an ingenious investigation showed that *Colpoda* were normally present as inactive cysts, and could not therefore be the predators that we were seeking. He found, however, large proteomyxan rhizopods in rich garden soils that fed on bacteria, also small amoebae and flagellates, but did not think that they or any other protozoa could be active in ordinary soils; those found by Hutchinson, he thought, could only have been cysts. C. H. Martin, however, an amateur Oxford protozoologist with his own laboratory at his residence near Abergavenny periodically worked at Rothamsted in collaboration with K. R. Lewin also from Oxford; they designed two ingenious methods of collecting protozoa from the soil so rapidly that they had no time to change their state. One was a flotation method which got the living forms out alive and was the prototype of the method Ladell used later for extracting the microfauna; the other consisted in stirring the soil rapidly with a saturated solution of picric acid which killed everything: on leaving the liquid to stand a scum was formed containing the microfauna in its natural state. It was picked up by floating cover slips on the surface.[1]

As a result of the controversy the old simple view that soil was inhabited solely by relatively small numbers of bacteria had to be abandoned, and evidence was obtained that the population was much larger and more complex, as will be shown later.

COCKLE PARK EXPERIMENT STATION, MORPETH, NORTHUMBERLAND[2]

Northumberland was among the earliest counties to promote agricultural education when the Whisky Money became available. In February 1891 its County Council made a grant of £500 to the Durham College of Science,[3] Newcastle-upon-Tyne, for the establishment of a chair of Agriculture. This evoked other support and later in the same year William Somerville was appointed to hold it.

He was born in 1861 on his father's 400 acre farm at Cormiston, Lanarkshire, and educated at the Royal High School; he also attended some lectures on agriculture by Professor John Wilson of Edinburgh. In 1880 at the age of 19 he succeeded to his father's farm and carried it on for the next 6 years; this was no easy task as the farm was poor and it was a time of depression. Like Middleton, therefore, he decided to give it up and in 1886 he sold it and returned to Edinburgh University to study under that remarkable character, Robert Wallace, who had succeeded John Wilson. Agriculture had only recently

[1] C. H. Martin and K. R. Lewin, *Phil. Trans.*, Vol. 205, B 77–94, 1914, and *Journ. Ag. Sci.*, Vol. 7, 106–19, 1915.

[2] Fortunately the history of this Station during its first sixty years has recently been written by Professor Cecil Pawson who has an exceptionally wide knowledge of the work done and the results achieved: *Cockle Park Farm*, Oxford Univ. Press, 1960, to which and to its author I am indebted for much of the material in this section.

[3] The College has had four different names: (1) (Durham) College of Physical Science (1871–1905). (2) Armstrong College (1908–37). (3) King's College (1937–63), (4) Newcastle University (1963 on).

become a degree subject, and Somerville was one of the small group of first graduates. He was very interested in forestry, and from Edinburgh he proceeded to Munich to study it systematically. On returning to Edinburgh in 1889 he was appointed to the newly established lectureship in forestry at the University; two years later he went to Newcastle as the first Professor of Agriculture and Forestry at the Durham College of Science.

The department had at first no farm. The acquisition of a small one was approved by the committee of management in principle, but deferred 'pending further developments': five years elapsed before it was actually obtained. One of Somerville's desires was to improve the large areas of poor grassland in the county, much of it little better than rough grazing, and in 1892, not long after his arrival, he told the Newcastle Farmers' Club what he wanted to do and how he would set about doing it. The experimental area would be divided into two acre plots, duplicate plots were to be dressed with various kinds of manures, at the beginning of the grazing season four or five sheep of known weight would be put on to each plot and weighed again at the end of the season. The gain in weight would show the effectiveness of the manure. He did not favour hasty conclusions, however; he suggested ten years as a suitable duration of an experiment, though it might be less.

Although Somerville had no farm belonging to the Department he was able to experiment on other people's farms: indeed the conditions of appointment required that each session he should organize six manurial demonstrations and deliver a hundred lectures. In doing this, he aroused so much interest among farmers that by 1896 there were no fewer than forty-six local demonstration centres and 817 plots.

In trying to acquire a farm the Committee had in 1895 sought the cooperation of the neighbouring counties of Durham, Westmorland and Cumberland, but failed. They therefore acted independently, and in May, 1896, took Cockle Park farm of 400 acres on the Duke of Portland's estate on a 21 year lease.[1] It was wretchedly poor, valued at 5s per acre per annum, some

[1] The Estate would not part with the freehold and the Governing body were unwilling to erect costly buildings on short leased land. In 1933 a 999 year lease was granted. In 1947 the farm was handed over to King's College Newcastle, thus ensuring its continued use for scientific and technological purposes.

of it at 2s 6d only, it was about 300 feet above sea level and 6 miles from the North Sea Coast. Most of the soil was an unkindly boulder clay, only a small area being lighter and more workable. It was a good site for reclamation experiments.

Somerville had the extreme good fortune that, unknown to most agriculturists, the ideal reclamation agent of proved efficacy was to hand cheaply and abundantly. Changes in the method of making steel had produced quantities of slag rich in a calcium phosphate which, though insoluble in water, dissolved readily in the weak acids occurring in soils like those of Cockle Park. John Wrightson had already in 1884–5 shown its striking effect on grass land by experiments at Ferry Hill in County Durham, and Munro of Downton College had made similar experiments with similar results. These experiments attracted little attention and few people acted on the results.

Somerville, however, knew of them and made basic slag treatment the central feature in his reclamation experiments. The most important group were made in Tree Field: they were started in 1896 and were continued without change till 1955 when the field was ploughed out: the longest spell of unchanged grazing experiment ever undertaken, and one which made Tree Field known all over the world. On five of the plots the treatments had remained unchanged during the whole period: they were: no treatment; basic slag 5 cwt. per acre and 10 cwt. per acre respectively; superphosphate; and a high protein diet fed to the sheep which would much enrich the urine and faeces in nitrogen. For the other five plots there had been some changes over the years but the final treatments were: (1) mineral phosphate, (2) dissolved bones, (3) slag plus lime, (4) slag plus muriate of potash, (5) slag plus nitrate of soda. There are special difficulties about long continued experiments of this kind; they require continuity of purpose and uniformity of treatment over long years possible only with very efficient and conscientious supervision. Fortunately this has always been available at Cockle Park, and the results can be accepted with the fullest confidence.

The adjoining field, Hanging Leaves, after slagging was grazed by a mixture of cattle and sheep instead of by sheep alone. This resulted in a better utilization of the herbage: the

cattle kept down the taller plants and so improved the conditions for the shorter ones, especially wild white clover, on
which the sheep by preference grazed, but there was no
evidence that the sheep had improved the grazing conditions for
the cattle.

It was reasonable to expect that the basic slag treatment
which had obviously increased the proportion of clover in the
herbage should also have increased the nitrogen and organic
matter content of the soil, and so enhanced its productiveness.
Long after Somerville left Newcastle he arranged for sufficient
soil to be sent to him from slagged and untreated plots, and
in pot experiments he found, as expected, a considerable store
of soil fertility resulting from the slag treatment.

In Palace Leas Field a long continued experiment was made
on the yield of hay under various fertilizer treatments on lines
similar to those of the park grass experiments at Rothamsted
except that the aftermath was always grazed. Pawson in his
book gives the results for the fifty-eight years 1897–1954, the
second longest series in the world.

Extensive use has been made of the material thus provided,
especially for chemical and botanical analyses of the herbage.
The series of ash analyses by B. Thomas and A. Thompson
reported in 1948 also quoted by Pawson, are among the most
complete in modern times as they include the trace elements
copper, cobalt and zinc, in addition to iron and manganese.

The striking results obtained both at Cockle Park and elsewhere on poor clay soils showed that basic slag was by far the
best agent known for reclaiming them.

The 'manuring for mutton' method, as it came to be called,
was almost perfect as a farmer's demonstration: in one operation which he could readily appreciate it gave him the information he wanted in a way that he could never forget. But it was
weak on the scientific side. There was no means of knowing
what food the sheep had eaten—they are selective in their
grazing—or how much; consequently no figure could be
obtained showing how much food was needed to produce given
amounts of live weight increase. Even this latter figure was
not known with certainty. The fleece of outdoor sheep can hold
some ten pounds of water and 'muck', and as the animals were
out of doors all the time and in all weathers there would

naturally be some variation due to this cause between one set of weighings and another. These criticisms do not affect the value of the method for demonstrating the improvement, which was what interested Somerville.

The Cockle Park programme included a wide range of subjects: animal feeding trials, arable crops, vegetables, fruit, and forestry. Somerville's idea at the outset was that 'the main use of a demonstration farm like Cockle Park lies not so much in the preparation of cut-and-dry manurial formulae, as in the supply of suggestions as to how a farmer may be likely to improve his own practice'. The Station provided all this and in addition it gave useful material to its Chemist, S. Hoare Collins. The grazing plots were so arranged that a strip of the herbage was inaccessible to the sheep and could therefore be sampled for botanical and chemical analysis.

One of the most interesting results obtained is recorded by Pawson in his book:[1] the weight per acre of phosphoric acid and of albuminoids (calculated from the nitrogen per cent) in the herbage, and the live weight increase of the sheep were all closely correlated. A change in the physical condition of the soil was produced by the roots of the plants developing on the slagged plots, which would repay investigation.

Somerville's final service to Cockle Park was the establishment of a meteorological station (second class). The Recorder was usually a student who had just completed his course: he also had charge of the experimental data in association with the farm manager. Interesting results might be expected from a study of the considerable accumulation of weather and field plot data by modern statistical methods.

Somerville left Newcastle in 1899 to become the first Drapers Professor of Agriculture at Cambridge; he was followed by T. H. Middleton who however, only stayed three years when in 1902 he also went to Cambridge in succession to Somerville who had been appointed to the Board of Agriculture.

Douglas Alan Gilchrist succeeded Middleton and held the chair till his death in 1927.

He was born in 1860, the son of William Gilchrist of Bothwell Park Farm, Lanarkshire, whose forbears had farmed in the parish for over 200 years. He was educated at Hamilton

[1] P. 48.

Academy near Glasgow till he was fourteen, then for the next twelve years (1874–1886) he worked on his father's farm and assisted in its management, acquiring thereby an intimate knowledge of the problems and difficulties confronting the working farmer. It was a time of growing difficulty: beginning at the tail end of a long period of agricultural prosperity and soon entering the long and dreary years of depression that did so much harm in England although fortunately less in Scotland; it drove him and other good men out of practical farming. He had already attended classes on agriculture and science at the Glasgow and West of Scotland Agricultural College, then in 1886 at the age of twenty-six he proceeded to Edinburgh University and working under Professor Wallace, graduated B.Sc. in Agriculture in 1889.

The University College of Bangor had just established a full time lectureship in Agriculture, the first to be set up at any University or University College in England and Wales, and on leaving Edinburgh Gilchrist was appointed to fill it. He proceeded vigorously to develop the Department. He set up a number of field trials with basic slag and other phosphatic manures, started dairy schools, and organized lecture courses for farmers and their sons both in the counties of North Wales and at the college—the first of their kind in Britain.

He remained five years at Bangor. In 1894 he was appointed Head of the new Department of Agriculture at the Reading University Extension College which ultimately became the University of Reading. Here also he vigorously organized outside lectures and field experiments in the five counties served by the college. He remained for eight years, and then in 1902 was appointed to Newcastle as Professor of Agriculture and Director of Cockle Park Experimental Farm.

He took up the problem of improving poor grassland where Somerville had left it, and while continuing and expanding Somerville's experiments, he developed the method of plough-ing and reseeding the land. This enabled him to start with the plants he wanted, but it raised the difficult problem of re-taining them, as they would from the outset be subject to the competition of native plants—otherwise weeds—and they might not be well adapted to the local conditions.

He had already studied wild white clover. He first realized its special qualities in 1891 while at Bangor. He was visiting some plots laid down by the Royal Manchester, Liverpool and North Lancashire Agricultural Society on Mr John Robert's farm at Saltney near Chester, and noticed particularly three sets of small plots of grasses and clovers which had been sown five years earlier with (a) grasses only, (b) grasses and cultivated white clover,[1] (c) grasses and wild white clover. Plot (b) had only a few clover plants living, (a) had as many, indicating that wild seed had blown in from outside and also on to (b), while (c) had an abundance of clover plants. The wild seed had obviously produced vigorous perennial plants, the cultivated had not, and so had soon disappeared.

The wild seed had come from Kent and he procured some from there and from other sources and started a collection of live grasses and clovers on a Lanarkshire farm. At Reading he extended these studies, and Messrs. Sutton, the well-known seedsmen, took an active interest in them; in 1895 he discussed his collected material in a paper entitled 'Hay and Pasture Management' read before the Farmers' Club in London. All this was done before Somerville had started the Cockle Park experiments. Gilchrist left Reading in 1902 for Newcastle where he made full use of the resources of Cockle Park and grew a wide range of grasses and clovers raised from seed obtained from various sources at home and abroad, noting their vigour and persistence, and their capacity for establishing themselves in Cockle Park conditions. On the basis of the knowledge thus gained he proceeded to devise the Cockle Park mixture for long leys which played an important part in the history of grassland management. The seed mixtures in common use were complex in the hope that some at least of the varieties might succeed: Gilchrist was able to simplify the formula by eliminating varieties that he knew could not. There was a novel feature about the new formulae that made them historic. Gilchrist recognized the importance of strain both in grass and in clover, and instead of merely red clover, white clover, and cocksfoot, he substituted late flowering red clover, wild white clover, and New Zealand cocksfoot. The

---

[1] Almost certainly of imported origin probably from Holland. The superiority of native clover over continental was recorded by Walter Blith in *The English Improver Improved*, 1652.

existence of 'strains' had of course long been known to botanists, and different strains of cereals, potatoes, etc. had long
been used by agriculturists, but Gilchrist seems to have been
the first to use strains of grasses. In place of the current mixture
of ten or fourteen different plants, Gilchrist had only six: three
clovers, wild white, later flowering red, and trefoil; and three
grasses, perennial rye grass, cocksfoot, and timothy for a three
year ley or permanent grass. His successors have simplified this
by cutting out the trefoil and in some cases the red clover. The
basis of the mixture remains wild white clover and basic slag—
normally at the rate of 200 lb. P_2O_5 per acre. In his paper to the
Farmers' Club in 1920 he was able to say that 'our temporary
leys at Cockle Park have within two years given turf far
superior to the best of our old land pasture' and he urged that
more old pastures should be put into long rotation.

It has since been objected that this simple mixture fails to
extract from the soil all the mineral nutrients needed by the
grazing animal and which the soil could supply. Stapledon had
noticed that sheep grazing on his improved pastures would
nevertheless turn away for a time to the surrounding waste for
a bite of some of the wild herbage: he therefore had recommended that wild herbage strips should be left intact in the
improved areas. In 1953 under R. W. Wheldon's regime the
question was tested. Inclusion of certain 'herbs' in the mixture
increased the proportion of both major and trace mineral constituents including copper and cobalt in the herbage, but there
was no evidence of higher nutritive value. Further investigation
seems desirable.

These investigations by Somerville and especially those of
Gilchrist have a high practical value. Their scientific value lies
in the large amount of factual material of a high degree of
reliability which they produced, and which poses many problems
for the agricultural biochemist and the physiologist. Beside
these grazing experiments there were as already stated many
others of considerable importance on arable crops and animal
nutrition: their interest, however, is agronomic rather than
scientific and the reader is referred to Pawson's book for an
account of them.

Gilchrist spent the remainder of his life at Newcastle, working
literally to the end. He was working at the College on the

morning of April 4, 1927, and died in the afternoon, aged only sixty-seven. He had accomplished twenty-five years of fruitful activity there, the longest period of service of any who had held that post before or since.

He never received the recognition he deserved for the work he had done. He lacked Somerville's impressive manner and Middleton's diplomatic suavity, qualities which had undoubtedly helped each of them along the pathway to the honours they attained. The reason probably was that the appropriate honours for work such as Gilchrist had done hardly existed at the time: they came later.

After his death there was a quiet period for a time so far as research was concerned, but from 1930 onwards to 1940 work was resumed under Professor Hanley. By that time, however, the Second World War was on and while it lasted was the dominant factor in determining the work of the station.

No account of the Cockle Park experiments would be complete without some reference to Sydney Hoare Collins who devoted the whole of his working life in this country to the Agricultural Department at Newcastle. Like Bernard Dyer he was trained in a public analyst's laboratory where he acquired analytical skill. Later he went to India where apparently his work decided him to devote his life to the development of agricultural chemistry. On returning to England in 1898 he became Lecturer in Agricultural Chemistry at the Durham College of Science two years after the Cockle Park farm was taken over and one year before Somerville left. He held this post for twenty-nine years, resigning in 1927, the year in which Gilchrist died. For a time he became Advisory Chemist to the Region when the Advisory Service was set up, but finally retired to Worthing where he died in May, 1963 at the age of ninety-four.

In the laboratory he was not only a good manipulator but an ingenious designer of improved techniques and appliances. His calcimeter[1] was an improvement on Scheibler's original form (then in common use) especially for soils containing only little calcium carbonate. This was estimated by measuring the volume of carbon dioxide evolved on treatment with acid, making allowance for errors due to its solubility in the solution and the

---

[1] Described in *J. Soc. Chem. Ind.*, 1906, Vol. 25, p. 515.

evolution of occluded air from the surfaces of the soil particles due to temperature and pressure variations. He designed a so-called 'slide rule' (really a nomograph) to convert the corrected readings direct into terms of calcium carbonate thereby saving much laborious arithmetic. He was among the pioneers in seeking mathematical expression for the relationships revealed by analytical data, and he rendered useful service by extracting from the Cockle Park experiments fuller information than could be obtained by the usual simple inspection. His book *Plant Products and Chemical Fertilizers* (1918) opened up some new ground. He made many analyses of food crops, turnips, etc. and determined unusual constituents, e.g. sugars in straw.

A bachelor till turned sixty he naturally developed various little eccentricities which marked him out as a 'character' in the days when they were expected at universities. These were such as endeared him to his students, among whom he enjoyed much quiet popularity; some of them visited him and wrote to him for at least forty years after they had left the department. To others he was rather shy and diffident, free from personal ambition, not particularly attractive either in appearance or in manner, and he never gained the recognition that those who knew him best thought was his due.

THE UNOFFICIAL ORGANIZATIONS

Leeds University: formerly (till 1904) Yorkshire College

Although the Agricultural Department of Leeds University did not develop a great research school there has long been much useful work done, always however personal and not during our period continuing over a succession of workers. It began with Herbert Ingle, the first lecturer in agricultural chemistry, appointed in 1899 after having been for sixteen years in the Department of Chemistry. He began some small investigations on milk production on the college farm. Before he had got far he was appointed as agricultural chemist to the newly organized South African Government and went there in 1903. He was followed by Charles Crowther who played an important part in the development of agricultural science and narrowly missed a notable research career. He was born in 1876 at Batley, Yorkshire and educated at the Grammar School there, also at Corpus Christi College, Oxford, and Leipzig University where he worked for three years under Wislicenus (1898–1901). For the next two years he was head of the Chemistry Department of the Harris Institute, Preston, and transferred to Leeds in 1903 as lecturer in agricultural chemistry, later (1913) raised to a professorship. He studied milk production problems, at first on a small scale, more extensively after 1913, when grants became available, and among other important results showed that the percentage of fat in the milk was not affected by variations in the ration, provided this was ample.

His work attracted the attention of T. B. Wood who wanted the results of milk production investigations to round off the general programme at Cambridge, and having research funds that he was not immediately using, passed them on to Crowther for the establishment of a small animal nutrition institute at Leeds to supplement the Cambridge programme by concentrating on problems relating to milk secretion and composition. The programme was in two parts, a chemical section under Crowther and a physiological under H. W. Dudley, a biochemist who later became Head of the Mount Vernon Medical Research Laboratory, Hampstead. The junior assistants included some who subsequently attained distinction, notably H. E. Woodman at Cambridge and H. Raistrick at the London School of Tropical Medicine. Crowther studied alternative methods of milking cows in order to find the most suitable for experimental purposes; he studied also their water requirements and the fatty acid components of milk fats. He made a long period investigation of the nitrogen metabolism of the cow at successive stages from non-pregnancy to parturition and normal milk production. Dudley made biochemical studies of milk proteins, and among other results proved the complete identity of milk globulin with serum globulin and the non-identity of lactalbumen with serum albumen. From 1916 to 1919 the war seriously interfered with the work and Dudley joined the forces. Wood set in train arrangements for transferring the Institute to Cambridge, Crowther included. But in the spring of 1919 Crowther accepted a very tempting invitation to take charge of the new Olympia agricultural research department described later.

Crowther was followed at Leeds by Norman F. Comber who, however, took soil as his subject for research during the 1920's. Much work was being done in Holland, the United States and elsewhere on the clay fraction of soils, and Comber, like Hall and Morison, studied the flocculation brought about by adding solutions of calcium hydroxide and other compounds to suspensions of clay particles in water. He concluded that the particles consisted of a solid core like silt coated with an emulsoid gel such as silica. This reacted with the calcium hydroxide producing a bulky precipitate which dragged down the clay (1921). He studied the rôle of electronegative ions in reactions between soils and electrolytes (1924) and showed also how a colloidal coating changed the properties of mineral particles. Little further progress was possible, however, till methods had been developed for elucidating the constitution of the clay minerals.

Charles Edmund Marshall was appointed in 1928 as Assistant Lecturer in agricultural chemistry. He studied some of the base exchange reactions (1931) and with H. Paver showed that aluminium acted as an exchangeable base (1934); its special relationship to clay was not yet fully realized in England. He also designed a centrifugal process for separating the clay particles into groups according to their size down to $0 \cdot 05\mu$. In 1937 just as his work was becoming most interesting he was tempted away to the United States.

The specialists of the Agricultural Advisory Service in the inter-war period were on the university staff and at times some research was necessary in connection with their problems. W. A. Millard worked on the common scab of potatoes, Powell Jones on *Actinomyces scabies*, and Miss B. M. Turner on the control of the Helminthosporium group of fungi by seed dressings. Already the potato eel worm was giving trouble and was under investigation by H. W. Thompson and L. R. Johnson. H. I. Moore made numerous comparisons of re-seeding and renovation for the improvement of old grass land and found re-seeding generally gave better results. He continued his grass land experiments at Seale-Hayne Agricultural College after he had left Leeds.[1]

[1] See p. 460.

T. S. Dymond. Essex Institute of Agriculture

As the result of public monies becoming available in the early 1890's for agricultural education a certain number of County Council Institutes of different kinds also engaged in education and advisory work and some of them carried out simple field trials; but at hardly any of them was any scientific work being done, there being neither suitable staff nor equipment.

The East Anglian Institute of Agriculture was an exception, however. It grew out of the County Laboratories established in 1892 at Chelmsford under T. S. Dymond. He did only one piece of scientific work, but it was of considerable significance which unfortunately was not appreciated at the time and was not further developed. On November 27, 1897, a great storm had broken the coastal defences in Essex. The sea had flooded large areas of agricultural land doing much damage. In co-operation with his assistant, F. Hughes, he investigated the cause of the damage.

The first effect of the flooding had been to kill the vegetation by the direct action of the salt. After the water was drained off and the rain began to wash out the salt there was an interesting sequence of changes. At first the soil was 'in remarkably good condition, ploughing well and forming a capital seed bed'. But as more and more salt was removed 'this condition gradually altered until the soil became difficult to work, and in dry weather hard and cindery'. The clay became more deflocculated, and would remain suspended for weeks in water while that from the unflooded land settled in a few hours. It was shown that calcium and magnesium had been removed from the clay and Dymond argued that sodium had displaced them. He attributed the initial favourable conditions to the flocculation brought about by the small quantity of salt still left; when this was gone the clay became highly deflocculated.[1]

These interesting observations have been in the main amply confirmed but it was some twenty years before their full implications were realized and the work was properly followed up.[2]

[1] He thus brought the change into line with the Way replacements, the displacing element being sodium.

[2] T. S. Dymond and F. Hughes, Report on Injury to Agricultural Land on the Coast of Essex by the Inundation of Sea Water on November 29, 1897. Chelmsford, 1899. It was shown later that sea water puts more magnesium than sodium into the clay.

In 1895 Dymond arranged for analysis of numerous Essex soils, the substances determined being nitrogen, lime, magnesia potash, phosphate and sulphate: totals only in most cases, Dyer's availability methods being very sparingly used. He commented on the smallness of the quantity of available plant food compared with the very large total supply. He showed also that except for potash and phosphate, the amount of plant food lost by drainage was greater than that taken up by plants. In the hope of alleviating the distress from which many of the arable farmers were suffering, Dymond also made numerous experiments on the manuring of grassland of several varieties including old grass, new grass and tumbled-down grass mostly on London clay or boulder clay soils. There were ten plots, $\frac{1}{4}$ to $\frac{1}{2}$ acre each all single, no duplication. Seven received one fertilizer or manure only: they were sulphate of ammonia, nitrate of soda, sulphate of potash, slag, superphosphate, lime and dung one had superphosphate and nitrate of soda, one had these two fertilizers plus sulphate of potash, and one was unmanured. The experiments were continued from 1896 to 1901. Slag (the old high soluble Bessemer type) gave the best results both for quantity and quality, and the effect was greater on old grass than on new: it was the only practicable agent for improving derelict land. Superphosphate was less effective. Nitrogen gave good returns, especially in conjunction with phosphate. Soil analyses were made at all centres and botanical analysis of the produce at one. Losses by drainage were estimated: lime suffered most, 2 tons of burnt lime per acre were needed each 8 years for full restoration. No phosphate or potash was lost, and the 4 cwt. of superphosphate per acre given was double the quantity taken up by most crops; more potash was taken up, however, than had been supplied. Only little sulphate had been taken up by the crops, but much was lost in the drainage water: there was a real danger of shortage for the plants unless liberal dressings of sulphate were given.[1]

In 1911 the Institute changed its name to the East Anglian Institute of Agriculture. In 1943 it moved out to Writtle and again changed its name, this time to the Essex Institute of Agriculture: its declared object was 'firstly to conduct original

[1] *Journal of the Essex Technical Laboratories*, the name by which the Institute was known from its beginning in 1893 till 1911.

research work and to keep itself abreast of what is being done elsewhere in the way of research into agricultural problems and to put the results before farmers' . . . and also to train students 'in the scientific principles on which the practice of agriculture is based'.

Dymond left Essex in 1906 to become an Inspector of Schools; when finally he retired he went to live at Hastings where he engaged in much public work, in due course becoming Mayor— 'one of Hastings' finest Mayors' was recorded of him—then Alderman, finally retiring into private life in 1945. He died in 1949 at the age of eighty-eight.

Grassland experiments were started by G. Scott Robertson in 1915 when basic slag was changing its character from the old high soluble to the new low soluble type; the new was compared with the old and also with the mineral phosphates. The comparison was made at several other widely spread centres, but the Essex group was the most extensive and included botanical and other studies of the herbage and of effects on the soil and the soil bacteria. They continued till 1920, and Robertson's full and interesting account of them was published as a monograph by the Cambridge University Press.[1] At no other centre was so much interesting material collected. In 1920 Robertson left Essex for Northern Ireland where he continued useful research work.

During the period 1908—14 Robert Robson the biologist was doing much pioneering in connection with Williams' campaign for the production of clean milk organized from Shinfield. He was away during the first World War, but returned at the end, and in addition to his other activities he did much useful work in the control of bacillary white diarrhoea disease of poultry. He is described as being in many ways unorthodox and unusual, but devoted to science and possessing much originality and charm. He retired in 1946.

Other useful research work began in 1921 when Frank Knowles joined the staff as agricultural chemist. He came immediately from the Midland Agricultural College, but had started his career at Wye College. His research work was done mainly in the 1930's, most of it with J. E. Watkin. The first scientific paper (1931) dealt with the assimilation and transloca-

[1] *Basic Slags and Rock Phosphates*, by G. S. Robertson, 1922.

I

tion of plant nutrients in wheat during growth; it was followe
by one on the amounts and distribution of phosphorus and nitr
gen compounds in wheat (1932). Then came a chemical stud
of sugar beet during its first growth year (1934), and a
important paper on the effects of fertilizer interactions on th
growth and composition of the potato plant (1940). This ha
been studied by Lawes and Gilbert, but analytical methods an
experimental procedure had been much improved since thei
time. Wet methods had been substituted for the ignition whic
had since been found to incur a loss of potassium chloride b
volatilization. Another paper by Knowles and Watkin issued i
1935 as a bulletin (No. 3) of the Institute, entitled the *Zone c
Soil to be Fertilized for Sugar Beet*, is an early demonstration c
the advantage of proper placement of fertilizers. The mor
technical papers included a series on goats' milk.

During the second World War (1939–45) all educationa
work was closed down and Knowles became Feeding Stuf
Officer for Essex, a post which he gave up in 1943 to assist i
the transfer of the Institute of Agriculture from Chelmsfor
to Writtle, a village three miles distant, where it still func
tioned in the 1960's. Knowles retired in 1955.

Essex has probably been the most active of the counties i
doing research. In a number of others, investigations have bee
made, usually as part of the advisory work.

The Saxmundham Experimental Field. East Suffolk, 189.
onward

East Suffolk was one of the first counties in England to b
actively interested in fertilizers. It supplied some of the minera
phosphate from which the early lots of superphosphate wer
made, and some of its sturdy inhabitants were not afraid to brav
Lawes' anger and make their own superphosphate, coming t
terms with him, however, after the lawsuit had settled th
position. The names of Packard, Prentice and Fison will alway
be associated with the superphosphate industry.

It was because of the failure of fertilizers to produce thei
expected effects on certain soils that experiments were starte
in 1899 under the Suffolk Education Committee, the guiding
spirit being Alfred Harwood—a great country gentlema
keenly interested in all that affected Suffolk agriculture. Tw

sites were chosen: Bramham, with a light soil, and Saxmund-ham, a rather unkindly clay. The Bramham experiments were discontinued after a short time but the Saxmundham rotation experiments are still going on unchanged since the beginning, the oldest of their kind in the world outside Rothamsted and Woburn. It includes the five crops most commonly grown on that type of soil in the district: wheat, barley, beans, clover and mangolds. The treatments were: no manure, farmyard manure; complete fertilizer (NPK); no nitrogen (PK); no phosphate (NK); no potash (NP). As on the Broadbalk field at Rotham-sted, the experiment is continued year after year on exactly the same lines, the only break occurring when a variety of one of the crops is no longer obtainable and a new one has to be chosen. Supervisor and operator—A. W. Oldershaw and Harry Fiske—remained unchanged for thirty-eight and forty years respectively: both were men of the highest integrity and their successors maintained their high standard. The experiment can be regarded as entirely trustworthy; it provides exceptionally good material for studying the relations of soil, fertilizer and crops.

The effects are cumulative: by 1964 the unmanured plot had been completely starved for sixty five years, while the dunged plot, though receiving only 6 tons per acre annually, had in all received 390 tons, and the phosphatic and potassic fertilizers had piled up to $6\frac{1}{2}$ to 16 tons per acre of chemical fertilizers over the whole period, thus intensifying their effects. The plots provide an exceptional opportunity for studying the effects of these various substances on the soil and on the crops. The plot receiving farmyard manure gradually stood out distinctly from the rest, the soil acquired a darker colour, became more friable, and could be cultivated earlier. The necessity for phosphate supply to promote root development is well shown by the mangolds: on the plots without phosphate they never grow up but remain always ridiculous little things yielding only 4 or 5 tons per acre. Superphosphate also acts well on clover and on beans but has less striking effects on wheat and on barley. The recovery of added phosphate by the crop is usually taken as 25 per cent: at Saxmundham, however, it appears to be con-siderably higher. For the first sixty years potassic fertilizers had little effect on wheat, barley or mangolds, the soil supplies being adequate for the level of growth permitted by the other conditions; beans and clover, however, benefited much earlier.

The phosphorus compounds in farmyard manure are usually supposed to have only about three quarters of the value of superphosphate: this is the figure used in Hall and Voelcker's tables for compensation for unexhausted manurial value. The Saxmundham experiments suggest, however, though they do not prove, that there is little if any difference between them. The plot receiving farmyard manure annually would furnish good material for studying the loss of organic matter and of nitrogen from the soil. During the first sixty years the manure probably added some 5,000 lb. of nitrogen per acre, but at the end, and in spite of some good crops of clover, the plot contained only about 1,500 lb. per acre more than the one which from the beginning has had no manure or fertilizer: some 3,500 lb. have disappeared of which not more than about one third or one half is likely to have been taken by the crops. The decomposition is brought about by the soil population which has not been studied: it has presumably reached an ecological climax and would probably be an extremely interesting subject for investigation.

Apart from their practical importance, which has been very considerable, the Saxmundham experiments have the scientific value of supplying material of known and trustworthy history for investigation of many subjects on which more information is sadly needed.

THE LAST OF THE AMATEURS

Besides the professional people there were some amateurs who were doing valuable pioneering work in agricultural science. One of the best known was E. S. Beaven, the most distinguished barley expert of his time. His father was a barley grower, and his father-in-law a maltster; Beaven entered this business in 1877 and devoted all his energies to the study of the barley crop: he knew it more intimately than any of his generation.

The usual variety at that time was Chevallier, which had been discovered about 1820 by a farm labourer, John Andrews of Debenham, Suffolk. The discovery is typical of the way that agricultural improvements were made in the days before science came in, and it shows also the character of some of the farm workers of the time. There are two accounts of it. One, contained in a letter written by the clergyman of the parish, the Rev. Dr John Chevallier, states that John Andrews passing through a field of barley 'plucked a few ears, and on his arrival home threw them for his fowls into his garden, and in due time a few of the grains arrived at maturity, and as the ears appeared remarkably fine I determined to try the experiment of cultivating them'. The difficulty of this account is to understand how the few grains managed to escape the attentions of John Andrews' fowls. The other account is much more picturesque: it appears in a history of Debenham dated 1845 and therefore some twenty-five years after the event. According to this John had been threshing barley with the flail and walking home was annoyed by an ear that got into his shoe and hurt his foot. When he got home he took off his shoe, and shook out the ear: he noticed it was better and more shapely than usual and so he kept it and at the proper time sowed the grain in his garden. The plants grew well and produced fine ears like the parent. The Rev. Dr Chevallier saw them and asked that they might be saved for him when ripe. This was done; he sowed the seed, multiplied and distributed it: finally it became very widely grown. It was named after him and not after John Andrews. This account may be nearer the truth: memories in the countryside are long, but there is always the possibility of some embroidering.[1] Accidents of that kind have given us some of our most useful varieties of crops. But it is unsafe to rely upon them.

Besides Chevallier other old varieties of barley were still cultivated: true landraces in that they had somehow emerged in the various localities in which they were found. Among them were Archer, better yielding than Chevallier, but of lower malting quality, with a stronger neck so that the heads were less liable to bend over as they ripened and to break off during harvesting; and Spratt, grown in places in the Fens and in Essex, a very stiff strawed variety that could stand up where other varieties would lodge. Beaven knew also of the Danish experiments on barley begun in 1882 and was much impressed by some of their varieties, particularly Plumage, a Danish

[1] The original statements are quoted by H. Hunter in his excellent book *The Barley Crop*, Crosby Lockwood, 1952.

selection of a Scandinavian type known in Sweden as 'Plumage-korn'.

Near his home in Warminster he began experiments in 1895 starting with single plant cultures of various established races of barley, and expanding his programme till finally his experimental ground covered four acres, and included a large bird-proof cage under which special cultures could be grown in safety. The best of these single cultures were further tested on a larger scale at Warminster and afterwards at Cambridge: two were soon taken up by farmers and came into general cultivation: Plumage, and Archer.

But he quickly realized the limitations of the selection method: it could emphasize existing characters but not introduce new ones. So he began hybridizing in his cage (with help from T. B. Wood and R. H. Biffen), discarding unsuitable plants from the F_2 generation onwards, and carrying on the most promising to the F_5 generation. The survivors were then transferred to small plots which were replicated but arranged systematically—not randomized as later practice would have required, but which Beaven never approved—the final selections were then multiplied and compared with the standard sorts in field trials.

He adopted an ingenious method of eliminating errors due to inequalities of the soil. The box of the seed drill was divided into two equal parts, one was filled with the seed under test, the other with seed of a standard variety; these half strips were separately harvested. The method was a great advance on the older ones and was long used. The best known of his crosses is the group of four hybrids of Plumage and Archer, all known as Plumage-Archer but each having a distinctive number: the group achieved great fame and for some time was probably the most popular barley in Great Britain.

Beaven's success was largely due to his amazing power of recognizing the qualities of barley. He knew intuitively which of his many seedlings to discard and which to retain. He combined the artist's eye with the scientist's recognition of the need for full and accurate records and for careful thought about what they mean. His studies of malting quality made in conjunction with J. H. M. Munroe were for long the best on the subject. He published little else, however, and it was feared hat his unique collection of data might be lost: but towards the end he was persuaded to summarize his results, though he did not live to complete the task. Fortunately his secretary Miss N. Stallwood, was able to do this, and his book was duly published.[1]

Beaven had done all this work at his own expense and with very little manual assistance. He was a typical Victorian: a sturdy, vigorous, forceful personality; outspoken, pungently critical of some of the scientists, scathing in his denunciation of anything State-aided; a stout believer in self-help, in some (but by no means all) of his contemporaries, and in himself. A. D. Hall dedicated to him the *Pilgrimage of British farming* made in company with him and T. B. Wood: 'I think of you as one of the last defenders of the old *laissez faire* position, a latter-day Athanasius, standing for self-help and honest individual work and denouncing government departments, county councils, development commissions and all such spoon-feeding agencies'.

Another distinguished amateur was Spencer Pickering, poles apart from Beaven in many ways but equally distinctive and like him, a solitary worker. Pickering came of distinguished ancestry on both sides, his mother being granddaughter of the great Coke of Norfolk, Earl of Leicester. He was born in 1858; his father was then Recorder of Pontefract; he was educated at Eton and in January 1877 entered Balliol College as a Brackenbury Science Scholar, and took final honours in Natural Science in 1879. Even as a schoolboy he had been devoted to chemistry and his father had allowed him to set up a laboratory at his home in Bryanston Square, London: an explosion unfortunately so injured his right eye that it had to be removed, leaving him for the rest of his life in impaired health. He was always fond of controversy; his first chemical paper published in his second year at Balliol College was to disprove some statement that his tutor had made.

He went down in 1880, and for a short time was Assistant Master at Highgate School and also Lecturer in Chemistry at Bedford College: he soon relinquished the school post and confined himself to the college, later the lectureship was changed to a professorship. He resigned in 1887 but continued

[1] *Barley, Fifty Years of Observation and Experiment*, E. S. Beaven. Duckworth & Co. London. 1947.

working in his own laboratory on various problems in inorganic chemistry, gradually developing a theory of solutions
which was much criticized at the time: by 1887 he had published some seventy papers on the subject and others followed
during the next ten years.

But they were not well received, and as his health was not
good he decided to spend some time in the country. He went to
Harpenden and worked as a labourer on the Rothamsted farm
lodging with a small farmer's family and sharing their life. It
may be doubted whether the search for health was his sole
reason for this: a young man in his position, a bachelor, well
connected, very good looking, in easy circumstances and
serious minded as the age required, could have found many
more comfortable ways of recuperating in the country. But
there was a streak of sentimentalism in his character:[1] he was
by no means a cold scientist but loved music and the works of
the pre-Raphaelites. His sister had married William de Morgan;
it is highly probable (although he did not himself state it) that
he had come under the influence of William Morris, Arnold
Toynbee and others then making themselves felt among
thoughtful young people and that it was in response to impulses
such as these that he broke away from his London laboratory
and began his life in the country. He decided to remain in
Harpenden, then an attractive small village including among
its inhabitants, however, no fewer than five Fellows of the
Royal Society. He had an interesting old house which he
adorned with William de Morgan's tiles and pottery; it was
set in spacious grounds in which he built himself a comfortable
laboratory where he worked solitary as ever, without even a
laboratory boy to do the washing up.

In 1894 he decided to apply science to fruit growing. He
interested the Duke of Bedford whom he had known both at
school and at college; the Duke in 1894 set aside 20 acres of
land for an experimental fruit garden, put up suitable buildings
and for the next 24 years bore the entire cost of the work.

Pickering drew up the experimental programme and devised

[1] Perhaps the only touch of sentiment in the tens of thousands of pages of the
Chemical Society's publications is to be found at the end of one of his papers where
he expresses his thanks to 'a little girl who had devoted all her spare time to the
laborious calculations involved in the present work': she afterwards became his
wife.

the methods: all the chemical work was done in his laboratory. All classes of fruit were studied, but the most important investigations were on apples; they included the preparation of the ground, methods of planting, manuring, pruning and the control of insect and fungus pests. The work was done with great care but many of the results conflicted with growers' experience. Trenching had no effect. Planting was best done by ramming the young tree into a hole in the ground as if it were a gate-post; the old-established ritual of carefully spreading out the roots, adding the soil and gingerly pressing it down so as not to damage them was not only unnecessary but detrimental. As to pruning: 'from every point of view' he wrote, 'it would appear that pruning is disadvantageous to a fruit tree, and the more it can be reduced the better'. Manuring, even with farmyard manure, was ineffective.

In the light of later knowledge it is possible to account for part at least of the abnormality of the results. The profound effect of root stock on the growth of the tree was not then realized: no precautions were taken to ensure uniformity of stocks, the trees therefore were not strictly comparable one with another. Also the method of treating the results was unsuitable. No actual weights were published. Instead the results for the different treatments were stated as percentages of those for the untreated plot, and the figures for the different varieties were averaged to obtain the final result. Equal significance was thus attached to results of all varieties. Inspection of the plots however, showed clearly that this was unjustified. A few sorts were doing well, notably Bramley's Seedling, but most of the others looked very unhappy and it was clear that something was wrong. The site and soil had been approved by horticultural experts before planting began, but later a fuller examination showed that only the surface soil was of the desirable loamy nature; the subsoil was a heavy Oxford clay not really suitable for fruit. Bramley's Seedling, which tolerated the conditions better than any of the other varieties and gave normal yields, responded normally to fertilizers.

Pickering was essentially a laboratory man; his work on fungicides and insecticides was very good, but unlike Hall or Percival he lacked the eye for a good tree. He enjoyed being provocative; he loved tilting at preconceived ideas and pre-

I*

judices in which gardeners are wont to indulge. The best of them recognized the value of provocation: 'The results', wrote E. A. Bunyard, the distinguished pomologist, 'aroused us from lethargy and while the "knocker up" cannot expect a warm welcome from the called, he performs an invaluable office, and has his reward in the sight of a busy and curious world which, but for his efforts, might still be deep in conservative slumber'. But all fruit growers did not take that view, and when in 1918 as the result of heavy taxation the Duke was unable any longer to finance the experiments perhaps the saddest feature of their abandonment was the refusal of the fruit growers to take any action for their continuance: the comment of one of their leading papers was: 'whilst regretting the cause, the writer is glad on the whole that the station is closed.'

He had a flair for discovering curious phenomena that most people would miss, but he did not always follow the matter up. He found, for example, that adding a small quantity of toluene to soil to kill the active micro-organisms increased its content of water soluble matter, but he did not determine what this was. He made a number of interesting observations which still await elucidation. Perhaps the most important relate to the harmful effect of one growing crop on another. Growing grass injured, and in the end killed, his fruit trees. He showed that this effect was independent of any interference with the supply of air, water, or nutrients to the roots. A definite toxic action seemed indicated and this was proved by a very ingenious experiment. Young trees were planted in glazed pots the level of the soil being several inches below the rim. Into this space in each pot was fitted a perforated iron or earthenware tray, several inches deep, annular in shape, leaving a central circular space through which the tree could grow. The trays were filled with sand: grass was grown in some, others were left bare. The watering was done through the sand. Where there was no grass the trees grew considerably better than where grass was grown, and Pickering concluded that the water had carried some toxic substance with it. The substance was apparently very unstable because the percolate from the grass-covered sand seemed to be beneficial when supplied to trees growing in pots of soil. But he could not identify it; once again a problem in agricultural chemistry was held up through lack of suitable methods of investigation. These methods have now been devised and when the problem is taken up again some interesting results may be confidently anticipated even if, as is possible, Pickering's assumption of a toxin should prove to be an oversimplification.[1]

He died in 1920 after a long and painful illness, the result of an internal haemorrhage for which in those days no treatment seemed available.

[1] A full account of Pickering's work is given in *The Scientific work of the late Spencer Pickering*, by T. M. Lowry and E. John Russell, published by the Royal Society in 1927. The toxin work is described in *Journ. Ag. Sci.*, 1914, 6. 136.

CHAPTER IX

THE BEGINNING OF STATE
AID: THE FIRST WORLD WAR

1910–1919

T HE year 1910 was a turning point in the history of agricultural science in the United Kingdom. Up till then the
state policy had been to leave it alone—*laissez faire* was the
phrase. Money would be provided for education but not for
research: Income Tax was already 1s in the £ and that was
enough. In the early 1900's, however, rural impoverishment
and depopulation threatened to cause serious economic troubles
and much unemployment might ensue. In 1909 the Chancellor
of the Exchequer, David Lloyd George, brought in an Act to expand the resources of the countryside and the coastal regions by
proper scientific development of afforestation, agriculture and
fisheries. It was to be done on a large scale, with guidance from
properly equipped experimental forests and experimental farms,
and the setting up of agencies for disseminating agricultural
instruction.[1] A development fund of £2,500,000, subsequently
raised to £3,000,000, was provided to last for five years.

It was an entirely new idea in British politics and needed
justification. The state will greatly benefit, Mr Lloyd George
declared in his Chancellor's speech. 'The resettlement of the
deserted and impoverished parts of its own territories may not
bring to its coffers a direct return which would reimburse it
fully for its expenditure, but the indirect enrichment of its
resources more than compensates it for any apparent and immediate loss'. Members of the House who remembered that

---

[1] It was recognized that development of the countryside would necessitate
improvements of the roads which were then in poor condition. Separate provision
was made for this and the Road Board was established.

the total grant for Agricultural Educational and experimental work in 1909/10 had been only £12,500, and in 1910/11 after a year's negotiations with the Treasury only £18,840 plus £425 special grants for 'experiments and research', may well have been astounded at Mr Lloyd George's courage in asking for such an amount: but he got it. The fund was to be administered by eight Commissioners: seven were part-time and unpaid and one was full-time and salaried.

The part-time members included two agriculturists, Walter Berry, a very able and enlightened East Kent farmer, and Hall, who soon became the dominant member where agricultural matters were concerned; Sydney Webb who was also a member quickly recognized Hall's remarkable qualities and gave him valuable support. The Commission soon got to work and decided on three main lines of action. The first was to set up a system of sound scientific investigation accompanied by a corresponding development of agricultural education to ensure that knowledge thus gained should speedily find appreciation and application by farmers. The second was to test the economic prospects of certain new or discarded crops: flax and hemp, formerly but no longer grown; sugar beet, not yet known to farmers in spite of Rothamsted successes with it in 1871–5 and 1898–1902; and tobacco. The third was an extensive campaign to develop co-operation among farmers in the hope of obtaining benefits comparable with those gained by the Danish farmers, or the Irish under Horace Plunkett's guidance.

In spite of much valiant and well directed effort the attempts to establish co-operation on any extensive scale failed. The countrymen of Britain are sturdy individualists; they are prepared under the guidance of a trusted Advisory Officer to follow a particular course to which they agree, or to consider adopting a particular policy on the recommendation of the National Farmers Union, but they insist on running their own farms in their own way—not out of sheer obstinacy but because they know that each farm has its own peculiarities to which they must conform. Of the new crops studied only sugar beet was adopted, and that has proved a great success.[1]

---

[1] A fastidious smoker who had tried a number of samples told me that the only possible use for British grown tobacco was to kill green fly. As a non-smoker I cannot offer an opinion.

It was with the first two of their objects that the Commission attained their greatest success. There was at first a struggle between the Board of Agriculture and the Board of Education about the agricultural education provided by the county councils out of the Whisky Money: did it count officially as education or as agriculture? In the former case it would come within the purview of the Board of Education: in the latter case it would be under the Board of Agriculture. It was an ideal topic for inter-departmental disputation, and it was settled early in 1912 in favour of the Board of Agriculture. Very fortunately its Secretary was T. H. Middleton,[1] the best that either the Board or its successor, the Ministry, had ever had for working with scientists: he and Hall worked well together, and they had the advantage of much shrewd advice from T. B. Wood of Cambridge. The details of the educational system do not concern us: it is sufficient to state that it catered for all concerned with agriculture: it provided Farm Institutes for the workers who wanted to become foremen, and small farmers' sons ambitious for a larger enterprise; and it strengthened Agricultural Colleges for young men who could afford the time and money for the longer courses. Associated with these were the County Advisers who were expected to be fully acquainted with the best existing farm practice and with possible improvements indicated by current investigations. They should also know leading farmers who would be willing to try possible improvements and pass the knowledge thereby gained around the district.

The research scheme was devised by Hall after its fundamental character had been agreed. Was the research to be of the so called 'practical type': the solution of particular problems important at the time though not necessarily of fundamental significance; or should it consist in building up a body of well tested information into a coherent science which experts and teachers could use with confidence? Hall strongly advocated the latter course with powerful support from Berry and Webb; and it was adopted. All agreed on the urgent necessity for a highly developed agricultural science as the basis of a permanent agriculture in this country. The attainment of this laudable objective was greatly facilitated by a valuable feature of the Act,

[1] See p. 202.

and a great tribute to the farsightedness and breadth of vision of Mr Lloyd George: the Commission's grants were not subject to annual review in Parliament; in consequence there has never been any pressure on the research workers to produce results. They were appointed after very careful scrutiny, and then left to get on with their work in peace. They would not be expected to find applications of their results to farm practice: that would be the province of the County Advisers.

The general framework of the scheme being thus agreed Hall proceeded to fill in the details. Agricultural science is too diffuse to be retained as a single subject for research purposes: Hall therefore divided it into eleven subjects, each of which was to be continuously and systematically investigated at a special institute, or in a few cases at two. These should not be gathered into one large organization as in the United States, France, and certain other countries, but established in or associated with the university that seemed most appropriate. The single large organization would have had the advantage of administrative tidiness with its pyramid-like structure, but the distribution of the institutes among the universities ensured that the workers were in constant touch with modern scientific thought and intellectual movements, and also could attract a constant flow of suitable recruits from the more able students.[1]

With Hall action quickly followed decision. During the year 1910 to 1911 four existing organizations became Research Institutes and received their first grants from the Development Fund: Rothamsted for soil and plant nutrition; Cambridge: one for plant breeding, a second one for animal nutrition; and Long Ashton for cider and West Country fruits. The Rothamsted grant was £2,000 for the year 1910/11: this was the first help Rothamsted had ever had from the Government. In the following year the grant was £2,500 and the Station was notified that a like sum could be expected annually in future. Two years later, however, it was raised to £2,850. The grants were described as temporary: Treasury sanction was required to make them permanent; the Commissioners recommended the grant,

---

[1] This accorded with an earlier decision. In 1895 the British Association had asked the Royal Agricultural Society whether it was desirable to establish one Central Government Agricultural Research Institute. The answer was in the negative.

the Treasury made it. Accordingly Hall put the scheme together and submitted it in August, 1911, to the Treasury: they accepted it, and Hall was charged with the duty of organizing the work of carrying it out.

At first Hall retained the directorship of Rothamsted as well as the commissionership, but, as he wrote, 'I soon found that a man cannot busy himself with committees, enquiries, and schemes, and at the same time think. Research demands that you must brood on it. So I had to choose and it seemed desirable that I should go and help to parcel out the straw from which others could make bricks'. So in September, 1912, he left Rothamsted and the writer became Director in his stead. Henceforth Hall devoted his time entirely to the Commission. Among other duties he had to prepare or examine schemes for agricultural and other rural developments. The Commission's income was above £500,000 a year and there were naturally many claimants, but from the outset all piece-meal and minor applications were refused and only large comprehensive schemes were considered.

Meanwhile, he continued to develop the research scheme and by August, 1914, twelve institutes and two minor research centres had been set up in England and Wales: four for the 'plant sciences', six for the 'animal sciences', two for fruit growing, one for dairying and one for agricultural economics. He realized that the agricultural colleges could not provide the scientific staffs for the new Institutes. Each member would be applying a particular science to the elucidation of the principles underlying a particular branch of agriculture, and while the necessary agricultural knowledge could be acquired at the Institute the basic scientific knowledge could not. Generous scholarships were therefore offered to promising young scientists to allow of three years training at the Institute preferred by the candidate.

Other developments were in progress till August 4, 1914, when the outbreak of the First World War dramatically ended these activities and set in train a chain of events that profoundly altered the position of agriculture and agricultural science in the national life. [1]

[1] A fuller account of the history of the Development Commission is given in H. E. Deal's *A. D. Hall, Pioneer in Scientific Agriculture*, London, John Murray, 1956.

The first World War differed from all previous wars in that as it progressed agricultural scientists were called upon to take an increasing part in dealing with its problems, particularly those relating to food supplies. Their ranks, however, were soon depleted: enlistment was at first entirely voluntary, and the best of the younger scientists at once joined the forces. As they went their work either closed down or was carried on by women or men who could claim exemption on grounds of health or conscientious objection. Until then there had been very few women workers in agricultural science, partly the result of custom, partly through lack of training. During the war, however, the science schools of the Universities, the Swanley Horticultural College, the Lady Warwick Hostel at Reading, forerunner of the present Studley College, provided a stream of well trained women who could efficiently complete the work entrusted to them.

During the early part of the war the general national policy was 'business as usual', and in consequence the scientific research already in progress was continued, subject to changes in staff and shortages of material—serious in some cases, as Germany at that time had almost a monopoly of optical glass, pure chemicals, and complex scientific apparatus. The economists had forecasted serious unemployment, and various schemes were put forward to alleviate it if and when it should arise: on some of these Rothamsted was asked by the Development Commission or the Board of Agriculture to advise: they included some large reclamations such as Pagham Harbour, the agricultural development of Foulness Island, and the utilization by afforestation or otherwise of the spoil heaps in the Black Country.

There was at first no food problem, as large quantities were still coming in from abroad and home production was not greatly impeded. Many people thought that intensification of the existing farming system would provide all that was required: Middleton did not. Knowing that the Germans had long been preparing for the war, he shrewdly surmised that they had worked out and put into operation a system that would ensure self-sufficiency when the need arose. The necessary statistical material was fortunately available, and from this he prepared a most illuminating memoir contrasting the agricultural systems of Great Britain and of Germany.[1] He pointed out that we had aimed at maximum profit per acre (or minimum loss) in order to ensure the continued survival of the farmers: this had meant concentration on live stock products necessitating a large proportion of grassland much of which, as then treated, yielded but little per acre; the system in consequence, resulted in a low level of national self-sufficiency. The Germans, on the other hand, had aimed at high calorie output per acre by concentrating on grain and potatoes, and although the resulting diet was less varied and less pleasing than ours it was physiologically adequate and home production could be much higher than was possible with our system. At the British Association meeting in Manchester in 1915 Middleton showed the relevant figures and boldly announced his policy for wartime agriculture: it was to plough up enough grassland to produce the additional corn and potatoes needed to supply the nation with the necessary calories.

Food produced under different systems of farming:
quantities per acre per annum. (Middleton).

Type of farming and produce	Food lb.	Digestible protein lb.	Calories thousand	No. of days' rations for one man	
				Protein	Calories
Grazing. Meat.					
Poor pasture	20	2·7	38·8	11	11
Medium pasture	105	14·3	204	57	58
Rich pasture	190	16·7	488	67	140
Dairy Farming.					
Good land: Milk, and meat.		74	674	296	193
Arable Farming.					
Good land		51·9	1036	207	296

Dairy farming had the advantage for protein production, but for calories arable farming was much superior. Early in 1916 a committee set up by the Royal Society to advise on the national food supplies concluded that if an ample supply of calories could be assured from the wheat, potatoes, vegetables and such animal foods as we might reasonably expect to produce and import, we should automatically obtain all the protein needed. The importance of vitamins and mineral nutrients

[1] *The Recent Development of German Agriculture* H.M.S.O. Cmd. 8305, 1916.

was not yet fully realized, calorie supplies appeared to be the key to the problem and Middleton's policy would secure them.

Nothing was done about it, however. Food supplies were adequate in 1915: home production of wheat had increased, though at the expense of other crops, especially barley; heavy crops were produced in Canada and the United States and safely brought to Britain.

But in 1916 the situation began drastically to change. The weather at home was unfavourable to food production, and the German submarine war was steadily intensified; finally food ships were being sunk at an alarming rate. By November the seriousness of the situation had led to the dissolution of the first and the setting up of the second Coalition Government, this time under Mr Lloyd George. The new President of the Board of Agriculture, Mr Rowland Prothero (afterwards Lord Ernle), fully accepted Middleton's policy and himself launched the ploughing-up campaign. The target set was the conversion of 3 million acres of grassland into arable. Quotas were assigned to the different regions, and the Woman's Land Army was organized to provide additional labour. County Agricultural Executive Committees were set up with considerable powers of compulsion and of allocating limited resources including fertilizers, feeding stuffs, labour, horses and tractors— albeit the tractor was then, as Middleton records, 'a new, untried and rather distrusted implement'; he might have added that it was uncertain and hated by the old farm workers, especially the horsemen.[1] More important still, the Food Production Department was set up in January of 1917 to co-ordinate and direct the whole of the campaign, and Middleton was appointed Deputy Director. The leaders in agricultural science, including the writer, were brought in as Technical Advisers and for the next two years devoted practically all their energies to its work: it was the first time that scientists had played an

---

[1] We had one at Rothamsted, and it not infrequently ceased work in the field. On one such occasion a little group of horse ploughmen in the same field had left their teams to watch the driver seeking the cause of the trouble and to offer their rather pungent comments. Unscrewing the jet of the carburetter he blew out from it on to his hand a small insect and said proudly: 'That's what done it'; to which one of the men at once replied with a quotation from St Paul, 'God hath chosen the weak things of the world to confound the things which are mighty'.

active part in the general food production operations of the country.

Middleton drew up a very comprehensive programme and in his quiet diplomatic way he helped to smooth out the difficulties that arose in carrying it out. The commonest of these arose from the circumstances that the ploughing-up programme required much larger quantities of fertilizers than did the old farming systems, while the war conditions greatly curtailed the supplies available. Before the war the farmers of the United Kingdom had used annually about 350,000 tons of sulphate of ammonia and 800,000 tons of superphosphate. Both the nitrogen and the sulphuric acid needed for their manufacture were, however, urgently required for the making of munitions; also imports of raw mineral phosphate fell off seriously. By 1916 the supply of sulphate of ammonia was reduced to a little over 250,000 tons and of superphosphate to 500,000 tons per annum, while the need for far greater quantities was growing more and more urgent. It was before the days of synthetic ammonia, and a wide search was made for nitrogenous materials that could be used as manure. The old Bessemer basic slag would have considerably reduced the shortage of phosphatic manure, but it was no longer made in the old quantities. The new open hearth process gave a slag containing phosphate, but in a form much less available to the plant than that in the Bessemer slag, and no method could be found of improving its effectiveness. Potassic fertilizers gave the most difficulty as even in pre-war days Stassfurt had been practically the sole source of supply, the Alsatian deposits not having yet been opened up. Extensive search was made. A number of industrial residues were found to contain potash but the quantities were usually too small or too contaminated to be of practical value: some blast furnace flue dusts, however, contained serviceable amounts and arrangements were made for their utilization.

Greater supplies of organic manure were needed; and investigations were made at Rothamsted to reduce the losses generally incurred during the making and storing of farmyard manure which was far the most important source of plant food available. A fermentation method was worked out for converting straw, which was now available in unusually large quantities, into a useful organic manure.

Elsewhere there were investigations on the fuller utilization of sewage, household waste, town refuse and other materials which in the spacious days of peace had been neglected.

Much of the ploughed up grassland soon carried a crop of weeds, but not uncommonly they were the weeds of arable land, not of grassland. This question was taken up at Rothamsted and it was shown that some seeds buried in the soil can survive for long periods. Land laid down to grass for ten years and undisturbed the whole time still contained many viable seeds of weeds of arable crops at all levels down to twelve inches at least; grassland thirty years old still contained a number, and sixty years old a few, but in grassland 200 years old there were none. The results compared favourably with those of the British Association Committee of the mid-nineteenth century, and show that grassland soil is at least as good a conserver of seeds as the ordinary museum cabinet.

While Rothamsted was the chief centre for dealing with fertilizers and soils the Cambridge School of Agriculture dealt with the many serious problems arising from the loss of grassland on the farms. Many farmers had relied almost exclusively on grass and purchased foods for their animals and were at a loss when the ploughing-up order was served on them. A list was issued monthly of the green crops that could be grown to replace the grass, and also pointing out economies that could be effected with the purchased foods to make them go further.

The Food Production Campaign served its purpose well. In spite of difficulties caused by shortage of fertilizers and other materials and the use of much unskilled albeit willing labour, by 1918 output of wheat, potatoes and oats (required for army horses) was 50 per cent above the 1909–13 average: wheat increased from 7 million to 11. 6 million quarters,[1] oats from 21·6 million to 31·5 million quarters and potatoes from 6·5 million to 9·2 million tons. But production of milk fell from 1,900 million to 1,500 million gals, and that of beef and mutton from 1 million to 0·83 million tons. The total calorie output from our own soil for the period 1909–13 had averaged 16·8

[1] The weights are not given but average weights about that period for one million quarters were:—

Wheat	Barley	Oats	
223	200	150	thousand tons

million million per annum: in 1918 it was estimated to be nearly twenty-five per cent higher. The plan for feeding the people of the United Kingdom had been carried out quietly, efficiently and economically and there had been no hunger. It was an epic that deserves to be remembered.[1]

On November 11, 1918, the fighting ceased and shortly thereafter agricultural experts began to work on a peace programme. 'The war to end war', as it was called, was won, and Britain was now to be made a 'Land fit for heroes to dwell in' to quote another phrase of the time. Hall, always socialistically inclined, had worked out a plan for the complete reorganization of the countryside of Britain: the whole of the agricultural land was to be taken over by the Government and laid out afresh in large farms where the best modern methods and appliances would ensure the best results. It was published in 1916[2] but ignored. He took this philosophically enough: he did not lose faith in his scheme, but 'at the back of my mind', he wrote to his son, 'there is a sneaking fear that human affairs do not move on planned lines but by irrational and unconscious growth'—one of his many sound *obiter dicta*. Nevertheless something had to be done. The anxieties of the closing months of the war had greatly disturbed the nation's equanimity about food supplies. No longer did one hear the proud boast 'We can always import all the food we want'. It was realized that we must grow a sizeable proportion of it here, within our own shores. The position of agriculture had changed from a pleasant occupation of little consequence to an industry of vital importance to the nation. Similarly agricultural science rose in importance.

Prothero, the President of the Board of Agriculture, had great faith in Hall and invited him to become Secretary to the Board of Agriculture which he did. Middleton took his place on the Development Commission and remained there from 1919 till he retired in 1941. From 1931 till his death in 1943 he devoted much time to the Agricultural Research Council and in 1939 became its chairman in place of Lord Cavendish. He

[1] The remarkable story of the campaign is modestly told by T. H. Middleton in *Food Production in War*, Oxford, 1923 (Carnegie Endowment Series).

[2] *Agriculture after the War*, John Murray, May 1916. He developed the scheme more fully in *Reconstruction and the Land*, Macmillan, 1941.

remained always the same: quiet, extremely efficient, deeply interested in agricultural science: he did much to help the development of the Scottish Research Institutes which had been impeded by the war. He was always accessible, and friendly and very helpful to scientific workers. These and other services were recognized in 1936 when the fellowship of the Royal Society was conferred upon him. The affectionate esteem in which he was held by the many he had helped found expression in the establishment after his death of a Middleton Trust which arranges for a Memorial Lecture to be given each alternate year. He was the first modern agricultural improver to be so honoured and for many years he remained the only one.

The move was good for Middleton but disastrous for Hall, who was quite unsuited for the Civil Service, and the years he spent in it were among the unhappiest of his life, aggravated by the death in the war of the elder of his two bright and promising sons and the severe wounding of the younger which led to the death of his wife. But he struggled on.

Soon after the war—in 1919—a Royal Commission was appointed to advise in regard to increased home production of food. It recommended the permanent adoption of the principle of guaranteed prices for wheat and oats[1] and this was embodied in the Corn Production Act of 1920. Other countries, however, were also increasing their wheat production, and sending their surpluses here with a consequent catastrophic fall in prices from 80s 10d per quarter in 1920 to 42s 2d in 1923. Before the Act was many months old it was evident that both the deficiency payment per quarter and the number of quarters would be very considerable: the total sum due to the farmers was so large that the Board of Agriculture had the Act annulled and no payments at all were made. Hall as Secretary to the Board had the unpleasant duty of explaining the position to the farmers which much impaired his popularity, already shaken by the publication of his plan for refashioning the countryside. The farmers were left to face the economic blizzard unaided; as their predecessors had had to do in the 1880's, and the same consequences ensued. Many went bankrupt, especially

---

[1] The oats were for horses which at that time were still the chief source of power for traction.

those who had tried to keep both their soils and their men in good heart; much arable land just went back to grass.

Farmers were furious with the Government at this breach of what they regarded as a solemn contract, and although the National Farmers Union was not as strong as it became later it pressed the farmers' claims for compensation. One item of special interest was that £1 million should be set aside for the extension of agricultural education and research, a request which would have been unthinkable twenty years earlier, and a great tribute both to the farmers and to the small but devoted band of agricultural scientists who, with meagre resources and often burdened with other duties, had striven to develop agricultural science in this country.

Efforts to increase production continued, however, and in 1921 the Board of Agriculture became a Ministry. A small group of enthusiasts headed by Viscount Fielding, afterwards the Earl of Denbigh, carried out a vigorous campaign for the cultivation of sugar beet which the Development Commission had already started. It was slow at first but gathered force: the crop proved very successful in the Eastern Counties and a valuable acquisition on the heavy soils where few crops did well. Farmers who learned to combine sugar beet and milk production achieved a modest degree of prosperity. Various aids were given by the Government, including from 1925 onwards a subsidy for growing sugar beet, but the fall in prices and the decay of agriculture still continued. 1927 was agriculture's worst year and the depression continued until 1932 but was greatly reduced by various government schemes for aiding agriculture and the old device of laying arable land down to grass—or leaving it to tumble down. By 1938 the arable area of England and Wales had fallen to 8·88 million acres, the lowest on record. In May of 1939 the further step was taken of giving a subsidy of £2 per acre for ploughing up grassland of seven or more years of age. None of these measures sufficed to restore agriculture completely, and four months later when the Second World War broke out it was still in a bad way, though much better than it had been.

The Agricultural Research Institutes naturally wished to help in overcoming the farmers' difficulties, but they themselves had their troubles during the immediate post-war period. Those of

Rothamsted will serve as an example. As each member of the staff had enlisted he had been assured that his post would be kept open for him, and this was done. But the salaries and wages of 1914 were of little avail in 1919, and the problem of adequate remuneration became acute. The Research Institutes obtained their grants through the Board of Agriculture but that body was not very helpful. It set up a Committee, of which the Director of Rothamsted was Chairman, to draw up a suitable salary scale; this was done on lines similar to those of the Carpenter scale adopted by various Government departments. But the Board was an inordinate time in taking action: it was said (though I accept no responsibility for the statement) that the scheme rested on one official's desk for twelve months before being passed on; meanwhile, discontent was growing in the Institutes, fostered also by the widely prevalent feeling of unrest in other occupations. Ultimately, however, a greatly improved salary scale was drawn up and linked with the Federated Universities Superannuation Scheme: this though somewhat inflexible overcame the immediate difficulties and enabled the Institute to attract a body of scientific workers of the calibre they needed.

There was another problem: not indeed a legal obligation but a moral one. As the men had gone their places were taken by women each of whom knew which man she was replacing, and she was clearly informed that if and when he returned her engagement would cease. But they gave such splendid service and had acquired such skill in dealing with our problems that it would have been a shocking waste of good human material to let them go, and it would have been unpardonable to turn them out into the seething mass of those seeking employment with the scales against them and in favour of any demobilized soldier that was applying. So the Director had to obtain extra funds in order that any of the women could remain if they wished.

Then arose the question of management of the Institute. So long as it was small the single pyramid type of organization sufficed, the Director having sufficient knowledge of all the work to be able to exercise general supervision. But the Agricultural Research Institutes were on a larger scale; each included a variety of subjects requiring specialist investigation, and no one person could contain all the knowledge needed to direct it adequately. In that way the Institute resembled a University College, and the appropriate form of governance was of the senate type to which the council responsible for the general conduct of the Institute delegates the details. The Rothamsted Staff Council was set up on those lines: it comprised all heads of departments and elected representation of the assistant and technical staffs. It met monthly and dealt with all domestic affairs. Major financial matters, however, were left to the Director; the grants never sufficed and under the rather grandiose title of 'The Society for Extending the Rothamsted Experiments' he had the task of collecting any sums needed to balance the annual accounts.

The system worked extremely well, and was an important factor in making Rothamsted a happy place in which to work.

The Development Commission had continued its labours during much of the war: when it ended there were fourteen Research Institutes and by 1930 seven more, with three smaller installations that later were called units.

List of Agricultural Science Research Institutes 1930.
England and Wales

Rothamsted:	Soil and Plant nutrition.	Cambridge:	Animal nutrition Plant breeding.
Long Ashton:	Cider and West Country Fruits	Shinfield:	Dairy.
Aberystwyth:	Grasses and Fodder Crops.	Oxford :	Agricultural Economics
		,,	Agricultural Engineering.
East Malling:	Fruit.	London:	Agricultural† Helminthology
London, Imperial College:	Agricultural Botany	Manchester:	Agricultural Entomology*
Cheshunt:	Glasshouse crops.		
Kew:	Agricultural Mycology*		

* Small units transferred in 1934 to Rothamsted to form a new Department of Plant Pathology.
† Small unit transferred later to Rothamsted.

Scotland

Aberdeen:	Rowett Animal nutrition (1922)	Corstorphine: Plant Breeding (1921)
		Ayr: Hannah Dairy (1931)
Macaulay:	Soil (1930)	

Note. Scotland has its own Board of Agriculture administering the grants but it participates in the Development Fund.

RESEARCH AT THE CAMBRIDGE SCHOOL OF AGRICULTURE 1910–1920

By 1910 the Cambridge School of Agriculture had overcome its preliminary difficulties and teaching and research work were proceeding actively. The group of distinguished Principals, Wood, Biffen and Marshall were at the height of their powers. Biffen's work has already been described.[1] Wood who at the outset had encouraged a wide range of investigations settled down to the study of animal nutrition. He had already greatly improved feeding experiments by designing them in such a way that the magnitude of the experimental error could be assessed. He and Stratton had shown in 1910 that the probable error of using one bullock in a feeding trial was about fourteen per cent of its live weight increase, but that this could be reduced to ten per cent by raising the number of experimental animals to twenty-nine. Pigs were less variable in live weight increase: the probable error of one animal in a feeding trial was ten per cent, and a table was worked out giving the number of pigs that would be needed to ensure that a given difference in an experiment was not due to normal variations.[2] Later in association with the well-known statistician Udney Yule a distinction was made between the starch equivalent needed for maintenance and that needed for production, and the latter was shown to follow the law of diminishing returns in that its utilization diminished as the period of fattening lengthened. Another line of investigation started by Wood was to determine the nutritive value of the various common foods. Digestibility cages and harness for sheep were constructed and tested by E. T. Halnan and valuable results

[1] See p. 208.
[2] G. W. Robinson and E. T. Halnan, *J. Agric. Sci.*, Vol. 5, p. 48, 1913.

might have been expected but unfortunately the 1914 war broke out and put a stop to the work.

Wood's versatility naturally attracted him to the Mendelian investigations carried out by Bateson, Biffen and others at Cambridge, and he proceeded to try whether Mendel's laws held for animals also. There was no room for the experiment on the small University farm at Impington, so it was done on Wood's own farm in Norfolk. He crossed the polled black-faced Suffolk sheep with the horned white-faced Dorset breed and found that the recombination of black horned and white polled occurred in the F_2 generation. Later when the University Farm moved out to Gravel Hill on the Huntingdon Road more space was available and experiments were made to see if the laws also held for the inheritance of the commercial characters, quality of wool and mutton. The difficulty then arose of finding proper objective tests for these properties. A research student, P. G. Bailey, was set to study wool quality in conjunction with Professor Barker, of the Textiles Department of Leeds University, and John Hammond studied meat quality in conjunction with Appleton of the Department of Anatomy at Cambridge. All was going well, and then as Hammond put it: 'the experiment and all the work connected with it was shattered by the onset of the 1914 war, during which Bailey was killed and the flock had to be slaughtered'. Later there was some salvage of the results already obtained: K. J. J. Mackenzie and F. H. A. Marshall collected some relating to the inheritance of mutton qualities,[1] and F. L. Engledow gathered others dealing with factors affecting wool quality.[2] Both collections formed the basis of much useful work after the war. Wood had also studied Emil Fischer's magnificent investigations on proteins, and had appointed a promising junior, F. W. Foreman, to study the proteins of wheat so as to see what if any light could thereby be thrown on the difficult problems of quality.

Meanwhile two important new subjects had been opened up. Gowland Hopkins at Cambridge had discovered the vitamins, substances essential to nutrition but previously overlooked because the quantities needed are very small; and Kellner, following the example of Lavoisier and Laplace, was using a greatly improved calorimeter for studying energy changes

[1] *Trans. High, Agric. Soc.*, 29, 37, 1917.   [2] *J. Agric. Sci.*, 6, 349, 1914.

taking place in the animal body: he described his work in his book *Grundzüge der Fütterungslehre* which had recently been well translated by William Goodwin of Wye. It speaks well for Wood's perspicacity that he recognized at once the great importance of these two new subjects and he made full use of them in his further investigations. Wood was fortunate enough to secure the help of A. V. Hill in constructing a calorimeter in which to study the energy exchanges of farm animals. Halnan thinks that he was led to this subject by an interesting observation that certainly intrigued him very much. Using a specially designed thermopile he showed that 'good do-ers' among fattening bullocks invariably have a lower skin temperature than 'poor do-ers'—the criterion of 'good do-ing' being ability to gain two pounds weight daily. Good progress was made with the calorimeter but the outbreak of war stopped further activity till peace came.

Marshall's work started later (1908) and was on animal reproduction. It began at a time when the close correlation often existing between remote parts of the body had been satisfactorily attributed to chemical substances; hormones—'messengers'—transmitted from one part of the body to the other and starting off the change. One of his early investigations was on fatness as a cause of sterility. Marshall found that the ovaries of fat cows and heifers often contained in their interstitial tissue large quantities of a bright orange-coloured lipochrome. An abnormally low condition, however, can also be detrimental to fertility, as in the case of cattle wintered in the open air, or cows that have suckled a large calf or more than one calf. An intermediate condition was found to be best.

The functions of the male organs including testicles and accessory glands were investigated and also the male reproductive cycle: for these experiments the hedgehog was found very suitable.

Detailed investigations on crop husbandry became possible when the School of Agriculture obtained its own farm. The experimental programme included three groups of enquiries: (1) the effects of farmyard manure and fertilizers in rotations of crops; (2) seeds mixtures for temporary leys, (3) manuring experiments on permanent and rotation grass: questions of technical rather than scientific interest.

THE JOURNAL OF AGRICULTURAL SCIENCE

Now that research was proceeding actively at Rothamsted and at Cambridge and was beginning elsewhere the problem of publication became important. Hitherto the papers had to be scattered over a number of Journals but this was very inconvenient. Hall, Wood, Biffen and Middleton decided to start the *Journal of Agricultural Science* and the Cambridge University Press undertook its publication. The first issue was in January 1905, and the first volume which was in four parts took two years to complete. It was produced in accordance with the high standards of those spacious days: beautiful paper, large type, ample margins, no double columns. The contents were worthy of the presentation. The first paper was Biffen's on Mendel's laws of inheritance and wheat breeding already described; later came two by Wood and Berry, the first on soil analysis as a guide to the manurial treatment of poor pasture, and the second on the variation of composition of mangolds. The second volume, which also needed two years for completion, contained more of the papers on wheat. The Journal has served an extremely useful purpose: for some forty years it published almost all the chief papers on agricultural science in Great Britain excepting a few that appeared in the *Transactions* or *Proceedings of the Royal Society*. In recent years, the specialist journals have taken an increasing number of papers, but those of more general interest still appear here.

THE AGRICULTURAL RESEARCH COUNCIL

In the early days of agricultural science in Great Britain it was so simple in its broad outlines that a single individual could obtain a good general grasp of the whole of the work going on at the research institutes. Both Hall and Middleton could advise the Development Commission on the merits of the work which it was financing. But as the various subjects developed and became more complex it was increasingly difficult for one man to express any useful opinion on the value of the work the various institutes were doing, or to decide on the merits of their applications for increased grants. So in June 1931 the Agricultural Research Council was established with the purpose of advising the Development Commission and the Agricultural Departments on their research programmes and advisory services on which some £390,000 of public money was being spent annually. Its wider functions were to review, co-ordinate and facilitate all agricultural research in progress, to promote new investigations when needed and to insure that manpower and resources were used to the best advantage. It did not attempt central direction of research, but it could exert considerable moral and financial suasion.

The Council consisted at first of ten members, six of whom were to be appointed after consultation with the President of the Royal Society 'on account of the qualifications in one or other of the basic sciences underlying agriculture' and four 'on account of their general experience of and interest in agriculture'. Later the total number was raised to fifteen, not less than ten being appointed in consultation with the President of the Royal Society.

It was, and is, the responsibility of the Ministry of Agriculture and the Department of Agriculture for Scotland to formulate the problems of the agricultural industry requiring research and to assess their importance. To assist them in this task, each of the two Agricultural Departments set up an Agricultural Improvement Council. The Improvement Councils had the dual function of advising the Agricultural Research Council on the problems requiring investigation and of advising departments on the best means of translating the results of research into farming practice.

Financial provision was made for some expansion of the research effort during the pre-war years, and in addition to making grants for special research projects in universities, the Council was able in 1937 to establish at Compton a field station, mainly for research on animal diseases requiring facilities on a scale not available elsewhere. The Council also made a beginning with its system of research units attached to universities. The war intervened, however, before the plans of the Council could take full effect. Towards the end of the war arrangements were made by the Agricultural Research Council, in conjunction with the Ministry of Agriculture and the Department of Agriculture for Scotland, through their respective Agricultural Improvement Councils, for a comprehensive review to be made by a number of survey groups of the adequacy of the various activities that together provided the agricultural research service of Great Britain[1]. These surveys revealed a number of gaps in the research effort and the recommendations for remedying these constituted a ten-year post-war programme of development which it was the responsibility of the Agricultural Research Council to implement. The most serious defects revealed by the survey were in animal research and the steps to remedy this included the setting up in the immediate post-war years of several new research institutes under the Agricultural Research Council. The Council also recognized that provision must be made for expansion of staff, and to this end scholarships were awarded to promising young graduates who wished to specialize in some branch of agricultural science.

[1] Accounts of the various Government organizations dealing with agricultural research in this period are given in a White Paper *Scientific Research and Development*, Cmd. 6514, 1944, and in *The Organisation of Agricultural Research in Great Britain* by Sir William Slater in *Jour. Science of Food and Agric.*, 1951, No. 8, pp. 337–341.

CHAPTER X

ROTHAMSTED

1919 – 1943

Normal research work began in the laboratories in 1919 when demobilization had liberated the men. Keen was the only scientific worker that returned: Lewin and Martin, our protozoologists were both killed, a new staff had to be formed. But the conditions differed greatly from those of pre-war days. The need for a much fuller development of agricultural science was widely recognized. Government grants were increased and posts were gradually made more attractive. An important change was made at Rothamsted. Research on plant pathology had hitherto been divided between Kew and Manchester University: mycology at Kew done by W. B. Brierley, and entomology at Manchester by A. D. Imms, each with one assistant. It was decided that the two should be combined and transferred to Rothamsted. A new block of laboratories was to be built for them when the rush of re-building was ended, but meanwhile they would be accommodated in existing laboratories. The advantage of having these two important subjects represented at Rothamsted outweighed the discomfort, and the staffs concerned made the arrangement work.

One of the first major problems of policy was the supply of junior scientific staff. The official provision for a department was one Grade I person, one Grade II, and two Grade III, thus providing one junior for each senior. We soon found that this was insufficient: we needed more of the scholarship type of man, well versed in one of the sciences that concerned us. Not being directly associated with any university, and forbidden by our Trust Deed from taking students, we had less opportunity for choice than we liked. I therefore made it my duty to accept whenever convenient invitations to address student scientific

K

societies and similar bodies, in order to describe the work don
at Rothamsted, its great scientific interest and growing socia
importance. I felt bound to add that there was little money t
be had, and those seeking wealth should turn elsewhere. Thi
of course put off the careerists, but we did not want them i
any case. At the same time I arranged with the University o
London that work done at Rothamsted and vouched for by th
head of the department could be accepted as a thesis for th
Ph.D. or the D.Sc. degree. An unusually able body of worker
gradually collected: the total number over all my time was onl
small by modern standards, but no fewer than sixteen had go
into the Royal Society by 1962, and I feel sure there are mor
to follow; thirteen, many of them different from the sixteen
got into the Honours List, three being knighted: here too I an
sure the full tale is not yet told. Of those that left us some be
came university professors, Heads of research stations, o
occupied other important administrative positions, and ye
others went into agricultural industry and prospered. W
organized a reunion at Christmastime and sent greetings t
those overseas.

When finally a sufficient biological staff was assembled
arranged for a comprehensive survey during the period 1918–2
of the soil population including bacteria, protozoa, nematodes
other small soil animals, fungi and algae. All these were know
to occur in the soil, but the controversy aroused by our soi
sterilization papers showed a widespread belief that only ver
small organisms the size of bacteria could lead an active life
larger organisms if present could exist only in dormant forms
such as cysts, and had got into the soil only by accident. W
soon found that this was wrong. Muriel Bristol found livin
algae, Brierley showed that fungi were undoubtedly active
T. Goodey showed that nematodes were also. Imms and H. M
Morris found a number of other active small animals, and D
Ward Cutler and Lettice M. Crump showed beyond doubt th
existence in the soil of an active population of protozoa feedin
on the soil bacteria. H. Sandon showed that protozoa were no
a peculiarity of the Rothamsted soil: he arranged to receiv
fresh samples from widely different parts of the world rangin
from Spitzbergen in the Arctic to Gough Island in the Antarcti
regions, and found protozoa in all of them; some species wer

o widely distributed that they could be regarded as the normal
oil fauna. He recorded his extensive observations in *The
Composition and Distribution of the Protozoan Fauna of the World*
Edinburgh, 1927).

The results of this mass attack were recorded in a Rotham-
ted monograph *The Micro-organisms of the Soil* (John Russell
nd others) published by Longmans in 1923, the first English
ook to deal with the soil population as a whole and the soil
auna in particular.[1] I should like to have brought in a chemist
o complete this mass attack but lacked the resources. The
umbers and variety of the different members of the population
ar exceeded our expectation and there appeared to be a wide
ange of interdependence of the groups, some feeding on the
ive bodies, some on the dead bodies of other organisms, some
ven on their excretions, but all helping in the general break-
lown of organic matter in the soil, one result of which is the
roduction of plant food. I spent some time trying to find ways
f controlling the population to make it more efficient for plant
roduction, but beyond partial sterilization I made little pro-
ress and gave up the attempt.

The protozoological department had been started during the
var under Lettice Crump, but could do little till expanded after
he war. It then proceeded to study the relations between the
umbers of protozoa and bacteria in the soil.

Cutler, Sandon and Lettice Crump had taken samples of a
ield soil at regular intervals and immediately counted the
umbers of bacteria and protozoa per gram of soil: in one
eries the intervals were two hours, day and night, in another
wenty-four hours. The numbers fluctuated considerably, but
sually in inverse directions: when the amoebal numbers were
igh the bacterial numbers were low and vice versa. The
umbers showed no clear connection either with temperature or
noisture conditions.[2] This was later (1936) confirmed by C. B.
Taylor for bacteria grown in plate cultures, but in the meantime
much better method of estimating the numbers by direct
ounting had been developed which gave far higher results than

[1] An earlier survey of the fauna had been made by A. E. Cameron in 1913:
Journ. Econ. Biol., 1913, Vol. 8; the first I can find. He had a later paper in
Trans. Roy. Soc. Edin., 1917.

[2] Cutler, D. W., Crump, L. M. and Sandon, H. *Phil. Trans. Roy. Soc.*, B. 1922,
211, 317-350.

the plate method, and when this was used there was no relation
with the protozoan numbers. The discrepancy was cleared up
later by B. N. Singh who showed that the amoebae were selec
tive in regard to the bacteria on which they feed; some were
taken readily, others not at all. This was an unexpected compli
cation: it showed that killing the protozoa by partial steriliza
tion would not necessarily lead to more ammonia production i
the organisms bringing this about were among those neglected
by the amoebae, and indeed experiments showed that there were
conditions in which both nitrogen fixation and ammonia pro
duction were increased by the presence of amoebae. The ex
planation suggested was that the amoebae by constantly re
ducing the numbers of bacteria kept the remaining population
at a level of increased activity. The question was left in abeyance
pending further investigation of the activities of the soil
bacteria which was too large and too complex a problem to be
undertaken on a wide scale at the time. Search revealed other
organisms feeding on bacteria: acrasieae, myxomycetes
myxobacteria (about 70,000 per gram of soil) which produce
enzymes that can 'lyse' (disintegrate and dissolve) the bacteria
and most remarkable of all, giant rhizopods some 250,000
times the size of an amoeba and present in the order of 1,000
per gram of soil. It is remarkable that bacteria survive in the
colossal numbers actually found: frequently several thousand
millions per gram of soil.

Studies of individual species of micro-organisms were for
some time confined to those decomposing naphthalene and
cellulose and those concerned in the building up and decom
posing the nitrogen compounds of the soil. The decomposition
of naphthalene is extremely interesting because it is difficul
to effect with mild agents at ordinary temperatures in the
laboratory, yet certain soil organisms bring it about relatively
easily. This is a nuisance to the agriculturist because naphtha
lene is a very effective agent against wire worms.

With the help of A. Appleyard, an able but consumptive
chemist sent to us from Leeds University, I was continuing my
investigations of the biotic conditions in the soil by making
analyses over a long period daily of the soil atmosphere of
some of the Rothamsted plots at the same time estimating the
numbers of bacteria as given by the methods then in use. (1915.)

After the war the Chemistry Department was completely re-organized and in 1920 was put under Harold James Page who had sufficiently recovered from his war wound to be able to take full charge. The department had always had to do much analytical work in connection with the field experiments, but this was done by a highly trained special staff and did not affect the research section.

Like Keen, Page came from Southend; indeed it was Keen who introduced him to us. He was born in 1890, educated at Southend High School and University College, London, then worked for periods at the Kaiser Wilhelm Institut für Chemie at Berlin and the Institut Pasteur in Paris. Before joining the forces he had been Head of the Chemical Department of the Royal Horticultural Society's establishment at Wisley. One of his first investigations at Rothamsted was on base-exchange in soils, a subject then attracting considerable interest in Europe and the U.S.A., largely through the work of Gedroiz in Russia and Hissink in Holland. He chose the Broadbalk plots, which offered a unique opportunity of studying the long-term effects of differences in the manurial treatments on the composition of the exchange-complex and the consequent effects on the reaction and other properties of the soils, also on the yields and mineral uptake of the crops grown on them. Similar studies were made of the exchange-complex in heavy soils on the N. Lincolnshire coast which had been flooded with sea water, in relation to the problems involved in their reclamation.

His chief work, however, was the study of the carbon- and nitrogen-cycles in the soil, with special reference to humus, the black humic material characteristic of the soil organic matter. This is a product of the decomposition of plant residues, straw and other cellulosic wastes applied to the soil as such or in the litter used in making farmyard manure. Page and his co-workers showed that lignin was the only plant constituent that produced humic matter; the other non-nitrogenous constituents,—cellulose, hemicelluloses, pentosans, etc.—left no black humic residue on decomposition. This brought the origin of soil humus into line with that of peat and coal which according to Fischer and Schrader had originated from lignin.

The relations were studied of the lignin with the nitrogenou‹ constituents of plant materials and bulky organic manures farmyard manure, compost, etc. These consist mainly of pro‹ teins and their breakdown products in the soil or manure heaɟ produced by fungi and bacteria. But for the presence of residua‹ lignin, these important compounds would all be rapidly los‹ from the soil, being taken up by roots of growing crops, o‹ leached into the subsoil or beyond, or even under some con‹ ditions, by evolution of gaseous nitrogen.

It was known that the soil humus contained nitrogen s‹ firmly held that it could long remain unchanged in the soil Evidence was obtained that this humic nitrogen consisted o‹ protein so firmly combined with lignin that it was release‹ and made vulnerable to proteoclastic agents only when an‹ to the extent that the lignin itself was slowly decompose‹ by oxidation or other process. This combination of lignin an‹ protein closely resembled that between hide and tanning agents; raw untanned hide is readily decomposed in th‹ soil and in glove-making districts waste clippings ar‹ much esteemed as organic manures, while tanned leather i‹ so resistant to decay that tanned waste products are valueles‹ as manures.

The extent to which soil protein becomes bound up in humi‹ matter was found to depend on the C/N ratio of the soil organi‹ matter. If the total nitrogen content of the soil was more thaɟ about one tenth of its carbon content (i.e. the C/N ratio les‹ than 10) the nitrogen cycle was not in equilibrium: the surplu‹ nitrogen was mobile and readily lost. But a C/N ratio highe‹ than 10 indicated a surplus of carbon in incompletely decom‹ posed vegetable matter. The soil micro-organisms causing thi‹ breakdown greatly multiplied during the process, and in s‹ doing absorbed much of the available nitrogen, converting i‹ into microbial protein in their cells. When, however, th‹ surplus of carbonaceous matter was broken down, the number‹ of micro-organisms rapidly fell, the protein in the dead cell‹ was liberated and at once combined with the adjacent residua‹ lignin to form the lignin/protein complex which is humic matter The C- and N- cycles were brought into equilibrium, with ‹ C/N ratio of 10.

Page left Rothamsted in 1927 to take charge of the new

research station of Imperial Chemical Industries at Jealott's Hill, and for a time this line of work was discontinued.

Page was succeeded as head of the department by Edward Mortimer Crowther who, as a member of the Society of Friends, had been excused active military service on condition that he undertook other work of national importance. He came to Rothamsted in 1917 and helped in the food production campaign so effectively that he was given a permanent appointment after the war.

He was born at Horsforth near Leeds in 1897, began his education at an elementary school and gained scholarships first to Archbishop Holgate's School, York, then to Leeds University, where he studied chemistry gaining an honours degree in 1917. At Rothamsted he was first attached to a small group working on the possible utilization of various waste substances as manures then desperately needed, imports of potash having been cut off and those of phosphate and nitrate much reduced. At the end of the war in 1918 he was appointed chemist in the soil physics department where, as reported later, he investigated soil acidity and the water relations of soil. Rothamsted at that time was widening its activities. In the winter of 1924–5 I had been asked to go to the Sudan, then under the co-dominion of Britain and Egypt, to advise on various problems including the cultivation of the Gezira for the production of high quality long-stapled cotton, and in the winter of 1925–6 Crowther went out to start some experiments pertaining thereto. His work proved so useful that he was retained on the Sudan Advisory Scientific Committee for the rest of his life.

When he became head of the Chemical Department in 1927 his research programme was to study the chemical aspects of soil formation and of soil fertility. He extended Page's work on base exchange and the related problems of soil acidity. One of his best papers dealt with the effect of climate in determining the chemical composition of the clay. Using American data he showed that the ratio of silica to alumina fell as the rainfall increased, and rose as the temperature increased; for similar parent materials constant silica/alumina ratios were found when an increase in mean annual temperature of 1° C. was accompanied by an increase of 4 cm. in mean annual rainfall.[1] He studied also the changes in soils continuously cropped, some with wheat, others with barley, for fifty years without a break at Woburn. He showed that plots receiving no organic manure had during this time lost about one-third of their nitrogen. It fell from 0·16 to 0·10 per cent; while on the farmyard manure plots the addition of manure supplying annually about 105 lb. N per acre for thirty years and about 82 lb. per acre for twenty years—about 9 or 10 tons of manure—just sufficed to balance the losses of nitrogen from the soil.

It had always been a weakness in the Rothamsted field experiments, and indeed in many others, that they did not yield the information they could give if more chemical analyses were done. To remedy this R. G. Warren from University College, London, was appointed in 1923, and in association first with Page and after 1927 with Crowther he made increasingly wide use of soil and crop analysis, steadily improving the methods. The value of his work increased with its repetition and was high by the 1960's.

In connection with Crowther's sugar beet experiments of 1933–49 he compared the results of different methods of soil analysis with responses to phosphatic and potassic fertilizers. The results, like some others, were not published during Crowther's lifetime, but jointly with Cooke in 1962.[2] He determined the quantitative effects of residues of nitrogen, phosphate and potash left in the soil in long-term experiments with fertilizers and farmyard manure.[3] The accumulation and loss of soil potassium in long-term experiments at Rothamsted and Woburn was studied in association with A. E. Johnston,[4] and with the same co-worker accounts were given in the Rothamsted Annual Reports of the soil exhaustion experiments (1959), the Barnfield mangolds (1961), and the Park grass (1963).

The analytical work was greatly widened in the 1930's when an extension of the laboratories allowed the installation of a

---

[1] *Proc. Roy. Soc.* (B), 1930, Vol. 107, pp. 1–30. He further developed the subject but died before the results were published.

[2] *J. Agric. Sci.*, Vol. 29, p. 269.

[3] *Proc. Fertil. Soc.*, 1956, No. 37 and *Rep. Rothamst. Exp. Sta. for* 1927 (Agdell rotation).

[4] *Proc. Fertil. Soc.*, 1962, No. 72.

properly equipped spectrographic laboratory where arc and spark methods could be used and also the Lundegärdh air-acetylene method. This latter was much used for diagnosing mineral deficiencies in crops and in following the uptake of nutrients in field experiments.

A young New Zealand chemist, H. L. Richardson, joined the staff in 1926 and made some useful studies of the soils of the Rothamsted grass plots. Earthworms were very active in soils with pH values 4·7 and higher, but not lower. Moles followed them so long as the pH was 5·5 or more, but with pH's between 4·7 and 5·5 they were safe. Very little nitrate was produced in the soils where the pH fell below 6 (1938). Shortage of calcium and of phosphate limited the rate of nitrification on some of the poor pasture soils, and in any case grassland soils had most of their mineral nitrogen in the form of ammonia. The typical nitrogen content of the old arable soils was about 0·11 per cent and of old grassland soils 0·25 per cent. About twenty-five years were needed for half the gain to take place.

In 1927 a brilliant young chemist, A. G. Norman, came to Rothamsted from Birmingham University and joined the group working on composts and their decomposition in the soil (1929). He studied the decomposition of cellulose, hemicellulose and the xylan of straw, and the accompanying immobilization of nitrogen from ammonia (1931), and showed that it was effected by various fungi and actinomycetes of the penicillia, aspergillia and tricoderma families. His work threw light on the constitution of the celluloses and particularly the distinction between pure cotton cellulose and structural cellulose. He studied the effect of lignin in protecting cellulose from rotting in the making of compost and also the immobilization of nitrogen during the rotting process, and found it greater with low lignin content than with high. In 1933 a biochemical section was set up under him in the Chemistry Department, but funds were inadequate for its development, and when in 1937 he was attracted to the United States the section was closed down.

In 1937 Richardson left for a post with I.C.I. which necessitated fertilizer experiments in various under-fed countries; later he joined F.A.O. at Rome and did much work on the World Hunger Campaign.

Crowther felt, however, that the department should serve the

κ*

farming community better, and shifted the emphasis more and
more to the fertility studies. His series of field experiment.
on the manuring of sugar beet and potatoes in Great Britain
rubber in Malaya and oil palm in West Africa are models of
their kind, rich in information of interest alike to the agri
culturist, the soil scientist and the plant physiologist. He did
much work also on phosphatic fertilizers, seeking alternative:
for superphosphate, supplies of which would be gravely affected
if the threatened shortage of sulphur should become a reality.

A brilliant young chemist, J. M. Bremner, who joined the
staff in 1945, made some remarkable studies of humus. He found
that about 30 to 50 per cent of the organic nitrogen in humus i:
in the form of amino-nitrogen distributed between twenty
amino-acids and the amides asparagine and glutamine (1950
1952). He showed also that up to 10 per cent of the organic
nitrogen in the surface soil and up to 20 per cent in the subsoil i
in the form of amino sugars, especially glucoseamine and
galactoseamine (1954). He found also sulphoamino acid:
liberated by acid hydrolysis. His work aroused much interes
outside Rothamsted, and in 1959 he was attracted to the
United States and lost to British agricultural science.

Like Schofield, Crowther was a perfectionist and always un
willing to publish a paper if he thought it could be improved by
further work. A severe illness in 1954 caused his death at the
early age of fifty-seven. Much of his work was still unfinished
but his colleagues arranged that it should be completed and
published posthumously. His death was a tragedy, for he wa:
one of the clearest thinkers and most critical-minded investigators Rothamsted had ever had, at the same time modest and
self-effacing, a loyal colleague and completely reliable friend

Schofield succeeded Crowther as head of the department but
did not remain long; in 1956 he went to Oxford University a:
Reader in Soil Science. He was succeeded by George William
Cooke, who came from University College, Nottingham. He
extended Crowther's investigations on the complex phenomena
associated with the uptake of phosphate ions by the growing
plant. Incidentally he estimated that 40 per cent of the phosphate present in 1957 in the soils of the United Kingdom wa:
derived from phosphatic fertilizers and manures added since
1837. He did much on comparisons of phosphatic fertilizers, on

methods of applying fertilizer for field crops, and, later, on the effects of crop rotations on soil fertility.

When R. Warington in 1900 published his *Lectures on some of the physical properties of soil* he had to rely almost entirely on American and German data: very little information was available in regard to British soils. Lawes and Gilbert had done something about soil-water relationships in the 1870's but had not followed the matter up.[1] A Physics Department was established at Rothamsted in 1913, and Bernard Augustus Keen, of University College, London, was appointed in charge. He had done a year's post-graduate research with Professor Porter and shown marked promise. He did not wish to follow the conventional course of taking a post at the National Physical Laboratory but wanted to break new ground: so he came to Rothamsted.

He was born in 1890 and attended school at Southend-on-Sea; a remarkable science master aroused an interest in physics which determined the course of his life. His people were engaged in commerce, transport, etc. in a modest way, but they had no agricultural connections whatsoever. While he was finding his way about his new subject the First World War broke out and he joined the forces: he did not return to Rothamsted till demobilized in 1919. It was in that year that normal research work began. E. M. Crowther was transferred from the Chemistry Department but continued his work on soil acidity: its measurement, on which there remained much to be done; and its relation to the fertilizer treatment of the soil, of which little was known.

The programme comprised two major items: the study of the physical structure of the soil, including air and water relationships and other physical factors influencing plant growth; and the building up of a science of soil cultivation corresponding with the science of manuring which chemists and plant physiologists had long been developing.

A start was made with water relationships. At that time the soil water was divided into three groups: the hygroscopic water held so firmly by the soil that it was unavailable to plants; the capillary water, held to the soil by surface tension so firmly that

[1] See p. 157.

it would not drain away though the plant roots could absorb it; and free water, not held at all, and lost by drainage wherever there was a clear way out. The capillary water was regarded as of chief importance for the plant: the free water might be objectionable by excluding air which was essential for root development. The capillary water was supposed to move in the soil in much the same way as it did in perfectly clean capillary tubes, being drawn up considerable distances by 'capillary attraction' from the water table to the plant roots, and replaced as rapidly as it was absorbed unless the plant was taking it too rapidly and then the plant wilted. Theoretically there was no limit to the height to which the water could rise. These ideas were discussed by Keen in *Journ. Ag. Sci.*, 1920, Vol. 10, pp. 44–71. Instances were quoted from the Great Plains of America of capillary rises of 30–35 feet in a year[1] while a competent English soil scientist had suggested the possibility of a rise of 200 feet. Experiment showed, however, that this rise never proceeded anything like so far: in soil cylinders containing a heavy loam set up at Rothamsted the water rose no more than 3 to 4 feet and the rate of movement was exceedingly slow. It thus appeared that a free water table much below this depth would contribute nothing directly to the water supply for the crop; it was of practical significance only where as in the Fens and in parts of Holland the level of the water table can be artificially controlled and kept within a few feet of the surface.

One deduction from this capillary hypothesis proved singularly harmful. It was supposed that hoeing the soil to make a fine surface mulch would break the soil capillaries and stop the movement of moisture to the surface where it would be lost. Prairie farmers were advised by some of the experts to maintain this fine mulch during the year of fallow when they hoped to store in the soil sufficient of the year's rain and snowfall to produce high yields for the succeeding wheat crop. Unfortunately the cultivation reduced the soil to a fine dust, and when a series of dry years set in, the hot scorching winds easily blew it away resulting in the terrible erosions of the 1930's. Rarely has an error in theory proved so harmful in agricultural practice.

Two years later (1921) W. B. Haines joined Keen and a much better picture of the capillary water was obtained by

[1] W. J. McGee, *U.S. Dept. Agric. Bur. of Soils. Bull.*, Nos. 92 and 93, 1913.

studying the pore spaces in the soil. These were not uniform like capillary tubes, but cells communicating with each other by narrow necks. These cells did not fill or empty gradually and uniformly, but at a bound, the movement being controlled by the pressure deficiency under the curved water meniscus. By a special feature of the geometry of the cells and their communicating necks the pressure deficiency for a cell to empty was higher than that at which it filled. The curve relating the moisture content of the soil with pressure deficiency as the moisture content increased therefore differed from that obtained when the moisture content decreased: there was a well-marked hysteresis loop.[1] A given pressure deficiency did not indicate a single value for moisture content: it had one value when the soil moisture was decreasing and another when it was increasing.

The department was greatly strengthened in 1928 when R. Kenworthy Schofield joined it. He was born in 1901, the son of a medical doctor, and I had first met him at Oundle School where he was studying with two of my sons. He impressed me greatly, and I decided if possible to have him at Rothamsted if his college career came up to his school promise. He did well at Trinity College, Cambridge, which he entered as a scholar in 1919 and remained till 1926, and then took a lectureship at Durham University which he held for two years as we had no funds to bring him to Rothamsted. He was one of the most brilliant thinkers we ever had. His output of published work was limited by the circumstance that he was a perfectionist, and loth to send a paper to one of the higher journals till all difficulties were clarified to his satisfaction. He communicated some of his results to the International Society of Soil Science: they are summarized by E. Walter Russell in the 9th edition of *Soil Conditions and Plant Growth*. He was interested in thermodynamics and made use of some of its concepts and methods. Whatever the subject he usually succeeded in bringing in a new idea.

Some of his best known work was on the intensity with which water is held in the soil capillaries, for which he devised an ingenious measure that he called pF. No sharp line, however, could be drawn between the so-called hygroscopic water and

[1] *Journ. Ag. Sci.*, 1927, Vol. 17, pp. 264–290; and 1930, Vol. 20, pp. 97–116.

the capillary water, nor between the capillary water and the free water; the vapour pressure of moist soil was very close to that of free water until the soil moisture content had fallen quite low.

The rate at which water drained through the soil was found to vary in the different seasons of the year; the differences were traced almost entirely to the changes in viscosity arising from the differences in temperature. The diffusion of air and water vapour into the soil was also studied: the ordinary process of diffusion accounted for the observed facts and the character of changes in atmospheric pressure sometimes assumed to pump air into and out of the soil proved negligible.

He made important studies on the electrochemistry of thin films of dilute electrolytes on charged surfaces, in particular soil water on clay. Also he demonstrated the simultaneous existence of both positive and negative changes on the clay particles: the older methods had measured only the balance of negative over positive charges. The attraction between these differently charged zones was shown to play an important part in stabilizing soil structure. The chemical groups in the soil organic matter likewise carried electrical charges, those on the carboxyl groups and hydroxyls being negative, while those on the basic groups were positive.

Meanwhile Keen was working on the other part of the programme, the search for a basis of a science of soil cultivation, but came across unexpected difficulties. A field that looked uniform and produced uniform crops would nevertheless show marked variations in dynamometer readings on ploughing. These represented some permanent property of the soil; although the absolute values depended on the conditions, the relative values remained the same from year to year.

G. W. Scott Blair joined the department in 1927 and introduced the concepts and methods of rheology, then a new science.[1] He showed that the variations in soil resistance to a cultivating implement recorded on the dynamometer chart were closely related to the variations in the shearing strength of pastes made from soil samples taken across the field. The investigations on soil cultivation had begun by trying to find out what the various operations actually did to the soil, but

[1] See p. 427.

they led to some unexpected conclusions. Only two of the processes had any important effects on the yield of crops: the preparation of a good seed bed, and the suppression of weeds, especially in the early stages of growth. Other cultivations including deep ploughing had little or no effect. The results were so contrary to expectation that they were received with some scepticism: but they were never disproved. Crumb formation in the field proved to be brought about mainly by clay particles, organic cementing matter, and the action of certain organisms. The process was studied by Edward Walter Russell, son of the Director, who joined the department in 1930 at the age of twenty-six after studying at Oundle School and Caius College, Cambridge, and specializing in soil science at the Zurich Polytechnic under Wiegner, and under Polynov in Russia. In his clay studies at Rothamsted[1] he found that strong clay crumbs could be formed only with water or a few other polar liquids; his explanation, which is still accepted, was that the clay particles are held together by bridges of orientated water molecules between the dissociated cations and the fixed positive charges on the surface of the clay particles.

Keen rendered great service to his subject by writing an admirable monograph, *The Physical Properties of the Soil*, (1931): he must be regarded as the founder of soil physics in Great Britain: he was elected a Fellow of the Royal Society in 1935. He left in 1947 to become head of the East African Agriculture and Forestry Research Organization, Kenya, and was succeeded first by Schofield and then by Howard Latimer Penman who had joined the department in 1954 and had made important studies of evaporation of water from the soil: he had shown that from a cropped soil it was largely done by transpiration from the plants; from soil carrying short grass with a water-table near the surface it was about three-quarters that from open water. Indirect evidence suggested that evaporation from a tall crop might be about the same as from short grass.[2] In extending the studies of soil—water—plant relationships he showed that the summer rainfall in the south east of England is frequently inadequate for the needs of modern higher yielding crops even after allowing for the water stored in the soil. He

---

[1] *Phil. Trans.*, 1934, Vol. 233A, 361.
[2] *Rothamsted Annual Rpt.*, 1939–45, p. 34.

devised a simple method of estimating the moisture condition of the soil and calculating its irrigation need: this was described in a bulletin issued by the Station in 1954. The lighter soil of Woburn was found to require irrigation during seven out of ten summers. Subsequent developments relating to Agricultural Meteorology and soil—water—plant relationships brought him into the Royal Society in 1962.

In the Botanical Department much quiet but useful work was done by Winifred Brenchley who directed it for 39 years, from 1906 to 1945, and must rank as one of the builders of modern agricultural botany. Her extensive and meticulous observations on the park grass plots continued during the whole period of her life at Rothamsted and were first published by the Station in 1924 as a book entitled *Manuring of Grassland for Hay*. A second issue was revised and brought up to date by Katherine Warington in 1958; they are a unique record of the effects of time, weather and manuring on the relations of the different species of herbage in a meadow undisturbed by grazing animals or by man.

Her observations on weeds in various parts of the country formed the subject of another book, *Weeds of Farmland*, 1920 (Longmans), which apart from its botanical value is very interesting for its accounts of her various journeys in the days before motorcars were available for agricultural scientists. She also joined with H. C. Long in producing *The Suppression of Weeds by Fertilizers and Chemicals* (Crosby Lockwood), published in 1946, which by 1949 had run into a third edition. Unfortunately this was prepared just before the advent of the synthetic herbicides so that it soon lost much of its interest. Winifred Brenchley also made an important investigation of the longevity of buried weed seeds. Samples of a 10 year old meadow soil were taken in inch depths down to 12 inches with an iron tool 6×6 inches in area; they contained up to 457 viable arable weed seeds throughout the whole depth of sampling of which 26 were 12 inches down, while the soil of a meadow 32 years old contained only 74 of which three were in the layer 12 inches down. A soil always in arable cultivation, however, contained just on 800 weed seeds throughout the depth of the whole sample, on which nearly 400 lay in the third, fourth and fifth inches. A meadow 58 years old contained only 30 weed seeds, 28 of which were in the top five inches, only two in the 7 inches below that. The most important Rothamsted studies were made during the period 1926–29 when the weeds on Broadbalk wheatfield had become so serious that drastic action had to be taken without, however, destroying the continuity of the experiment. Sections of each plot were fallowed and clean cultivated for two years and four years respectively. Soil samples were taken before, during and after the fallow and the weed seeds allowed to germinate. They showed considerable differences in length of dormancy of the two chief weeds, alopecurus and papaver, the alopecurus seed had practically no dormancy period and was rapidly eliminated by the fallow, while the papaver seed had a long dormancy period and was reduced much more slowly. Some seeds including polygonum and bartsia germinated only in spring; others, including alopecurus, germinated in autumn.

Very small quantities of poisonous salts did not stimulate plants grown in nutrient solution, but provided many interesting observations which were recorded in *Inorganic Plant Poisons and Stimulants* (Cambridge University Press) of which the first edition was published in 1914, and the second revised and enlarged in 1927. Katherine Warington took a very active part in all this work and became extremely expert in the manipulation of nutrient solutions, greatly improving the technique then in use.

An important achievement was the discovery in 1923 that a small quantity of boron is essential for the growth of plants. J. Davidson of the Entomological Department had been trying to make the bean crop distasteful to aphids as an alternative to spraying, and among the various compounds which he fed to the crop was borax. It had no particular deterrent effect on the aphids, but it did increase the growth of the plants. He passed the information on to the Botanical Department where it was tested thoroughly, and boron was shown to be an essential nutrient for beans, though needed in very small quantities only. Later work showed the need was general: all plants required it. The work aroused much interest and was followed by many investigations with other elements. An experiment made with Chilean nitrate of soda gave the interesting result that it was more effective than the pure nitrate used in chemical laboratories. In 1941–2 solution culture experiments were made with six of the 'impurities' found in it by spectroscopic analysis: chromium, molybdenum, strontium, titanium, vanadium and zinc: these showed that molybdenum was essential for lettuce.[1]

The main object of the classical field experiments had been to determine the effect of fertilizers on the yield of crops. Observation showed that there were also differences in the habit of growth which could be fully interpreted only by a good plant physiologist. At first it was intended to set up a Plant Physiology Department, but our relations with the Plant Physiologists of the Imperial College of Science and Technology at South Kensington were so close that they were invited to build a small laboratory adjoining ours and use a plot of land on which they could carry out experiments not possible in London. Rothamsted thus got the help of Professor V. H. Blackman, and with the aid of a good assistant could undertake detailed physiological observations of growing plants at all stages of life. The first appointed (1924) was E. J. Maskell of Cambridge, who later became Professor of Botany at Birmingham University. He was followed by W. O. James, afterwards Professor of Botany at Imperial College who, as lecturer in the Oxford Botany Department, brought small groups of his students to study some of the plots and to visit the laboratories in the long vacation. Maskell and James studied the effects of potassic fertilizers on the potato plant. Eden and Maskell studied the relationship between the growth of wheat and swedes with the physical condition of the soil as measured by the force required to pull a plough through it. A. R. Clapham (1927–8), also from Cambridge, succeeded James and studied an important problem in experimentation. The physiologist had to work on samples of the whole crop, and fortunately the Statistical Department had been making a thorough investigation of sampling procedure. Clapham devoted much time to working out a statistically sound technique for sampling for yield of wheat. Observations of growth were made periodically in conjunction with meteorological observations so that the effects of seasonal weather conditions could be worked out. The ultimate purpose was to provide a sound basis for the fore-

[1] *Ann. Rept. Biol.*, 1946, Vol. 33, pp. 249–54.

casting of yield. Work began in 1928 and was carried on at ten centres in England and Wales until the outbreak of war in 1939 brought it to an end. Other investigations included comparative studies of the growth of sugar beet and mangolds in relation to date of sowing and climatic conditions, the physiology of sugar storage in the root, the extent of utilization of stored sugar when the plant flowered during the second year of growth, and the variation of net assimilation rate and other quantities.

In the late 1920's the prime physiological subject under investigation was the form in which nitrogen was taken up by plants. It was recognized that the usual form was as nitrate, but there were some difficulties. Sulphate of ammonia and cyanamide were equally effective as sources of nitrogen, yet cyanamide depressed nitrification whilst sulphate of ammonia did not. There were problems in connection with the behaviour of phosphate in acid soils: was it all retained as on neutral soils or was some washed out? There were questions about potash; it was supposed to be beneficial in sunless seasons but harmful in sunny seasons. Was this so?

The information provided by these physiological studies of crop growth and yield made in the field proved so interesting that a permanent section was set up in 1930 under Donald J. Watson to develop them more fully. Like his predecessors, W. O. James, E. J. Maskell and A. R. Clapham he came from the Botany School at Cambridge where he had been taught by F. F. Blackman with whom he had also done three years' research on the effect of oxygen concentration on the respiration of apple fruits. The programme put before him was both broad and vague: it was to study in the field the physiology of crop growth and yield. He soon found that the ordinary field experiments designed only to measure crop yield were usually much too complicated for his purpose, and he used instead simpler field experiments designed to allow frequent repeated sampling to study the progress of growth.

He started from the obvious fact that yield is the accumulated net product of photosynthesis throughout the growth of the crop or some specific part of it, and so depends on the size of the photosynthetic system, (leaf area), its efficiency, (net assimilation rate), and the length of time during which photosynthesis can continue. Net assimilation rate could be estimated from the changes with time in total dry weight, and changes in leaf area could be determined by sampling at intervals throughout the growth period. This procedure had been developed by G. E. Briggs at Cambridge and F. G. Gregory at the Royal College of Science, but Watson was the first to apply it systematically to field crops. He found that different species differed in their net assimilation rates, cereals having smaller rates than dicotyledonous crops like sugar beet and potatoes, but variation in yield of any species with season, variety or fertilizer treatment, was mainly the result of differences in the leaf area of the crop. The best measure of this was leaf area per unit area of land, which he called the leaf area index. The various cultivation and management processes evolved by the husbandman over the centuries had for their unconscious purpose the control of this factor.

As the leaf area index increased, the growth rate of the crop increased more and more slowly to a maximum and then might decrease. This was because of mutual shading of leaves, which eventually caused the lower leaves to receive so little light that their photosynthesis did not exceed their respiration, so that they no longer contributed to dry weight gain. The leaf area index at which crop growth weight was at a maximum, i.e. the optimal leaf area index, varied between crop species because of differences in the spatial arrangement of the leaves. The efficiency of a crop as a convertor of solar energy thus depended not only on how much leaf surface it had and on the photosynthetic efficiency of the leaves, but also on the size, shape and position of the leaves which determined how much light penetrated the crop canopy. This was still being studied in the 1960's.

These field studies are a great advance on older attempts to analyse yields, which usually tried to relate them to morphological attributes such as number of ears and grain size in the case of cereals. These, however, give no insight into the physiological processes involved.

When Dr Brenchley retired in 1948 the Botany Department was reorganized and combined with the Crop Physiology Section under Dr Watson.

The most important investigations in the bacteriological

department dealt with the fixation of free atmospheric nitrogen by bacteria in the roots of clover and lucerne plants. Hutchinson had started the work soon after he came to Rothamsted and had made considerable progress, but he left in February, 1916, for a much more lucrative post with the Distillers Company, and after the war his place was taken by Henry Gerard Thornton, son of an old Northamptonshire family. He was born in 1892 and educated at Radley College and New College, Oxford, where he studied zoology. He had served with the Royal Air Force during the war and took up his post directly after demobilization in 1919. He was at once attracted to the idea of becoming a bacteriologist and studying the organism then called *Bacillus radicicola*, later renamed Rhizobium, that produces nodules on the roots of leguminous plants within which elementary nitrogen from the air is built up into organic nitrogen compounds. Hutchinson and W. F. Bewley had already before the war traced out its life cycle in laboratory media: Thornton and N. Gangulee found that the same cycle occurred in the soil.

The relations of the nodule organism to its legume host proved extremely interesting. The roots of the seedling plant were found to secrete substances that stimulated multiplication of the bacteria in the root surroundings. The bacteria in turn secreted indolylacetic acid which was in some undiscovered way concerned with the typical deformation of the root hairs, by means of which the bacteria usually entered. Only those specific to the host legume could, however, infect it. They grew along the root hairs, and on reaching the root induced the formation of the nodule and multiplied in its cells. In the presence of nitrate, however, nodule formation was reduced or inhibited. But in healthy conditions the relationship of bacteria and host plant is one of mutual benefit, the bacteria obtaining food and freedom from competition, while in return they supply the plant with essential nitrogen compounds. This symbiosis was associated with a change in the bacteria some of which became curiously swollen, the so-called 'bacteroids', whilst others remained in the rod stage. These bacteroids seemed to be incapable of multiplication but their presence was associated with nitrogen fixation. In unhealthy conditions such as lack of boron or of light, and in old nodules, the rod form of the bacteria multiplied and became parasitic, attacking and ultimately destroying the nodule tissue.

The nodule bacteria specific to most agricultural legumes in Great Britain were found to be widely distributed, but the lucerne organisms tended to be restricted to areas in which the crop had been grown. A successful method for inoculating lucerne seed with a potent strain of bacteria was developed and placed in the hands of a firm of chemists for distribution: it was quickly taken up by farmers and has since been widely practised in Great Britain. Numerous strains of clover nodule bacteria were found varying widely in nitrogen fixing ability, some fixing considerable amounts with consequent benefit to the clover crop, while others that usually produced many small nodules fixed little or none: these 'ineffective' strains were usually most prevalent in wet hill districts. Thornton and Hugh Nicol found competition between strains of nodule bacteria in the soil.

Philip Sadler Nutman who came in 1939 from the Institute of Plant Physiology, Imperial College, where he had studied botany under Professor F. G. Gregory, widened the investigation by showing that the genes in the clover plant could bring about the production of different types of nodules with a normally 'effective' strain of bacteria, in some cases producing an 'ineffective' result on the plant. He found that a normally 'effective' strain of the red clover organism could even in healthy conditions produce an 'ineffective' association, and he showed that this is the result of genetic defects in the host plant. These can interfere with the symbiosis either by upsetting the normal nodule development or specifically by preventing the formation of bacteroids.

As mentioned above, nodule bacteria before infecting the plant produce secretions which deform the root hairs, and there was evidence that this was connected with the formation of indolylacetic acid. This compound not only caused root hair deformation of sterile clover seedlings but was also toxic in high dilutions to the clover plant. In unsterile soil, however, it had little effect, being rapidly destroyed by other soil bacteria. Introduction of chlorine atoms gave ample protection and P. S. Nutman, H. G. Thornton and J. Quastel found that 2.4. dichlorophenoxyacetic acid was stable in soil and also toxic to clover and a number of other plants in fresh soil at very high dilutions, but very little toxic to wheat. Unlike indolyl-acetic acid this compound and others related to it are fairly persistent in fresh soil since, as shown by Norman Walker, relatively few soil organisms can attack them. This suggested the possibility of creating a new and very useful type of weed killer and the work was deflected to that end: it is described in Chapter XV.

Thornton much improved the plate methods of counting bacteria, but in view of the fact that no medium permits all species to grow, no plate method can give the total numbers of bacteria in the soil. He and P. H. H. Gray devised a method of making direct microscopic counts of bacteria in films of soil suspensions in water.[1] It was later improved by P. C. T. Jones and Janet Mollison who used suspensions in agar. This direct method gives far higher numbers than the plate methods: in the Rothamsted soils they are of the order of 2,000 million or more per gram. In one instance the $3 \cdot 3$ thousand million bacteria per gram were estimated to occupy $3 \cdot 3$ cubic milli-metres of space and the fungus mycelium $0 \cdot 7$ cubic millimetres.

Other work on soil bacteria and related organisms included the isolation and description of a number that decompose phenol, cresol, toluene and naphthalene and of interesting organisms that will form indigotin from indol.

Thornton retired in 1957 and P. S. Nutman succeeded him as Head of the Department.

The bacteria bringing about the vitally important production of nitrate in the soil were studied by Jane Meiklejohn. The first stage, the oxidation of ammonia to nitrite is effected by an autotrophic bacterium, *Nitrosomonas europaea*, first isolated by Winogradsky about 1890 but had been so rarely found since that many agriculturists doubted its existence. She found it, however, on the Broadbalk dunged plot in 1949 and confirmed the accuracy of Winogradsky's description. In 1950 she isolated his other organism, *Nitrobacter winogradskyi*, and sought un-successfully for organic stimulants, A $0 \cdot 02$ M solution of glucose sterilized by heat killed the organisms, but if sterilized by filtration, only delayed nitrification in mixed cultures. Both organisms needed calcium, magnesium and phosphate, but the

---

[1] *Proc. Roy. Soc.*, 1934, Vol. 115B, p. 522.

minimum requirement was very small: 0·003 mg/litre of phosphate and 0·0002 mg/litre of magnesium sufficed. Small amounts of iron (0·1 mg/litre acted as stimulant for nitrosomonas and 0·3 mg/litre for nitrobacter; large quantities—560 mg.Fe/litre—delayed oxidation both of ammonia and of nitrite. The importance of the work lies in its greater accuracy than was possible for the earlier investigators. Ecological studies were also made, and altogether the work has been a useful addition to knowledge of the organisms concerned.

The improvement in soil structure effected by soil microorganisms during the decomposition of rapidly decomposable substances was studied by R. J. Swaby. Fungi were the most effective agents, and a high correlation between improvement and length of mycelium per gram of soil was found by the Jones—Mollison method. Soil actinomycetes were less effective, gum-producing bacteria almost ineffective, and those not producing gum completely ineffective.

Bacteriophages that attack nodule bacteria were studied by Janina Kleczkowska from 1939 onwards using a new method for obtaining plaque counts with plates poured with a thick suspension of nodule bacteria in agar to which dilutions of bacteriophage were added. The lytic process and the reactivation of phage after inactivation by ultra-violet light could thus be studied quantitatively. The different ways in which polysaccharides and the enzymes chymotrypsin and ribonuclease inhibit phage multiplication were also investigated.

In 1913 the Hon. Rupert Guinness, realizing that the growing use of motor cars and tractors would reduce the production of horse manure on which dairy farmers, potato growers and market gardeners in the neighbourhood of London and other large cities were largely dependent, decided to foster experiments on the direct conversion of straw and similar organic wastes into useful manures. He therefore provided the funds for a chemist at Rothamsted who would make the necessary investigations. Eric Hannaford Richards was appointed. He was 35 years of age, son of a medical doctor. He had been educated privately and had been on Dr George McGowan's chemical staff of the Royal Commission on Sewage Disposal. He began by studying jointly with me the losses of nitrogen and organic matter during the making and storing of farmyard manure, showing how the losses occurred, and how they could be reduced.

In another investigation he studied jointly with Hutchinson the microbiological decomposition of straw. The essential conditions were found to be an adequate supply of nutrients for the organisms, particularly nitrogen which was generally deficient in the straw; not too acid a reaction; and adequate supplies of air and moisture. This was the first clear statement of the principles of compost making, and a patent was taken out in the name of the Adco Company for the large-scale exploitation of the process. It proved so successful that for some time 100,000 tons of manure a year were said to have been made by it, chiefly by private gardeners and market gardeners using garden waste in Great Britain and by planters overseas. Later, in collaboration with the bacteriological group, he studied the purification of effluents from sugar beet and milk factories which when run into rivers had been harmful to fish.

All his life Richards had suffered from a deformity, the result of an accident during babyhood, which would have crushed the spirit of a less courageous man. But he was indomitable and he let nothing stand in the way of his work. He had to renounce many of the pleasures of life but there was no repining, and he won the affection and respect of all his colleagues. He died in 1929 at the age of fifty-one.

Entomological work at Rothamsted began during the first World War to deal with two very serious problems: the swarms of house flies produced in the great horse manure heaps in army camps, and the large population of wireworms that had been building up in the pastures that now had to be converted to arable land growing wheat instead of grass. Our solution was to move the manure heaps further away from the kitchens and canteens: usually the distances were sufficiently short to make both breeding and feeding almost ideally easy. The Cambridge workers had a better scheme: a spray that was an effective deterrent. The wireworm problem was studied by A. W. Rymer Roberts, a member of the Society of Friends sent to work at Rothamsted in lieu of military service. He was an able investigator and added much to our knowledge of their life history. No practicable improvement on the current in-efficient methods of control could be found, however, and wireworms caused great loss of badly needed wheat. Reference has already been made to the work of H. M. Morris who came in 1920 and stayed till 1927 studying the insect populations of the various fields at Rothamsted: he then left to become entomologist to the Government of Cyprus. Meanwhile Imms was greatly helping the increasing body of young entomologists by writing his very useful *General Textbook of Entomology* (Methuen 1925).

Imms retired in 1931 and was succeeded by Carrington Bonsor Williams whom I had first met in Egypt in 1925, where he was entomologist to the Government but neither happy nor appreciated. I was so pleased with him and his work that I decided to get him to Rothamsted if at all possible. He was within our age group, born in October 1889 and educated at Cambridge; in addition to Egypt he had worked in Trinidad and in Tanganyika at Amani, a research station established by the Germans during their occupancy and which as a matter of national pride we had felt bound to carry on though it was neither very suitable nor convenient. He willingly agreed to come and on Imms' departure in 1931 he became head of the department and retained it for twenty-three years. He started almost immediately to investigate the movements of insects and their relations to climatic conditions. A light trap set up in one of the fields was in continuous use every night for four years and about 850,000 insects were captured. They were sorted out and the numbers studied by proper statistical methods in their relation to the meteorological data. Temperature was the main controlling factor, especially minimum night temperature. Much work was also done on the migration of insects, especially the lepidoptera. Two of them received particular attention as being serious pests. The cabbage white butterfly migrates over the greater part of Western and Central Europe and there were particularly large migrations in this country in 1940 and 1941. The silvery-moth (*Plusia gamma*) becomes at times a major pest; large migrations occurred in 1936 and were closely studied. This work involved the organization of a group of reliable and competent watchers, but Williams arranged that successfully. Evidence was found of return flights to the south in autumn of several of our immigrants which arrive here from the south in spring.

Williams showed that in Britain the numbers of Lepidoptera are so dependent on temperature and rainfall during the preceding three months that it is possible to predict them from a knowledge of these quantities.

He had a great gift for dealing with abstruse problems and finding the underlying bonds if they exist: he showed that the numbers of different species appearing in a sample collection follow a logarithmic series and that the same law describes numerical findings of many sorts in nature. He was one of the most ingenious minded men Rothamsted had ever had. He retired in 1954 but still continued his population studies.

After Morris left in 1927 little was done on the small soil animals till 1935 when W. R. S. Ladell came to Rothamsted. He had spent his working life in the tropics but on retirement took up research and did some very valuable work. Instead of using Morris's sieve method for extracting the small animals from the soil he modified Martin and Lewin's water washing method. The soil was stirred up in a strong solution of magnesium sulphate through which a fine stream of air was blown carrying the insects, which were all lighter than the solution, to the top in a froth which was shed off into a settling chamber from which they were collected. The method proved very effective and was still in use in modified form some thirty years later. It supplied rich store of soil animals for investigation. The solution was not toxic, and eggs washed out could be hatched and identified. He also extended the search for agents to destroy wireworms and eelworms in the soil.

Some remarkable population studies of soil animals were made by H. C. F. Barnes who came from Wye College and joined the Rothamsted staff in 1927. His extensive studies of gall midges, many of them jointly with James Davidson, were in their day the most exhaustive yet made; they continued for a number of years and dealt particularly with midges affecting grass seed, especially cocksfoot, foxtail, ryegrass, as well as chrysanthemums, red clover and willow. In association with J. Weil he made an intensive survey of slugs in Harpenden gardens during the years 1940–43 in the course of which they dealt with some 100,000 of them.

In 1923 the Ministry of Agriculture decided to transfer their Bee Section from the Plant Pathology Department to Rothamsted. It was only small, consisting of D. M. Morland and his assistant, W. Bolt, and we were very glad to have them with us, particularly as Imms, head of the Entomological Department, was very interested in bees. Morland was a teacher and adviser rather than a research worker; and although a number of interesting and useful observations were made, there was nothing of outstanding importance.

In 1937 Seale Hayne College decided to start a department on bees, and their programme happened to require the qualifications that Morland possessed; as it was a larger and more important position than he had at Rothamsted he was advised to transfer, which he did in 1938. He was followed in 1939 by Colin Gasking Butler of Monkton Combe School, Bath, and Queen's College, Cambridge, (1931–33). He had obtained a First Class in Part II of the Natural Science Tripos in 1935, his subjects being Zoology and Entomology and was awarded a Bachelor Scholarship. The next two years were spent in research under A. D. Imms at Cambridge, then from 1937–39 he had been Superintendent of the Cambridge University Entomological Field Station at Cambridge doing also research and teaching. Besides being able to help the bee-keepers with the difficult problems they sometimes had to meet, he proceeded to investigate the ways in which insect communities are organized, the pollination problems in crops and the mechanisms controlling behaviour in the hive. Important studies were made of the queen substance and its production in the mandibular glands of the queen; he found that its distribution through a colony of bees inhibited the workers from rearing queens and then swarming. Studies were made of the production and synthesis of this substance and of another inhibiting substance which is volatile, but production of which was not confined to the mandibular glands. In conjunction with R. K. Callow of the Medical Research Council the queen substance was analysed and found to be 9-oxodecenoic acid. This is the sex-attractant of the honey bee. Its actual discovery was made in America, but much work was done at Rothamsted to find from what distance drones are attracted by it towards the queen. He obtained evidence that actions other than queen rearing are also governed

by specific substances and that chemical control of social behaviour applies to other gregarious insects besides bees. The
work was still continuing in the 1960's.

Among the new recruits who joined us in 1919 one of the most
useful was Frederick Tattersfield. As a member of the Society
of Friends he had served in the non-combatant ambulance corps
and had been wounded but never fully recovered. He was a
Yorkshire man educated at the Wheelwright Grammar School
and Leeds University, and was older than most of the Rothamsted staff having been born in 1881, but that did not prevent
him from mixing freely with them. He was a competent organic
chemist, and with William Roach, C. T. Gimingham and other
assistants undertook the investigation of insecticides, the general
purpose being to find the relations between toxicity and the
chemical constitution and physical properties of the substance.

The first paper[1] showed that aromatic hydrocarbons and
their halides were on the whole more toxic to wireworms than the
corresponding aliphatic compounds; it also dealt with the effect
of substituting various groups in the benzene ring in modifying
the toxicity: chloropicrin was found to be highly toxic. There
was a fairly close relationship between toxicities and vapour
pressures of compounds of the same chemical type. The effects
of a wide range of chemicals on insects that attack the aerial
parts of plants were studied, and during this investigation the
high ovicidal value was discovered of 3:5 dinitro-o-cresol[2]
which subsequently came into wide use as winter wash for
fruit trees.

During this period—the 1920's—chemical manufacturers had
little confidence in the development of synthetic organic
chemicals as effective agents for pest control. Lead arsenate was
both effective and popular for this purpose, but it was liable to
cause public scares prejudicial to the sale of the fruit. Tattersfield and his colleagues therefore turned to plants as sources of
high biological activity. The dried powdered root of *Derris
elliptica* was first investigated; this is a Malayan plant used by

---

[1] F. Tattersfield and A. W. R. Roberts, *J. Agric. Sci.* 1920, Vol. 10, pp. 199–232.
[2] F. Tattersfield, C. T. Gimingham and H. M. Morris, *Ann. Appl. Biol.*, 1925,
Vol. 12, p. 218; also Tattersfield and Gimingham, *J. Agric. Sci.*, 1927, Vol. 17,
pp. 162–80.

the natives to poison the fish in the streams so that they might more readily be gathered in. It is so deadly that a small quantity of the dried and powdered root thrown into the river killed the fish, and as the dead bodies floated to the surface they were easily collected by the natives. Human beings could eat the fish with impunity; in these small quantities the derris did not affect them, nor other large animals. But it was deadly to insects. Why fishes and insects should be so susceptible and not mammals is not at all clear. Its main active principle, rotenone, was isolated and was shown to be at least as toxic to aphids as nicotine but it was harmless to mammals. *Tephrosia, Lonchocarpus* and other fish-poisoning plants were found to yield valuable insecticides the activity and chemistry of which were studied by Tattersfield, J. T. Martin, Harper and C. Potter. These were wild plants which might not readily become available in large quantities.

Tattersfield therefore turned to pyrethrum, *Chrysanthemum cinerarifolium*, the flowers of which contain potent insecticides. They can be obtained in any desired quantity since the plant is easily cultivated as a field crop, and Tattersfield in collaboration with Sir John Fryer and C. T. Gimingham of the Ministry of Agriculture's Plant Pathology Laboratories at Harpenden studied methods of growing, harvesting and drying pyrethrum flowers in order to obtain the maximum amount of the insecticidal substances. Mainly on the basis of this work, and with seed from this country, the cultivation of pyrethrum was started on the large scale by British farmers in the White Highlands of Kenya. It grew well and sold well and was quickly taken up by both British and African farmers as a very useful cash crop. In due course Kenya became, and in the early '60's still was, the chief source of the world's pyrethrum supply. In order to deal with problems that might arise, the growers set up their own research organization. Pyrethrum proved to be the quickest acting and safest insecticide available. Potter showed that films of pyrethrum in white oil effectively protected stored foods against some of their more important pests. During the period 1940–43 Tattersfield, Potter and J. T. Martin were studying and standardizing the pyrethrum-oil insecticide.

During the 1940's the possibility of using DDT against

agricultural pests was studied: hitherto its use had been confined to carriers of human diseases. This was quickly followed by the introduction of other synthetic complex organic compounds, DNC, the organo-chlorine, organo-phosphorus and other compounds, and methods were devised for using them for the control of wireworms, aphids on field beans, and the carriers of potato leaf roll virus: all, especially the aphids, causing serious losses. When Tattersfield started his work there were no quantitative methods of procedure, and with the help of his colleagues he and R. A. Fisher devised a method and the appropriate apparatus for the quantitative assessment of insecticidal action which has served as a model for later patterns.

Tattersfield rendered great service to the whole subject. Throughout he insisted that mere descriptive qualitative results were insufficient: quantitative results were required and meticulous accuracy in the work was essential. The chemists were accustomed to this, but to the biologists it was a new idea. By the additions to the knowledge of insecticides made by him and his co-workers, and by putting the subject on a quantitative basis he greatly raised its status. Before he took it up it was hardly deemed worthy of attention by a scientist of repute: when he ended his work its importance was widely recognized, and it was receiving the attention it deserved.

Tattersfield retired in 1946, and Potter was appointed head of the department; with the increased resources available after the end of the war in 1945 he was able to work on a larger scale. During his first ten years studies were made of the effects of various physical, chemical and biological factors on the toxicity of insecticides; A. H. McIntosh did useful work on the effects of particle size of suspensions, while Potter and colleagues studied the effects on the insect's susceptibility to insecticides of its stage of growth and of the species of plant on which it was feeding.

From 1950 onwards more work was done on the action of insecticides. For this purpose Potter designed a precision spraying apparatus for laboratory use which was adopted in many other countries. Definite quantities of insecticides, even very small, could thus be administered to insects and the effects observed. K. A. Lord used it to compare the effects of old and modern insecticides on insect respiration, and later with C. Potter he worked on the biochemical mechanism of poisoning by organo-phosphorus insecticides. Previous work with insects had dealt solely with inhibition of cholinesterases of the nervous system, this being assumed to be the critical reaction by analogy with mammals. Lord and Potter, however, showed that insects contained aliesterases more sensitive to inhibition than the cholinesterases present, and showed that any consideration of poisoning insects with organo-phosphorus compounds should not be restricted to any one group of esterases.

The work on natural pyrethrum was continued and extended to study the relationship between the structure and the insecticidal activity of the pyrethroids and synthetic molecules allied to them. This led M. Elliott to the synthesis of a number of very active compounds.

The most notable achievement during this period, however, was the isolation and identification of the four known insecticides contained in the pyrethrum flowers and of a fifth previously unknown. This was done in a long investigation in the 1950's by Potter and his colleagues jointly with the Tropical Products Institute.

A Mycology Department with a staff of two was started in 1918 in a single room under William Broadhurst Brierley who had been doing the work at Kew. In such cramped conditions as were then available at Rothamsted possibilities were limited, but Brierley managed to make a detailed analysis of the strains of *Botrytis cinerea*, which contributed to theories about the significance of mutation.[1] In 1924 a special block of laboratories was opened for entomology and mycology, and the staff was increased. Among those added was Mary Dilys Glynne who had come to Rothamsted as a voluntary worker during the first world war and stayed on as a member of the permanent staff till her retirement in 1962. She had been educated at the Bangor Grammar School and the North London Collegiate School where her mother had taught under Miss Buss, the distinguished pioneer of women's education. From there she proceeded to University College, Bangor, and obtained a good science degree.

[1] *Phil. Trans. Roy. Soc.*, 1920, Vol. 210B, p. 83.

She developed a flair for studying difficult plant diseases and had much success with wart disease of potatoes, *Synchytrium endobioticum*. Her investigations led to the introduction of a new method for testing the susceptibility of new varieties of potato by using the rapidly germinating summer sporangia produced on living warts to give infection in 2—3 weeks; this replaced the laborious field method which had taken a year or two.[1] Varieties hitherto regarded as absolutely immune were found to be hypersensitive, producing necrotic areas which prevented further penetration by the fungus. Attempts to kill the fungus-infected soils with chemicals proved impracticable on a large scale, although sulphur gave a considerable measure of control. (1925).

Sydney Dickinson, using his own 'isolator' studied the covered smuts of oats and barley and showed that single sporidial isolates produced mycelia with different 'genders' whose hyphae could fuse to give infective cultures (1931). Attempts were made to assess the numbers and kinds of fungi in the variously treated soils of the classical field experiments, and the role of soil algae was studied by Muriel Bristol Roach.[2]

J. Henderson Smith, a medical research worker whose lung trouble had compelled him to leave the Lister Institute in London for the purer air of Rothamsted, contributed to the theory of disinfection by his studies of spore killing by heat and by chemicals (1921, 1923). R. H. Stoughton investigated the angular leaf spot of cotton, *Bacterium malvacearum*. Using specially constructed chambers to control temperature, light and humidity, he determined the conditions for infection and showed that this tropical disease could be studied successfully in Britain and the results used to help field experiments in the Sudan (1930, 1933).

In 1932 Brierley left to become Professor of Agricultural Botany as also did Stoughton to become Professor of Horticulture, both at the University of Reading. Henderson Smith became Head of the Department. With the advent in 1933 of Geoffrey Samuel, who had been plant pathologist at the Waite Institute, Australia—where I had met him in 1928 and hoped to welcome him to Rothamsted—the work of the Department

---

[1] *Ann. Appld. Biol.*, 1925, Vol. 12, p. 34, and 1926, Vol. 13, p. 355.
[2] *Journ. Ag. Sci.*, 1927, Vol. 17, p. 563.

L

moved from some of the more academic problems to the study of soil pathogens, to cereal diseases and to the rôle of fungi in the decomposition of organic matter. Working with *Plasmodiophora brassicae*, which causes club root in crucifers, he devised the first quantitative method for determining the amount of infection in soil by counting the number of root hairs infected (1945).

I had also met in Australia Stephen Denis Garrett, and hoped he would join the Rothamsted staff. He was in his 22nd year he had been educated at Eastbourne College, Cambridge University and the Imperial College of Science, South Kensington, and worked for a time as plant pathologist on the West Indian Banana Research scheme. He came to us in 1936. Using his own neat 'tumbler' technique, he studied the nutritional requirements and the survival in soil of the fungus *Ophiobolus graminis*, which causes 'take-all' in cereals (1942). In 1944 he published *Root Disease Fungi*, the first of his two authoritative books on root infecting fungi. Three years later he transferred to Cambridge where in 1956 he published the second, *Biology of Root Infecting Fungi*, embodying the results of his 20 years' investigations of the subject.

In most of England the oat crop is immune to 'take-all' and so can safely be grown before or after wheat or barley, but Elizabeth Turner (1940) showed that a distinct strain, *Ophiobolus graminis* Sacc. var. Avenae, attacked oats in Wales; it also occurs in Scotland and parts of northern England.

While surveying the diseases of crops on the experimental plots, Mary Glynne (1936) found that eye spot disease of wheat, caused by the fungus *Cercosporella herpotrichoides*, though not previously recorded in this country, was common on Broadbalk, where it had probably been for many years, and on some of the other wheat crops at Rothamsted, causing serious loss in yield as well as increasing the tendency to lodge.[1] Later, extensive surveys (1942) showed that it was most severe where wheat or barley were taken often on the same land. Hitherto field experiments at Rothamsted had been mainly concerned with effects of chemical and physical conditions on plant growth. In 1940 a long series of field experiments was begun to measure effects of fertilizer and other treatments

[1] An important bulletin on this disease was issued by the Station in 1935.

(including in later years rotation) on eyespot, take-all and other soil-borne diseases of cereals. They showed the marked depressing effects of these diseases on yield of wheat and on its response to fertilizer and other treatments (1956).

Meanwhile, virus diseases where becoming increasingly troublesome. In 1927 the Imperial Agricultural Conference had recommended that 'funds should be provided for the more extended study of the fundamental nature of virus diseases in plants', and two years later this had been done by the old Empire Marketing Board. With these new resources Henderson Smith had begun some exploratory work on virus diseases of plants in 1928 and expanded it in 1929. I went to F. Gowland Hopkins at Cambridge to see if he could provide a virus botanist and also a biochemist: fortunately he had in his laboratories two that were entirely suitable, Frederick Charles Bawden, born in 1908, who had obtained the Diploma in Agricultural Science at Cambridge as virus botanist, and Norman Wingate Pirie as biochemist. I liked both, and decided to bring them to Rothamsted if at all possible. Unfortunately financial stringency still prevailed, and while it was not proposed to curtail the Research Institutes nor to forbid the filling of posts as they became vacant, sanction would not be given for new appointments unless absolutely essential. The virus work was deemed essential and Bawden was duly appointed in 1935. No equally strong case could be made for a biochemist, but Pirie was appointed as virus physiologist.

The Rothamsted Centenary (1943) was approaching, more laboratories were being built to celebrate the event, but no Government grant could be obtained and I had to collect the money myself, as I had to do when the Lawes' family had decided to sell the estate. Fortunately the Earl of Iveagh had generously provided funds that allowed a biochemical department to be included and the laboratories were built. Pirie was consulted about their design and it was my full intention that he should be Head of the Department. But the necessary funds were not in sight, and before long the war broke out. Some of the leaf protein work was actually started, but there could be little done and no recognition of the Department till the war was over. That was not till 1945, and meanwhile, in 1943, I had retired so that to my disappointment the official establishment of the department actually occurred in the time of my successor.

The appointment of Bawden and Pirie led to a rapid expansion of the work on virus diseases, and it soon became the major occupation of the department. Viruses at that time were generally thought to be living and essentially similar to small bacteria, but nothing was known of their nature, and little of their properties and behaviour. Kenneth Smith at Cambridge had shown that the one causing potato leaf roll was carried by an aphid, *Myzus persicae*, and this turned out to be a frequent carrier. Work in the department began with tomato aucuba mosaic virus and dealt with the formation of the characteristic intracellular inclusions and the way in which the virus moves through the infected plants. This virus is not transmitted by aphids, and the entomologist, Marion Hamilton (later Watson), who had come from Liverpool University, at first worked with a henbane mosaic virus, but later with many others to elucidate the factors affecting the spread of viruses by insects of various kinds.

From 1936 onwards increasing attention was given to the physico-chemical properties of viruses. Bawden and Pirie isolated several including the tomato bushy stunt virus and showed them all to be non-living and crystallizable nucleo-proteins containing nucleic acid of the ribose type. Different viruses were shown to differ in size and shape and to contain characteristic proportions of nucleic acid to protein.

From 1940 onwards the spread and control of virus diseases in field crops was studied, starting with potatoes which especially in eastern England suffered greatly: so much, in fact, that seed had to be imported from eastern Scotland where the aphis carrying the virus could not survive and the disease therefore could not spread. The virus diseases of lettuce, sugar beet, brassicas and leguminous crops were also studied.

Marion Hamilton first showed, with hyoscyamus, that the spread of a virus disease could be checked with insecticides, but it was only when persistent and systemic brands became available after the second world war that they could be applied to farm crops. They were then extensively used to control sugar beet yellows and potato leaf roll. They proved effective against viruses of which the insect vectors did not become infective immediately after feeding briefly on diseased plants, but much less so against those that did. They were mainly useful in preventing spread from diseased to healthy plants within a crop, but less so in preventing viruses entering crops from elsewhere.

The increased knowledge of the factors governing virus multiplication and of their distribution in infected plants had important practical results in leading to the production of virus-free plants from clonal varieties that had become wholly infected. Maintaining the plants for long periods at 36°C. freed them from many viruses, and this method was widely used to obtain nuclear stocks of plants as different as potato, strawberry and chrysanthemum. When heat treatment failed culturing the apical meristems might succeed since they were often virus-free; a notable success of this method was to bring into cultivation a virus-free line of the widely grown King Edward potato.

Not all viruses are spread by insects active above ground; soil-borne viruses were later discovered. Their ways of survival and transmission by nematodes or fungi were much studied later, but this work lay outside our period.

The introduction of new appliances facilitated further studies of viruses. W. J. Elford's new collodion membranes with more uniform pore sizes enabled estimates to be made of the diameters of the spherical types, and above all, the invention of the electron microscope made it possible to obtain photographs of an 80,000 magnification which showed the crystalline structure and the arrangement of the molecules therein. Much interesting work has continued on the viruses, which are among the most extraordinary and fascinating objects in nature.

A NEW VENTURE: THE STATISTICAL DEPARTMENT

On taking charge at Rothamsted I found great files of records which I knew I could never deal with adequately. Lawes and Gilbert had extracted much information by personal observation at the time and Hall had taken five or ten year averages to find general results; he had also compared results obtained in wet seasons with those of dry seasons. I knew that the Census authorities had methods for extracting information from great masses of data, and in 1919 after the war I applied both to

Oxford and to Cambridge Universities for a young mathematician familiar with similar methods who would be prepared to examine our data and elicit further information that we had missed. Neither could help. A member of the Committee, Dr Horace Brown, introduced to me Ronald Aylmer Fisher, a former mathematical master at one of the Public Schools who wished to change over from teaching to research work in Statistics, and I invited him to inspect our records to see if they were suitable for statistical investigation. He found that they were, and he spent 14 very fruitful years from 1919 to 1933 at Rothamsted.

He was born in 1890 at East Finchley; his father, George Fisher, was a member of a well-known firm of auctioneers in King Street, St James's, London. His schools were Stanmore Park and Harrow; he was fortunate that at each place a brilliant teacher had discovered and fostered his love of mathematics. From early days his eyesight was bad and he was forbidden to work by electric light. One of his Harrow masters, W. N. Roseveare, however, taught him in the evenings without pencil, paper or other visual means; he thus acquired unusual ability in solving mathematical problems in his head which often brought upon him the criticism of using intuition instead of strict mathematical procedure in his work. He obtained a scholarship to Caius College, Cambridge, and entered in 1909; he became a wrangler in 1912 and spent another year in studies under James Jeans and F. J. M. Stratton. He also became interested in evolution and genetics.

But Cambridge had nothing to offer him and he left in 1913. For the next two years he was unsettled; he volunteered for military service in the 1914–18 war but was rejected on account of his eyesight, and for some time he worked on a farm in Canada. From 1915 to 1919 he taught mathematics and physics at various public schools; he was constitutionally unfitted for the work and was neither happy nor successful at it: when I first saw him in 1919 he was out of a job. Before deciding anything I wrote to his tutor at Caius College whom I knew personally, asking about his mathematical ability. The answer was that he could have become a first class mathematician had he 'stuck to the ropes', but he would not. That looked like the type of man we wanted, so I invited him to join us. I had only

£200, and suggested that he should stay as long as he thought
that sum should suffice, and after studying our records he should
tell me whether they were suitable for proper statistical examination and might be expected to yield more information than
we had extracted. He reported weekly at tea at my house and
always favourably. It took me a very short time to realize that
he was more than a man of great ability: he was in fact a genius
who must be retained. So I set about obtaining the necessary
grant; he stayed with us and revolutionized many of our ways
of thinking out our research programmes and in particular our
methods of doing field experiments. It became quite usual for
new research programmes to be discussed with him before
starting work on them.

He began by studying the long sequence of yields on the
Broadbalk field on which wheat had been grown continuously
since 1843. Using a series of averages related to the temporal
order of the sequence he separated out the annual changes due
to weather conditions and experimental errors from the slow
changes due to soil deterioration, weed infestation, changes in
variety or method of cultivation. These groups were further
analyzed. The effects of rainfall were much studied in the 1930's,
the average effect of 1 inch of rain each month on the Broadbalk
wheat plots[1] and Hoos barley plots at Rothamsted were determined, and also those on the chief wheat and barley plots at
Woburn and on the Barnfield mangold plots at Rothamsted;
similarly the effects of sunshine on Rothamsted wheat yields
were studied (1926). The effects differed considerably according
to the fertilizer treatment. The Broadbalk wheat plots receiving
nitrogenous fertilizers showed a considerable loss of yield due
to rain in January, while the dunged plot and certain others
showed an even heavier loss due to rainfall in July and August.
Behind all this investigation lay the hope that it might be
possible to construct tables of the expectancy of crop yield on
which a sound system of yield insurance might be based analogous to the tables for the expectancy of human life used by life
insurance companies. So far this hope has not been realized.[2]

[1] R. A. Fisher, *Phil. Trans.*, 1924 Vol. 213B, pp. 89–122, the most important
of the series.

[2] The position in 1940 was discussed by B. A. Keen in *Quart. Journ. Roy. Met.
Soc.*, 1940. Vol. 66, pp. 156–166.

Later studies by W. G. Cochran[1] showed that some other factors not identified are concerned besides rainfall.

Another set of investigations produced results used much more widely, related to the design of field experiments. I had long been unhappy about this and felt that there had been little or no real improvement since the days of Augustus Voelcker. Reference has already been made to the earlier attempts of Wood and Hall to estimate the magnitude of the error in agricultural experiments.

Gossett ('Student') showed that the lack of precision in the estimation of a 'probable error', consequent upon the small number of observations available in agricultural experiments, necessitated modifications in the theory of errors. Fisher found that some of the procedures widely used were wholly misleading, and developed Gossett's ideas so as to give exact tests of statistical significance for many circumstances. He established principles of good design for agricultural and other experiments: adequate replication, random allocation of treatments to plots, and, where practicable, combination of several questions into one comprehensive enquiry.

His first principle was already well recognized, but the other two were entirely novel and came in for much criticism. Hitherto plots had been arranged in systematic order, with the advantage that an ingenious arrangement could catch the eye and make an excellent demonstration to farmers. By comparison Fisher's randomized designs looked untidy and were less effective as demonstrations. On the other hand they made possible a strict scientific estimation of standard errors and tests of significance.

The simplest, most flexible, and most widely used design was the Randomized Block. In it, plots were grouped in blocks with one plot of each treatment on a randomly chosen plot in each block. There might be two or any larger number of blocks, but each must have its own random arrangement of treatments. The extension to a Latin Square design required that the number of replications be equal to the number of treatments and that the plots were laid out in an equal number of rows and of columns. Each treatment appeared once in each row and once in each column, the particular arrangement being selected at random from all possibilities. These, and other more general

[1] *Journ. Agric. Sci.*, 1935, Vol. 25, pp. 510–522.

designs, permitted valid estimation of experimental error, and hence assessment of the difference between mean yields that was to be regarded as statistically significant. By 1933 these two types of design had come into general favour at home and overseas, although surprisingly they had yet to win acceptance in France, Germany and Italy.

Fisher's third principle, inclusion of several questions in one enquiry, ran counter to the general view then held that scientific investigation should proceed by asking one question at a time. It was widely held that, unless a simple question were asked, the answer could not be correctly interpreted. In rejecting this opinion, Fisher combined tests of one or more fertilizers with comparisons of cultural or other treatments in what he termed 'factorial' experiments. For example, he might test three alternative quantities of phosphatic fertilizer in all combinations with two alternative quantities of potassic; the six compound treatments could be arranged in randomized blocks of six plots each or in a 6 x 6 Latin square. He might further use each of the six fertilizer combinations with each of four varieties of a crop, now having twenty-four alternative combinations of the three factors phosphate, potash, and variety; the experiment might have two or three blocks of twenty-four plots. Even larger numbers of treatment combinations (e.g. 36, 64, or 81) could be tested simultaneously.[1] Very little true replication might be needed, and the internal or implicit replication of factors might contribute to or suffice for estimation of experimental error.

Not only does a factorial design economize by enabling effects of several factors to be tested in one experiment; it has the agricultural advantage that each question is examined in an assortment of subordinate circumstances. Thus one amount of phosphate may produce a certain increase in crop when given by itself to a particular variety, but a different increase when potassic fertilizer is also applied or when given to a different crop. Only by factorial experiments can these interactions between fertilizers and other factors be studied, and some may be of great agricultural importance. Intrinsically less interesting interactions are sometimes 'confounded between blocks' in

---

[1] The largest number of plots known to me in one factorial experiment was 270 in one of Frank Crowther's cotton trials in Egypt about this time.

L*

order to permit the use of smaller blocks and better control of soil heterogeneity.

These later types of experiment proved more difficult to organize and they did not come as widely into use as the simpler Latin squares and randomized blocks, but they proved particularly appropriate for complex investigations such as those involving residual effects of fertilizers and organic manures, or for comparing modifications of a rotation.

The same principles were applied to other types of biological investigation: plant physiology, genetics, studies of insect populations, marine biology and other subjects.

The application of these new principles to field experiments involved a considerable amount of investigation in the field ably carried out by E. M. Crowther, T. Eden and E. J. Maskell. Practicable methods were evolved and demonstrated at Rothamsted and then used from 1925 onwards by H. V. Garner in the experiments done on commercial farms in various parts of the country. So the practice of the new methods improved and agriculturists were made familiar with the idea of appending to each table of results a statement of their standard error or their degree of significance. As a rough rule in field experiments a quantity was regarded as significant if it was greater than twice the standard error, and a difference between two quantities having the same standard error was significant if it was three times the standard error. This corresponds to an odds of 20 to 1 in favour of the result. In farmers' demonstrations the statement of odds was sometimes better appreciated than statements of standard errors. 'Least significant differences' were later given. In due course the new procedure received well merited recognition from workers in other branches of science: Sir Harold Jeffreys in his Presidential Address to the Physical and Mathematical Section of the British Association in 1953 stated that, thanks to these new methods 'the standard of presentation of results in agriculture is better than in any of the so-called exact sciences'; adding also 'this is a state of affairs that physicists should cease to tolerate'. The new methods are now widely used here and elsewhere including tropical Africa.

Another line of investigations started by R. A. Fisher related to methods of sampling. It is usually impracticable in agricultural investigations to deal with the whole of the material involved: samples only can be used. The study of the method has been greatly developed by F. Yates and his colleagues and numerous surveys have been carried out which would have been impossible by the older methods.[1] The work was still proceeding in the 1960's.

In 1929 Fisher's work received well merited recognition by the Royal Society and he was elected a Fellow. He continued to develop his interest in genetics and in 1933 finally abandoned agricultural science and left Rothamsted to become Galton Professor of Eugenics at University College, London. He held this post till 1943 when he returned to Cambridge as Arthur Balfour Professor of Genetics and remained there till he retired in 1957. Two years later he visited Adelaide and liked it so much that he remained there till his death following an operation in 1962.

His first and best known book, *Statistical methods for research workers* (1925), has been widely used (13 editions and reissues: translation into six languages) in spite of its difficulty in places which some considered unnecessary. Ten years later came *The design of experiments* (1935) in which he discussed the basic principles concerned and the various complexities involved such as factorial design and confounding. Later and fuller developments are described in W. G. Cochran and G. M. Cox *Experimental Designs*.[2] The underlying principles are clearly set out by D. J. Finney in *An Introduction to Statistical Science in Agriculture* (1953, 1962,) Oliver and Boyd. Records of actual experiments are given in the Rothamsted Annual Reports: some especially interesting ones in 1938, pp. 170–191 (sugar beet) and pp. 118–137 (Rotation and residual effects).

Fisher summarized his work for agricultural science in the Rothamsted Annual Report for 1933 (pp. 43–50).[3]

[1] Set out in F. Yates, *Sampling Methods for Censuses and Surveys*, Griffin & Co. (2nd. ed. 1953, 3rd. ed. 1960). W. G. Cochran, *Sampling Techniques*, John Wiley & Sons: Chapman & Hall (1953, 1963).

[2] New York, John Wiley and Sons; London, Chapman and Hall (1950, 1957)

[3] A very good account both of the man and his work is given by F. Yates and R. Mather in *Biographical Memoirs of Fellows of the Royal Society* 1963, Vol. 9 to which I am indebted for some interesting information for which my thanks are due. I wish also to express my thanks to D. J. Finney who has given me great help in the preparation of the statistical section of this account.

Frank Yates was appointed in 1933 to succeed Fisher. He has since greatly developed the subject and widened the range of application of statistical methods so much that a large modern computer has had to be set up to do work for other stations and for advisory officers. The Department, started in 1919 with Fisher and one trained mathematician, had in 1963 Yates with twenty-three mathematicians and twenty-four assistants.

CHAPTER XI

ANIMAL AND PLANT INSTITUTES

THE interest in wheat started by Biffen was still maintained at the School of Agriculture and much chemical work was done by H. E. Woodman who had transferred to Cambridge when Crowther's group at Leeds was disbanded in 1918. He showed that the gliadin proteins of strong wheat were identical with those of weak wheat but the glutenine proteins differed in chemical structure. He concluded (1922) that the size of the loaf was determined by the diastatic capacity of the flour as indicated by Wood, but its shape was apparently associated with the physical properties of the gluten. P. Halton (1925) found strength of wheat to be associated with a glutenine of high specific rotation and weakness with low rotation.[1]

In the investigations on animal nutrition and reproduction F. W. Foreman studied the proteins of perennial rye grass and wild white clover at various stages of growth and found that in the rye grass leaf they occurred in complex association with phosphorus compounds (1928). J. W. Capstick and Wood continued their calorimeter experiments with a young pig to study its basal metabolism; combining these results with chemical analysis of the carcase at different ages they constructed data from which the daily food requirements of pigs could be calcula-

---

[1] The investigation of 'strength' and 'weakness' in wheat grain was taken over by the Research Association of British Flour Millers when its Institute was established at St. Albans in 1924 under the direction of E. A. Fisher, a Rothamsted Chemist who retired in 1939 and was succeeded by T. Moran. The subject proved very complex, involving not only chemical but physical properties: it was concluded that the strength of wheat was best measured as the ratio Modulus of elasticity/Viscosity.

ted for any given level of live weight increase (1922–26). T. Deighton continued these studies, making them more accurate by improving the calorimeter and obtaining better measures of the animal's surface area (1932). Later he made a small calorimeter suitable for poultry and with J. C. D. Hutchinson (1940) measured among other properties the energy quota for standing and squatting and the net energy of Sussex ground oats and white maize meal for fattening cockerels. Unfortunately the war put an end to all further calorimeter work.

Meanwhile, in attempting to apply laboratory results on animal nutrition to farm practice, Wood had come up against the difficulty of measuring the energy expended by the animal in walking about looking for food. He found no direct way of doing this, but with much ingenuity he devised indirect methods of evading the difficulty. He found the production requirement of fattening sheep to be $2\frac{1}{2}$ lb. of starch equivalent per lb. of live weight increase (1927). He also devised a formula R = M + GK for calculating the starch equivalent of the foods forming the main part of a ration (R) from the average live weight increase per head per week in lb. (G), the average maintenance requirement in lb. of starch equivalent (M), and the weight in lb. of starch equivalent required to make 1 lb. of live weight increase (K). Wood enjoyed devising formulae of this kind.[1]

Woodman and Arthur Amos studied the chemical changes occurring during several types of ensilage (1922–25). In 1925 Woodman began extensive studies of the nutritive value of pasture grasses as affected by various conditions of environment and management and found the conditions under which young leafy herbage could be obtained which when dried artificially yielded a cake of high protein content. A sample shown by Wood at a meeting of the Farmers' Club aroused great interest. Unfortunately it proved too costly for general use; some manufacturers included it in their compound cakes, while the drying and much of the improved pasture management were widely

[1] Wood and Capstick summarized their work on basal metabolism, maintenance and production requirements of farm stock in *Journ. Agric. Sci.*, 1928, Vol. 18, p. 486. Wood's very successful *Rations for Livestock* first appeared in 1921 and was in its fifth edition when he died in 1929. Woodman then took it over and saw it into its 14th edition (1957) which came out after his death. W. B. Mercer then took charge and brought out the fifteenth in 1960.

adopted by good farmers. Woodman also made digestibility experiments with the pig, and in view of the importance of fibre as a nutrient for farm animals he studied the mechanism of its digestion in the rumen.

John Hammond sen. organized an interesting and new type of investigation. The British housewife was becoming more fastidious about the breakfast bacon, and the factories had to supply a product that not only tasted well but looked well. There were specific requirements in regard to weight and shape of the carcase, the proportion of fat and lean and the way the fat was laid on. Hammond undertook the physiological studies and W. S. Mansfield those of the farm. Hammond studied the growth and development of the different parts and tissues of the pig's body and the effects of food on various physical characters: length of side, thickness of fat at various points, thickness of lean, proportion of fat to lean, character of fat, its softness, etc. Never before had such a mass of data relating to the pig been assembled.

In 1923 poultry were included in the programme, and E. T. Halnan was put in charge of the work. Knowledge of fowl nutrition was meagre and empirical and the purpose of this new investigation was the development of a scientific basis on which standards for the feeding and fattening of poultry could be established, and the acquisition of knowledge of the nutritional factors affecting the quality of eggs and of poultry meat. This involved analytical determination of the changes in carcase composition during the various stages of growth of a typical egg-producing breed, the White Leghorn, and of a typical meat breed, the Light Sussex. The information thus obtained about protein and energy requirements was checked by actual trial. During 1936 and 1937 Halnan carried out metabolism and digestibility studies, having overcome the difficulty that with poultry there is no separation of urine and faeces, as with larger animals. A wide range of other problems was studied including the causes of various defects in eggs. The work went on to the end of the 1940's.

Marshall continued his work on animal reproduction taking as his subject the female pig, particularly the effects of removing the ovaries (ovariotomy or spaying) to avoid the waste of time while she is excited by getting on heat when she ought to be quietly laying on fat. The uterus was generally removed as well but this was found to be unnecessary; both ovaries had to go, however, for desexing and prevention of the development of the accessory genital organs and mammary glands. This work was done in association with K. J. J. Mackenzie (1912–14). The most complete of the investigations on small animals was by John Hammond on the rabbit (1928). The changes occurring in the whole oestrous cycle were fully described and it was shown that the rabbit, like the ferret, requires the stimulus of coition or other specially applied sexual stimulus to effect the discharge of the ova from the ovarian follicles. The ovum of the rabbit can be fertilized after it has been shed for not more than four hours; spermatozoa must be present in the female tract ready to meet the ovum as it passes to the fallopian tubes or oviducts in order that fertilization may be accomplished. The spermatozoa can live in the female and be capable of fertilizing for only about thirty hours, but in the male they may survive inside the generative passages for thirty-eight days.

This was followed in 1927 by a memoir on the physiology of reproduction in the cow, dealing with the sexual organs and also the udder. Studies were also made of post-oestrous changes in the generative organs of the non-pregnant bitch.

Other investigations dealt with the effect of light and ultra-violet radiation. Ferrets do not naturally breed in midwinter, but they will do so if exposed to artificial illumination for a couple of hours or so at the end of each day so as to give the impression of spring time. Other animals, but not ruminants, react in the same way. Marshall in 1940 showed that this acceleration of the oestrous cycle varied with the degree of the intensity of the illumination. J. Hammond, Jn. and F. Bhatta-charya (1944) showed that a substance produced by the an-terior pituitary gland, and one (possibly the same) obtained from the blood serum of mares at certain stages of pregnancy will, if injected into cattle a few days before service, induce the production of twins or of triplets according to the amounts used. They also caused sheep to breed out of season and to have three crops of lambs in two years, also goats to have kids in autumn thus increasing the winter milk supply. Some re-markable effects can be produced on animals now that human beings are learning to take charge of the directing glands.

Of the investigations relating to artificial insemination the most astonishing were those leading to the transfer of a fertilized ovum from the mother to another female which can feed, incubate and deliver it without imparting any of her own properties to it. As the mother may have more than a thousand ova the possibility is indicated of a high class mother producing a very large number of high class offspring incubated without loss of quality by lower class foster mothers. This transplanting has already been tried successfully with rabbits, but the difficulties with larger animals had not been overcome by 1964. Other investigations dealt with the fertility of the male, milk secretion, and the growth of the mammary glands and the inheritance of meat qualities.

In these investigations on animal production the outstanding personality was John Hammond. He was born in 1889 at Briston, Norfolk, the son of a Norfolk farmer, one of the few modern English agricultural scientists to come from a farm. He was educated at Gresham School, Holt, and Downing College, Cambridge. In 1912 having taken his science degree he was awarded a Board of Agriculture research scholarship, but he gave this up to join the forces in 1914: he rose to be a staff captain in the 201st. Brigade. On demobilization in 1919 he was given a Board of Agriculture appointment connected with the reorganization of the milk supply, but he soon returned to Cambridge, and under Marshall's guidance began his researches on animal production which continued throughout his working life. He attracted research workers from all parts of the world and built up the strongest postgraduate school in animal husbandry of his time in Great Britain. He retired on age limit in 1954 but retained his active interest in his subject till his death in 1964.

He was best known to the farming community through the important part he played in the extension of artificial insemination. The first A.I. centre in England was set up at Cambridge in 1941: the method was quickly accepted by farmers and by the early 1960's some two million cattle were annually bred in this way in Britain. Two of his books, *The Physiology of Reproduction in the Cow* (1927), and *Growth and Development of Mutton Qualities in the Sheep* (1932), record much of his early research work, while two of the later ones, *Farm Animals*,

Their Breeding, Growth and Inheritance, 1st ed. 1940; 2nd ed. 1952, 3rd ed., 1960; and *Progress in the Physiology of Farm Animals*, 3 vols., 1954–57, covered a wider range.

He was a most modest man, quiet and unobtrusive, but greatly admired both by the farming community and his scientific colleagues. Fortunately the value of his work was recognized during his lifetime, and he received many honours from Universities and scientific Academies at home and abroad, all richly deserved. He was elected a Fellow of the Royal Society in 1933 and knighted in 1960.

In 1948 the Cambridge Institute for Research in Animal Nutrition was closed along with one or two others because, as was officially explained, they would require 'in the judgment of authority, a physical capacity and administrative responsibility exceeding what can be provided in a University'. Already, it was stated, some were in process of detaching themselves. The Staffs were absorbed or found other work. Research continued, but on an individual basis: Hammond's son, also John, followed in his father's footsteps and carried the investigations several stages further, outside our period.

THE ROWETT RESEARCH INSTITUTE

In his account of its early days Lord Boyd Orr wrote: 'The most interesting thing about the early history of the Institute is that it originated in a misunderstanding on the part of the first worker appointed.' The University of Aberdeen and the North of Scotland Agricultural College had decided jointly to carry out research on animal nutrition and in 1913 appointed E. P. Cathcart of the Institute of Physiology, Glasgow, to be in charge. He, however, decided to accept a London post and recommended instead John Boyd Orr who was then doing research under him in Glasgow. Orr was 33 years of age and had been trained as a medical doctor at Glasgow University, but had had neither training nor experience in agriculture. He was, however, offered the post and accepted it under the impression that he was to be Director of an Institute of Research on animal nutrition. He went to Aberdeen on April 1, 1914 (an ominous date), enquired the way to the Institute and was told there was no such place, only a scheme for research under the College

and the University in a wooden laboratory to be erected on a
farm a few miles away 'in the wilds of Aberdeenshire' as he
put it. He was given a copy of the scheme: it had been drawn
up mainly by James Hendrick and J. Arthur Thomson—but
did not appeal to him: its most interesting item was the analysis
of turnips to be fed to cattle. The total recurrent expenditure
including salaries and wages was not to exceed £1,500 a year,
which would have provided for one scientific worker and two
laboratory boys. The capital grant for the erection of the
laboratory was to be £5,000. He hesitated whether to give it
up and return to the well equipped laboratory and group of
research workers he had left at Glasgow, but decided to stay
on and 'push for an Institute'. He put up an alternative scheme
involving a capital sum of £50,000 and £5,000 annually for
maintenance: if his proposals were not accepted he would tender
his resignation. Meanwhile the original scheme was started,
but before it had got far the 1914–18 war broke out. Orr enlisted and did not return till 1919. He then found that nothing
had been done about setting up an Institute. He took the
matter up with T. B. Wood who, in addition to his professorship, was also Head of the Animal Nutrition Institute at
Cambridge. Wood agreed that there was a case for a second
Institute in Scotland and together they visited the Development
Commission who accepted their view and offered a capital
grant of £25,000 on condition that an equal sum was raised by
the Institute, also an annual grant of £4,000.

Then began for Orr the wearisome business of collecting
money which afflicted all directors of agricultural research in
those days, myself included: we had either to be persistent and
successful beggars, or like Williams of Shinfield, have a
wealthy patron. Orr proved to be very successful: he got some
substantial donations including £10,000 from Mr John Quiller
Rowett who later gave another £2,000 for the purchase of a
farm, and for this, which today seems a small sum, his name is
perpetuated with great distinction.

The new building was opened in 1922 with a scientific staff
of eight: within three years no fewer than sixty-two papers had
been published including those of the earlier broken period
back to 1913. Orr continued his successful fund collection. In
1923 he obtained from Mr (later Dr) Walter A. Reid the

sum of £5,000 which led to the establishment of the Reid Library; in 1925 the Duthie Experimental Stock Farm was given by John Duthie Webster to commemorate his uncle, William Duthie, a well-known shorthorn cattle breeder. In 1929 Strathcona House was set up as a hostel for overseas visitors and a social centre for the staff: it was named after Lord Strathcona who had contributed £8,000 towards the £20,000 the house was expected to cost: the only one in the country till 1952 when the beautiful old Rothamsted Manor House purchased in 1934 became available for the same purpose. In 1932 came another endowment from Dr Reid, unique among the Agricultural Research Institutes and showing the very human side of Orr's nature: an Annual Dinner for the senior staff and distinguished visitors. Dr Reid's next gift—the last recorded in the jubilee volume—was a suitable residence for the Director.

The first Annual Report of the Institute was issued in 1922 and among the investigations described was one by A. Crichton on leg weakness in growing pigs, then prevalent in north east Scotland. The usual diet had been grains, wheat offals, potatoes and turnips. Skeletal abnormalities suggested defective calcification as the cause of the trouble and a mineral supplement rich in calcium was therefore added to the ration with marked beneficial results. Addition of cod-liver oil led to further improvement which was more marked when mineral matter was deficient. Investigations with laying poultry showed that the ash components of all-vegetable rations supplied insufficient calcium for high levels of production and the addition of a mixed mineral supplement considerably increased egg production and in some cases improved the growth of young laying birds. Then followed studies of the mineral composition of grassland herbage in relation to the productive performance of the grazing animal which traced some of the leg disorders of sheep to lack of calcium.

In 1922 also work was started at the Institute on the quality of protein in feedingstuffs for non-ruminants by R. Aders Plimmer, John Crichton and others who showed the value of a protein supplement with a high lysine content for chicks reared intensively. Whey was then available in quantities and there was much searching for its profitable use. Orr and Crichton showed its value as a food for pigs, which was already known in a general way; they also suggested that it could be used as infants' food.

In his account of the history of the station given in the jubilee volume in 1963 Orr writes nothing about the research done during his 32 years of office. He had been trained as a medical doctor and his interest tended more to human than to animal nutrition. He began in 1928 with a large-scale demonstration of the nutritive value of milk for children, done to promote increased demands for milk which would have benefited the dairy industry. This was followed in 1930 by a dietary survey of about 600 of the children's homes which revealed much malnutrition and deficiency of the more expensive health foods due partly to ignorance and largely to poverty. David Lubbock, a Cambridge graduate working at the Institute, collected a team of well qualified young women and a young medical graduate who carried out under Orr intensive dietary surveys during the years 1937–39 with funds provided by the Carnegie United Kingdom Trust. They found widespread malnutrition. This attracted much interest and aroused a general feeling that something should be done; gradually a movement developed for a national food policy which later broadened out on international lines.

In 1932 Orr was elected a Fellow of the Royal Society.

During the 1939–45 war the Institute became a hostel for the Women's Land Army and the farm and energies of the staff were entirely devoted to food production. At the end of the war in 1945 Orr resigned the directorship and went to work for the United Nations; soon afterwards he was appointed the first Director General of the Food and Agriculture Organization (F.A.O.) where his activities brought him world wide fame.

His successor at the Rowett Institute was David Paton Cuthbertson. He had started his education at Kilmarnock Academy and then like Orr had taken a medical degree at Glasgow University; this was followed by a period at Leipzig University. He was now in his forty-fourth year. Like Orr he had had no training or experience in agriculture before his appointment to the Rowett Institute. He found the Institute in poor condition after the war but pulled it together. There was no further need to be greatly concerned with human nutrition although interest was never lost: in Cuthbertson's words the object was 'the advancement of our understanding of the energy and material requirements of animals of agricultural importance so as to enhance the quality and quantity of their production to meet the needs of man'. The work done is summarized in the jubilee volume, *Progress in Nutrition and Allied Sciences* to which I am indebted for much useful information.

An important series of investigations arose from the observation that while a considerable proportion of the hay or herbage on which ruminants—cattle, sheep, goats, etc.—feed consists of cellulose the animal possessed no means by which cellulose could be digested. Ruminants have, however, a complex stomach system including three sacs before the true stomach, the abomasum, is reached, and it had been shown at Cambridge that one of these, the rumen, contained a considerable microbial population which decomposed the cellulose. Little was known, however, of the process or the products. From 1945 onwards Frank Baker, P. N. Hobson and others at the Institute made a thorough investigation of the microbiology of the rumen and the chemical changes occurring there. The most important organisms were the bacteria; protozoa were also found though playing only a minor part. Much of the work was done with sheep, but as the micro-organisms isolated from sheep were very similar to those from cattle it was assumed that the chemical changes were similar also.

The cellulose and other carbohydrates were found by A. T. Phillipson to break down to acetic and other volatile fatty acids, lactic and succinic acids, carbon dioxide and methane. These two gases are excreted by the animal and the lactic and succinic acids converted by the bacteria into fatty acids: so also are the fats contained in the animal's food. The fatty acids are absorbed by the animal and become an important source of energy: this indeed, is the greatest contribution of the bacteria to the energy supply of the animal. The protein in the feeding stuffs is broken down to peptides and to amino-acids which can be deaminated to fatty acids and ammonia or re-synthesized into bacterial cells. Ammonia is either absorbed and excreted mainly as urea by the host or used for the synthesis of bacterial protein. The bacteria thus fed are carried forward to the abomasum and intestines where they are digested by the host's enzymes and duly assimilated.

In herbivores other than ruminants the digestion of cellulose is also effected by micro-organisms but in the large gut.

Corresponding studies on lipid fat production in the animal did not begin till 1951 and hence lie mainly outside our period. They fell into four groups: digestion and absorption of lipids in the ruminant; body fat composition of pigs in relation to the digestion and absorption of dietary fat and of Vitamin E; metabolism of plasma lipids in the lactating mammary gland; and the composition of the milk fat of beef cows with special reference to the development of muscular dystrophy in calves. This was mainly done by G. A. Garton, W. R. H. Duncan and A. K. Lough. Orr, Scott Robertson and others had shown (1926 onwards) that milk was a valuable supplement to cereals in chick rations, separated milk being as good as whole milk, but buttermilk and dried milk were less effective as also were fish, meat and bone meals. Various vegetable proteins gave as good growth as fish meal as long as they were supplemented by minerals, but they did not produce as good a carcase. This inferiority of vegetable to animal protein could with certain exceptions be corrected by adding methionine, an amino-acid.

Investigations were also made of the digestive secretions and the flow of food material in the sheep. The amount of water consumed by the sheep was $2 \cdot 2$ litres daily but the amount flowing from the abomasum to the duodenum was approximately 8 litres, the difference being made up of saliva and abomasal secretions. The total volume of the secretions was about 10 to 20 litres daily, about half the sheep's body water. The flow of food residues into the large intestine varied between $1 \cdot 3$ and $4 \cdot 8$ litres per 24 hours according to the food intake which had ranged from 700 to 800 grams. The salivary glands secreted large volumes of liquid: those of sheep about 10 litres daily and of cattle 98 to 190. The flow of fluid down the digestive tract is very important; sheep rapidly lost condition when it was stopped and if losses of water and electrolytes were not replaced. Much of this work was done by A. T. Phillipson (1939–1963), R. W. Ash (1957 onwards), and R. N. B. Kay (1958 onwards).

Investigations of the epithelial cells of the intestine showed more active metabolism and dynamism than in most other tissues. Their columnar form gives them a large absorbing surface, but the cells are very ephemeral and after a short life die and are replaced by new ones. Selective absorption of a variety of substances takes place in the gut rumen. Many of them are probably digested *in situ*, but absorbed macromolecular and particular matter is passed into the lymphatic drainage system. The animal absorbs little carbohydrate from its alimentary tract, but it has a remarkable power of synthesis. A short chain fatty acid, propionic acid, was known to be a precursor of carbohydrate in the dog: M. W. S. Hitchcock and Phillipson showed that this was true of the sheep also; when metabolized in presence of CO_2 it produced lactic acid and could also produce succinic acid; tentative evidence suggested that acetic and butyric acids could act in the same way.

The substances with which the biochemist has to deal in investigating problems of animal nutrition and growth are often very complex and require correspondingly complex methods of procedure. Marked improvements were effected in the 1940's by Richard L. M. Synge. He showed that N-acetylamino-acid could be separated by using counter-current liquid-liquid extraction. In collaboration with A. J. P. Martin this led to the development of partition chromatography which they applied with conspicuous success to problems relating to the composition and structure of proteins, particularly wool keratin. The new methods enabled Synge to gain considerable new knowledge about the composition and structure of the granicidins, and were applied later by him to the study of herbage constituents. So highly was this work esteemed that he and Martin were elected Fellows of the Royal Society in 1950 and given the Nobel Prize for Chemistry in 1952.

Interesting studies were made of animal behaviour by D. E. Tribe in 1948 and 1949, usually with J. G. Gordon. They showed that for Cheviot sheep on lowland pastures the working day ranged from 10 hours in February to 15 hours in June: of these about $9\frac{1}{2}$ hours were spent in grazing whatever the season, and the rest of the time their habit was to walk about 3 miles a day and, in the words of W. H. Davies, 'to stand and stare'. They lay down and ruminated mostly at night. Detailed studies were also made of the nutrition and growth of pigs and the effects of vitamins, fats, growth stimulants such as antibiotics and other substances fed to them. Among the early workers were also H. Bussett, Walter Elliot in the 1920's: later ones (1950's) included I. A. M. Lucas, G. Lodge and A. F. G. Calder.

Although the Institute has changed in many ways it still includes man among the animals it studies. Human growth and stature, energy expenditure including basal metabolic energy expenditure were studied, also energy expenditure during walking and its relation to the weight and sex of the subject, and the gradient and speed of walking. For equal weights and gradients women have the advantage over men.

As with other Institutes this account does not attempt to include all the research work done, but only enough to show the general character of the Institute's work and its contributions to the branch of agricultural science that it serves. The full account must be obtained from the Institute's Collected Papers or the admirable summary in the jubilee volume.

The National Institute of Agricultural Botany, Cambridge, is not itself mainly engaged in research but it is indispensable to the Plant Breeding and other research Institutes, and must therefore be included with them. It was founded in 1919 largely through Lawrence Weaver. He was not an agriculturist but an architect brought into the Food Production Department of the Board of Agriculture during the 1914–18 war for his clear-sightedness in seeing what wanted doing and his ability to decide how best it should be done. It was he who voiced the strong desire within the agricultural industry for more knowledge about seeds and crop varieties as a means to increased production; he knew how useful the Botanical Institutes were in the Scandinavian countries and he helped to form one here. Its objects included 'promoting the improvement of existing varieties of seeds, plants and crops in the United Kingdom and aiding the introduction and distribution of new varieties.' The idea was welcomed by Biffen who was in charge of plant breeding at Cambridge and recognized the need for an organization to take over the plant breeders' products and to ascertain which of the many potential new varieties compared favourably with established kinds and with the introductions from abroad and from private breeders. The discovery of Mendel's paper in 1900 had greatly stimulated plant breeding and new varieties were being produced more rapidly than ever before.

R. G. (later Sir George) Stapledon was largely responsible for planning the technical side of the new Institute in 1919 until he was elected to the Chair of Agricultural Botany at Aberystwyth. The Institute's first Director was Wilfrid Parker who held office from 1919 to 1937; he was followed by M. A. Bailey who, however, died after one year; in the war period 1939–45 Herbert Hunter, Director of the Cambridge University Plant Breeding Station, became also Acting Director of the Institute, but he gave it up at the end of the War, and in 1945 Frank Horne, Head of the Botany Department at the Seale-Hayne Agricultural College, was appointed to the post and was still holding it with distinguished success in 1964. The potato crop was the first to receive attention. Since 1913 John Snell, a native of Cornwall, had been trying to find varieties of potatoes acceptable to the market and resistant or immune to wart disease which had not long before entered this country, apparently by way of Liverpool. Growers in South Lincolnshire, Lancashire and Glamorgan suffered seriously when these areas were scheduled as wart infested, and the growth of Up-to-date, Epicure and other susceptible but popular varieties was forbidden. Numbers of potato varieties claimed as new and resistant to the disease were neither new nor resistant: one of them, Up-to-date, was said to have been sold under 200 different names; no less than 75 per cent of the potatoes first submitted to the Institute were in this class. The appointment of the Potato Synonym Committee in 1920 soon put an end to this practice. When the Institute commenced its trials the practice of renaming old varieties ceased.

New varieties of crops submitted to the Institute for approval were, and still are, subject to a series of stringent tests. The seeds are sown in preliminary trials and the emerging plants carefully watched to detect any weaknesses in growth, liability to disease, etc. If they prove superior to existing varieties they are passed to a number of the Regional Trial Stations of which there were nine in 1946 and fourteen in 1961. The tests and trials usually take three years. These regional stations are distributed throughout the country so that the plants are tested over a wide range of climatic and soil conditions. The most important property is the yield of material suitable for the market, but field characters such as suitability for mechanical harvesting and resistance to the main diseases take a very high place. If the Institute is satisfied that the new variety is a sufficient improvement on existing sorts it is included in the recommended lists and in the Institute's descriptive farmers' leaflets. Improvements in yield do not necessarily constitute all the improvements. In certain regions 7 to 10 days earlier ripening of barley may be well worth achieving even if there is a slight decrease in yield.

Around 1960 some 60 new varieties of cereals were tested each year, but only about one in ten fulfilled a new need or gave better performance. Help in regard to wheat intended for baking is obtained from the Cereals Research Institute of the Millers Association at St Albans; some of the English wheat, however, is used for biscuit making and household flour as well as for bread, while a large proportion goes into poultry or other animal foods. Barley for brewing is discussed with the Brewing Industry Research Foundation, Nutfield, Surrey, who conduct special malting tests on varieties taken from the Institute's trials.

The need for the Institute's work was well shown in 1948 when it was found that at least one quarter of our acreage of wheat was sown with varieties known to be inferior. The rusts of cereal crops cause difficulties in testing because there are distinct biological races. Thus it is necessary for the Institute to distinguish between the sister selections from the same cross Nord Desprez which proved to be susceptible to certain races of yellow rust, and Capelle-Desprez which proved to be more resistant. In the rusts and other diseases such as cereal mildew new and potent biological races are liable to appear and to change the classification of a variety from 'resistant' to 'susceptible'.

The value of the Institute's variety testing work is shown clearly from the fact that five replicated yield trials of spring oats at the Institute's stations gave more useful and significant results than 103 County trials using single plot comparisons on ordinary farms.

The Cambridge Plant Breeding Institute submits all its new

varieties to the N.I.A.B. at least three years before releasing them to the seed merchants, and then releases only those recommended by the Institute. Similar arrangements are made by the Welsh Plant Breeding Station and the National Vegetable Research Station.

Another line of work is the technical inspection of crops grown for seed. This is done during their growth to ensure that 'rogues' are eliminated. During the early stages of multiplication the utmost care has to be taken to avoid contamination with the pollen or seed of other varieties. By means of the advice and technical supervision offered by the Institute, seed growers are able to produce the quantities of certified and other high quality seeds needed by the industry.

Much work has been done to avoid the spread of virus diseases especially of potatoes. Some viruses are carried by aphids; these thrive in the eastern counties of England but not in those parts of Scotland, Northern Ireland and Northern England where the climate is unfavourable to them. The Institute has arranged for the production of stocks of virus tested potatoes first under greenhouse and laboratory control and later in isolated seed growing districts.

Stapledon at Aberystwyth and J. W. Gregor in Scotland had demonstrated the special value of leafy and persistent varieties of herbage. But these varieties can lose their valuable characteristics rapidly if multiplied without suitable technical supervision. The Institute has devised methods in co-operation with the Welsh Plant Breeding Station whereby they may be conserved.

There are, however, special difficulties in maintaining crop varieties and seed stocks at the optimum level of uniformity to meet agronomic and marketing needs, and the Director and his colleagues were still investigating this important matter in 1964.

The above account shows the general character of the Institute's work. It covers, however, all crops grown on a field scale, fodder crops, sugar beet, vegetables and others, accounts of which are excluded by limitations of space. From its foundation the Institute has administered the official Seed Testing Station for England and Wales and about 60,000 samples are tested annually for purity and germination. Improvements in the techniques for these and the other tests conducted by the Institute are constantly being investigated.

PLANT BREEDING. THE CAMBRIDGE INSTITUTE

Reference has already been made to Biffen's pioneering investigations in wheat breeding which led to the introduction of some greatly improved varieties, and even more important, to the formation of the Cambridge Plant Breeding Institute in 1912. During his régime the chief interest had been in wheat with the purpose of increasing winter hardiness, stiffness of straw, resistance to disease, chiefly rust, and quality of grain: hardness for millers and bakers, softness and whiteness for biscuit makers.

One of Biffen's best known colleagues was Frank Leonard Engledow (later Sir Frank). He had started his educational life as a mathematician. From boyhood he had always been interested in the wild life of the countryside, but no biology was taught in the country grammar school in Kent which he attended. A scholarship took him to University College, London, where he studied mathematics and physics and gained an Exhibition in Mathematics at St John's College, Cambridge. There he became greatly interested in genetics and their agricultural possibilities through some lectures by R. C. Punnett, and realizing that botany and other biological sciences were also Tripos subjects he forsook mathematics for them, against the strong resistance of his Tutor and went over to agriculture, obtaining a Board of Agriculture scholarship in 1913. He spent a year working with Biffen on genetics and plant breeding, but on the outbreak of the First World War in 1914 he enlisted and was sent to India and Mesopotamia. Here one of his duties was to grow wheat to feed a ravished countryside.

In 1919 the war being over Biffen offered him a post, and he returned to resume plant breeding which he continued for the next eleven years. Among other achievements he overcame a difficulty that had arisen in regard to Biffen's Yeoman; it had admirably suited the conditions common at the time of its production, but it was too long in the straw to stand up to the higher manuring that later became good farm practice. He shortened the straw by crossing with another Canadian variety,

White Fife, and produced Holdfast which was the best combination of yield, good straw and baking quality of any variety of its time. It was marketed in 1935 and was highly praised. Unfortunately it had white grain, which made it liable to sprout in the field in wet harvests, so that it failed to achieve the popularity it otherwise deserved. The excellent quality of its grain, however, made it valuable for hybridization. He produced a second wheat, Steadfast, by crossing Little Joss and Victor; it was primarily a biscuit wheat and did quite well. The demand for biscuit wheats, however, was never very strong and it had to compete with varieties of poorer quality but rather higher yield. He produced several other wheats and started on what he described as the over-ambitious idea of studying the inheritance of yield in cereals. This led to statistical studies of population density in field crops of wheat, the first of their kind in Britain; he studied also the stages of development of the wheat plant in small experimental plots.

In 1930 he was elected to the chair of agriculture which so completely occupied his time that he had to pass on to Garner, Hudson and Saunders his personal researches, covering the major problems of yield in relation to population density.

His experiences in the East had given him a wider view of agriculture than usual, recognizing not only its technical and economic aspects but also its social factors which meant considerable change in the teaching. His advice on the development of agriculture in the tropical and subtropical regions of the British Commonwealth was much sought and during the period 1927–62 he paid a number of visits to deal with the problems on the spot.

He was knighted in 1944 and retired in 1957.

Biffen retired in 1936 and was succeeded by Herbert Hunter who had for some years been working at the Institute, and prior to that had become well known for his success in Ireland in breeding barley for Messrs. Guinness and the Irish Department of Agriculture. His chief success had been Spratt Archer, a cross between an old English variety Spratt, a little of which still survived in the Fens, and Irish Archer, a strain of Archer which had originated in eastern England. It had been produced in 1908 and released in 1914. This, and Beaven's Plumage Archer, were for long the chief barleys grown for malting in England,

and for many years they were unsurpassed for quality. Unfortunately they had longer straw than some of the Scandinavian varieties, and therefore less power of standing up against wind and rain; they were also later in ripening. Hunter's most important early work at the Institute was, however, the improvement of winter oats by crossing winter and spring varieties, and he produced two varieties, Resistance and Picton. But he continued his investigations to elucidate the factors underlying yield and malting quality in barley, and his breeding work in this crop resulted in the varieties Earl and Camton.

In 1932 George Douglas Hutton Bell of Selwyn College started work at the Institute. He had come from Swansea Grammar School and the University College of North Wales, Bangor, and later became University Lecturer in Agricultural Botany. He early showed his interest in barley by producing in 1932 a classification of cultivated varieties of barley based on vegetative, developmental, and grain characters. Vernalization was a very live topic owing to the interest stirred up by the Russians in Lysenko's work. Bell confirmed Lysenko's claim that low temperature pre-treatment of the seeds of wheat, barley and oats stimulated the development of the young plants, but could find no significant gain in yield (1935 and 1936).

During the years 1933–39 much work was done on field peas and beans: important crops, but in an unsatisfactory position at that time. Some of the Institute's varieties of peas ripened a month earlier than the older sorts and also had shorter haulm, an advantage in cultivation. Engledow selected a high-yielding, late-maturing variety of Maple pea which he called Marathon Maple: it was released in 1937, and Bell produced an early ripening variety called Minerva Maple in 1951.

During the 1939–45 war the Institute was asked among other things to help in the provision of sugar beet seed. Breeding work was started later with emphasis on bolting resistance, and these investigations resulted in two varieties—Cambro (1963) and Camhilt (1964) being released to growers. Sugar beet breeding subsequently expanded to include the study of breeding for tolerance to Virus Yellows, improvement of juice quality and the exploitation of polyploidy and male sterility. Much work was done in the breeding of lucerne and sainfoin during the period, while field beans continued to occupy serious attention.

Bell's great successes, however, were still with barley of which he early produced two remarkable varieties. The first was Pioneer, a cross between Spratt Archer and Tschermak's two-rowed winter barley. It was liberated in 1943, and was the first winter barley to satisfy both farmers and maltsters; it was still the standard winter barley in 1964. In 1951 he liberated Proctor, a spring variety; it was an outstanding success, combining some of the best Scandinavian field qualities, strength of straw, early ripening and other properties with British high malting quality. At its most popular it occupied 75 per cent of the acreage of barley in England and Wales, and even in 1964 was still the most widely grown variety. It was remarkably free from Loose Smut. In 1954 came another spring variety, Provost, followed later by the spring varieties Maris Budyer and Baldric (1963) and an improved winter variety Maris Otter (1964). These and other achievements brought Bell the Gold Research Medal of the Royal Agricultural Society of England, and in 1965 election to the fellowship of the Royal Society.

Before the Research Institutes were set up the production or finding of new varieties of potatoes was done by private individuals who had the gift of recognizing a better potato when they saw it, though they could not always arrange for its multiplication. Some of the most popular of the older sorts, King Edward, Majestic and others originated in this way: nothing is known of their parentage and little of their early history. What is known is recorded in two interesting books by R. N. Salaman[1] who did so much for plant breeding and in its earlier days for the Institute that an account of him is given later.

The potato being an exotic plant, the genetic diversity of the genus *Solanum* which the breeder would need as a source of genes had to be sought overseas before more comprehensive breeding could be started. In 1938 an expedition under J. G. Hawkes and E. K. Balls was therefore sent by the Commonwealth Agricultural Bureaux to Central and South America to search for all available varieties of wild potatoes and near culti-

[1] *Potato Varieties* (1926) and *The History and Social Influence of the Potato* (1949), both Cambridge University Press.

vated relatives. They brought back over a thousand, and these, with others, were grown in special glasshouses at the Potato Genetic Station, Cambridge until 1954 when they were transferred to the John Innes Institute which still held them in 1964. In 1939 the Plant Breeding Institute took over Salaman's potatoes which he had used for the breeding of varieties resistant to Late Blight (*Phytophthora infestans*); they were mainly crosses between *Solanum demissum*, a Mexican wild potato highly resistant to this disease, and commercial varieties satisfying the housewife's demands. The work was continued at the Institute by S. Dickenson, H. W. Howard and G. P. Carson; it necessitated much cross breeding to eliminate undesirable morphological and other characters derived from the wild parent without detriment to the power of resistance. Fundamental research had also been done on certain cereal obligate parasites, including Yellow Rust (*Puccinia glumarum*), Brown Rust (*Puccinia recondita*), Powdery Mildew (*Erysiphe graminis*), and Downy Mildew of sugar beet (*Peronospora Schachtii*).

While the breeding was in progress important genetical and cytological studies were being made at the Institute to give a better understanding of what the breeder was actually doing. The purely scientific subject of cytogenetics was being developed by others elsewhere, including Kenneth Mather at Birmingham University, and Cyril Dean Darlington, first at the John Innes Institute where he was concerned mainly with horticultural plants, and later at Oxford University. At the Plant Breeding Institute A. E. Watkins was working from 1924 to 1940 on genetical and cytological problems presented by the *Triticum* family, and greatly extended our knowledge of this group, besides doing much to elucidate the evolutionary and systematic relationships of the cultivated wheats. Similar genetic, systematic and cytological work was done by H. W. Howard between 1938 and 1947 on the genera Brassica and Nasturtium. This has done much to clarify the polyploid and systematic relationships of the cultivated members of the two genera, which include swedes, cabbage, kale, mustard and watercress. Their whole breeding systems and possibilities of improvement depend on these relationships particularly with regard to chromosome numbers.

In Bell's experience the chief value of genetical and cytological

M

investigations has been to provide background illumination enabling the breeder to see more clearly what he is doing. They have also contributed important fundamental knowledge on evolution, phylogenetic relationships, taxonomy and genetic architecture in particular groups of plants thereby helping to define breeding methods and objectives. Unfortunately they do not enable him to predict the best parental combination for inter-varietal hybridization which he would most desire them to do. Breeding for disease resistance has, however, improved considerably as a result of greater knowledge of the genetical principles involved, and since the 1940's there has been considerable development of scientific method in plant breeding.

Hunter retired in 1946 and was succeeded by Bell which proved to be an entirely suitable choice. He was in his forty-first year, had known the Institute and its problems for some fourteen years, and had already shown unusual ability as a plant breeder by producing Pioneer, as already stated.

During Bell's directorship there were great developments in the Institute itself. When he took charge it was still small and a section of the School of Agriculture of Cambridge University. During his tenure of office it expanded greatly and became an independent research station with its own Governing Body reporting to the Agricultural Research Council, which gave it a much higher status.

During its earlier years the Plant Breeding Institute had been housed at the School of Agriculture with its breeding plots on the University farm. In 1948 the Agricultural Research Council, the Ministry of Agriculture and the University announced that it was to be considerably enlarged and set up as an independent Institute of the Agricultural Research Council. A suitable site was found at Maris Lane, Trumpington, and in 1952 the new Institute was set up, still under Dr Bell. Here its responsibilities were considerably widened. Besides undertaking the breeding of all the major crops in England including grass, and much cytogenetic investigation, it became a storehouse of knowledge on fundamental research on plant breeding methods, genetics, cytogenetics, plant pathology and plant physiology which is available to help other organizations engaged in similar work. The new school of cytogenetics and of cereal pathology quickly acquired world-wide recognition and in particular the cytogenetics of the Triticinae has made outstanding contributions to fundamental knowledge on polyploid structure and behaviour.

No account of plant breeders in Cambridge would be complete without special reference to Redcliffe Nathan Salaman, one of the pioneers who gave much help in the early days.

He was born in London in 1874, educated at St Paul's School and Trinity Hall, Cambridge, took a medical degree and became Director of the Pathological Institute, London Hospital. In 1905 he developed tuberculosis and left London for Barley near Royston, where, being comfortably endowed, he made a beautiful country home. Here he became interested in William Bateson's genetical investigations, and in his garden he studied intensively the potato, particularly its resistance to blight. As early as 1909 he had observed that some of the wild potatoes planted in his garden remained free from blight while others caught it: he showed that this property of immunity was heritable. Selfed seedlings from immune plants were supplied to the Scottish potato breeders seeking new immune varieties. Later he studied virus diseases of the potato with such success that a special research institute was set up at Cambridge to extend the work, and he was appointed Head. Among other useful activities he initiated the building up of virus-free stocks of seed potatoes afterwards carried on by the National Institute of Agricultural Botany at Cambridge.

Like many other of the older scientists he was a man of wide culture and extensive interests. He did much public work, was an active Governor of the Hebrew University, Jerusalem, and a kindly and sympathetic friend to many of the refugee scholars of the 1930's. He died in 1955.

VIRUS INVESTIGATIONS

It had long been known that potato varieties usually lost vigour the longer they were in cultivation and that they degenerated more rapidly in the south and east of Britain than in the north and west. This was widely attributed to a supposed deleterious effect of vegetative reproduction, though some even in the eighteenth century attributed it to an infection, but without evidence until well into the twentieth century, when the causes of degeneration were shown to be the invisible pathogens, then called filterable viruses, the existence of which had been first demonstrated in 1892 by the Russian botanist, Iwanowski, who showed that juice from plants with tobacco mosaic was still infective after being passed through bacteria-proof filters.

In Britain the first to work on potato virus diseases was R. N. Salaman. In 1926 the Potato Virus Research Station was founded at Cambridge under his direction with the chief purpose of producing healthy stocks of seed potatoes. Many different viruses and virus strains were identified and much of the previous confusion was clarified by showing that different potato varieties could react differently to the same virus, that two viruses together often produced very different diseases from either alone, and that plants of one variety though seemingly healthy, could be harbouring viruses that caused severe diseases in other varieties. Salaman also showed that, although plants infected with one virus were still susceptible to infection with other viruses, they were resistant to infection with other strains of the same virus. The rapid degeneration of potatoes in the southeast of England was shown by Kenneth M. Smith to be caused by two viruses transmitted by the peach-potato aphid, *Myzus persicae*, and the reason for the better health of potatoes from the north and west was that aphids were fewer and less active there. Seed classification schemes based on this knowledge have greatly reduced the losses of yield formerly caused by potato viruses.

Although most of the early work at Cambridge dealt with viruses of the potato, Smith also identified those affecting many other plants, and showed that different viruses were transmitted by different species of aphids or by other insects such as thrips. The value of serological techniques for identifying plant viruses and for assay work was demonstrated by F. C. Bawden and E. T. C. Spooner. Smith also in the 1930's made the first estimates of the sizes of some of the viruses, by filtering through the collodion membranes with pores of known and uniform sizes made by methods devised by W. J. Elford.

Work on the purification of potato virus X by Bawden and Pirie gave the first conclusive evidence that viruses contained protein and later led to the identification of the viruses as nucleoproteins. Between 1936 and 1943 several viruses were isolated in crystalline or liquid crystalline forms, which allowed them to be studied by X-ray diffraction techniques, by which J. D. Bernal and his colleagues not only produced the first accurate measurement of particle sizes but showed that viruses differed fundamentally from living organisms and were built up from many similar unit pieces arranged in a perfectly regular manner. This settled a long standing uncertainty whether viruses were a very low form of life or a remarkable inanimate entity with power of reproduction under certain circumstances.

The invention of the electron microscope made it possible to photograph virus particles and the combination of electron microscopy with X-ray diffraction revealed the detailed structure of many of the viruses.

The widening activities of the Potato Virus Research Station were recognized by the change of name first to Plant Virus Research Station and later to the Virus Research Unit of the Agricultural Research Council.

SCOTTISH PLANT BREEDING STATION: PENTLANDFIELD, ROSLIN, MIDLOTHIAN

The Scottish Society for Research in Plant Breeding was founded in 1920; its operations were to be exclusively scientific and its object was the promotion of agriculture, arboriculture and horticulture. Its very limited resources, however, compelled a restriction of the programme to plant breeding for agriculture and in 1921 a station was set up at Craigs House, Corstorphine. It was fortunate in receiving from the late Dr J. H. Wilson's estate a collection of breeding material containing 200 or more potato clones, selections and known varieties of oats and numbers of strains of swedes, so that breeding could be started immediately with these crops. The potato programme included the raising of commercial varieties resistant to blight and wart disease, both of which were causing considerable losses at the time. For swedes the emphasis was on feeding value, and for oats the suitability for poor districts of low soil fertility and high rainfall. The first new oat, Elder, was liberated in 1930; it was stiff strawed and of the potato oat type; it was followed in 1932 by Bell, an earlier ripening variety with good yield of grain and quality of straw intended to replace the old Sandy oat. As the horse population fell, however, more importance was attached to suitability for oatmeal, and the aim became an improved general purpose type.

As the work expanded, two new oat selection centres were set up in 1953, one in Inverness and the other in Argyll, and in 1954 the Station was transferred to Pentlandfield.

Work was also done on the improvement of herbage plants, particularly perennial rye grass, cocksfoot and timothy. Pollination and conditions of fertilization in the more important grasses were studied, and then the origins and inter-relationships of species and intra-specific races, using timothy and the sea plantain for the purpose.

A fairly representative collection of perennial rye grasses became available, and the exceptional leafiness and peculiar growth habits of certain populations from uncultivated localities stimulated enquiries as to how such characteristics had been acquired. The evolutionary aspects of the intra-specific variations were studied. The striking difference between the wild perennial rye grasses and the types in commercial use suggested that the latter would in due course be replaced by the leafy indigenous strains. Much attention was given to the grazing problems of hill farms and other grasslands, and a striking feature of the Institute's early work was the realization of the potentialities of grass as an arable crop.

Work on the fodder crops was from the early days affected by the declining popularity of swedes and the increasing use of kale.

When the station was established little was known about the genetics and cytology of the potato or the potentialities of wild and cultivated species in Central and South America. The research at the station had the twofold purpose of obtaining scientific information about the potato and potato breeding and also to produce improved varieties. In the early years the chief studies were the inheritance of characters such as pigmentation in tubers and flowers, shape of tubers, depth of eyes and colour of flesh. It soon became clear, however, that resistance to disease and pests was more important, especially wart disease, blight, virus diseases and eelworms. Resistance to diseases therefore became a main subject of potato research. Fortunately, immunity to wart disease was common, this being a dominant factor, but the others had proved more difficult. Salaman had found in 1909 plants immune to blight among some of those in the Cambridge collection of wild potatoes from South America. At the station it was observed that some of Dr Wilson's seedlings remained free from blight while adjoining plants succumbed. These formed the initial parents for blight resistant plants. A few years later, however, a new race of blight appeared capable of attacking them, although the wild species from which they had been bred was completely resistant. In 1932 therefore, the search for a new variety was started; it was complicated by the different numbers of chromosomes in the different varieties and their irregularities. A complex series of crossings overcame the difficulty, and a resistant variety was in due course obtained. The station's first blight-resistant variety was Craigs Snow White introduced in 1947, followed in 1950 by Craigs van Riebeck resistant to A, C, and D; then in 1951 came Pentland Ace resistant to strains, A, B, C and D.

A potato root eelworm (*Heterodera rostochiensis*) had long been a menace in some of the best potato areas, but during and after the Second World War it was probably the most serious of all the pests. Nothing effective could be done by breeding till 1951 when Ellenby at Newcastle discovered that resistant forms occurred among the wild potatoes in the Cambridge collection. Seeds of some of these were obtained and the plants grown from them were used in research for eelworm resistant varieties.

The search for varieties resistant to virus diseases was begun in 1930 with grants from the Empire Marketing Board. Many cultivated varieties were found to be immune to viruses A, B, C and X, but virus Y caused more difficulties which, however, were ultimately overcome. Varieties relatively resistant to leaf roll virus were first recognized during 1933–35. This work on virus diseases was still being continued in the 1960's.

In 1947 the station was asked to help the Cambridge breeders in the production of a non-bolting sugar beet: the climate of Edinburgh, however, is not suited to this crop and no success was attained. Sugar beet had nevertheless become a Scottish crop since a factory was set up at Cupar in 1926 and investigations at this station were still continuing in the 1960's.

The work is not confined to the practical problems of breeding new varieties. Much purely scientific work has been done in the study of genetic mechanisms which operate within organisms and between organisms and their environment at the level both of the individual and of the population. This indeed has become a new branch of science called Genecology which seems likely to become a great aid to plant breeders,[1] and its study and that of inheritance of resistance to potato blight and viruses are probably the station's contributions of widest significance up to the early 1960's. The Sections are organized as teams making it difficult to mention particular individuals.

[1] An interesting account of the bearing of genecology was published by Erna Bennett in the Scottish Plant Breeding Record for 1964.

CHAPTER XII

FRUIT RESEARCH STATIONS

LONG ASHTON RESEARCH STATION 1914–1950

THE history of the Long Ashton Experiment Station from its foundation in 1903 to the outbreak of the first World War in 1914 is given in Chapter VII. The station was small, and confined almost entirely to cider problems. It had, however, another task which was given the first place in its Articles of Association: the investigation and demonstration of 'the best methods of cultivation of all kinds of fruit and vegetables' which, combined with its duties to the cider makers, constituted a big order for an Institute with a scientific staff of one. Nevertheless Barker, ever resourceful, contrived in 1910 with the help of an old Cambridge friend, A. H. Lees, son of a London physician, to commence investigations on the factors governing fruit bud formation in apple and pear trees. This was widely believed to be antagonistic to vegetative growth, a view on which were based the pruning methods then adopted. The East Malling dwarfing and semi-dwarfing stocks were becoming available, and these enabled Barker and Lees to develop dwarf pyramid trees which came thick-set with fruit buds. They were so small that they could be planted much more closely in the ground than the standard trees, they also came much earlier into bearing and yielded more heavily per acre than the old standard trees. The crops, however, were still irregular: a heavy crop one year tended to be followed by a poorer one the next; and high rainfall in June, July and August caused the food reserves to be used for a continuance of growth instead of laying down fruit buds. But although they had discovered how to increase the number of fruit buds on the tree they could not explain why this had happened nor indeed is it yet known.

M*

A profound change in the Institute occurred in 1912. The Development Commission expressed its readiness to include Long Ashton among its Research Institutes on condition that it became associated with the University of Bristol which had recently received its charter. Both parties agreed and the Institute forthwith became the nucleus of the University Department of Agriculture and Horticulture which was also to include the Provincial Advisory Centre. The Development Commission thereupon supplied funds for the provision of a chemist and an entomologist.

C. T. Gimingham, assistant chemist at Wye College, was appointed to the former post, and Lees, who at Cambridge had studied entomology under Cecil Warburton, to the latter. Barker and Gimingham began with studies of the fungicidal action of bordeaux mixture, and showed that the fungus acted on the insoluble copper compound contained in the mixture, producing a soluble compound which the fungus absorbed and which killed it. This was later the subject of much research.

Before they could get far the first World War broke out and the Institute had to help with food production. Among other activities the expected scarcity of jam and sugar was met by making fuller use of fruit. A cold-process preservation of fruit pulp by sulphur dioxide was devised. A method was worked out for preparing pectin, valuable as a basis for jam making, from pomace, hitherto a waste product which was either fed to the animals or used as manure: in neither case was it particularly useful. A method of making apple orchard jelly from concentrated cider apple juice and pectin was devised; thus giving a welcome addition to the rather dreary dietary of the time. The station was given supervision of the experimental centre for work on fruit and vegetable preservation which had been set up at Studley College and was later transferred to Chipping Campden. There it was put under the control of the Director of Long Ashton until 1935 when the resident director assumed full responsibility, remaining, however, associated with the University till 1953.

After the war ended it became possible to concentrate on the study of the many problems presented by fruit trees, particularly apple trees, In 1918 a new turn to the subject of fruitfulness was given when E. J. Kraus and H. R. Kraybill of the Oregon

Experiment Station showed that in tomatoes it was associated with moderately low nitrogen status combined with high carbohydrate. The important factor was not the absolute amounts, but their relative proportions in the cell sap; the carbon/nitrogen ratio, as it was later called. The old idea that vegetative growth and fruiting were in some way opposed, and trees must be pruned accordingly, had to be abandoned or modified: growth could be increased by nitrogenous manuring without detriment to fruitfulness if the carbohydrate supply was correspondingly increased. This was limited by the light intensity and leaf area and the efficiency with which the leaf area was presented to the light: the light intensity could not be controlled but the other two could by suitable pruning.

A complete change in the theory and practice of pruning resulted: the aim was no longer to induce fruitfulness by restricting vegetative growth, but to maintain a high level of carbohydrate. In order to give greater precision to these ideas detailed studies were made of the various types of nitrogen compounds and carbohydrates in fruit trees grown under different conditions and worked on different root stocks.[1] These investigations did not fully explain fruit bud formation, but the possibility was raised that a specific flower-forming hormone was made in the leaf, and that the absence of lower buds on the stem during the development of growing shoots at the apex might be due to the formation of some inhibitor—the theory of apical dominance. Investigations were still continuing in the 1950's; the work already done, however, had led to great improvements in the pruning and general management of the trees.

Meanwhile two subjects were being studied to which Long Ashton subsequently made great contributions: the nutrition of fruit trees and the control of pests and diseases by insecticides and fungicides. This extension became possible directly after the first war as a result of the expansion of the Development Commission's research scheme. Thomas Wallace, a young chemist from Rutherford College and Armstrong College (later King's College) Newcastle on Tyne, was appointed in 1919 to deal with soil and nutrition problems while insecticides and fungicides were to be studied by S. P. Wiltshire who came

---

[1] D. V. Karmarkar, *J. Hort. Sci.*, 1934, Vol. 12, p. 177. Elsie S. Smythe, *ibid* p. 249, and 1938, Vol. 16, p. 185.

from Cambridge in the same year as mycologist, G. T. Spinks having turned over to pomology; F. Tutin came a year later as chemist. As a result of these and later appointments the work widened out greatly and although the cider department remained as active as ever it gradually became only one of several, some of which became larger than itself and even more widely known. The expansion was greatly helped by the Empire Marketing Board which from 1927 till its winding up in 1933 made substantial grants towards investigations likely to assist the overseas Dominions.

The nutrition studies were started on two different lines: pot culture experiments with apple trees, later extended to other fruits; and field experiments and soil surveys in the chief fruit regions of the West Midlands.

In Pickering's earlier experiments on the nutrition of fruit trees he showed that potassic fertilizers increased growth on light soils, and in those of Dyer and Shrivell[1] there had been some response to nitrogenous and potassic fertilizers in absence of dung, but little information was available about their general nutritional requirements. Wallace in 1921 began a long series of pot experiments, and using the sand culture method was soon able to clear up three important practical problems. A deficiency of nitrogen produced effects similar to those observed on grassed orchards poorly managed. Deficiency of potash caused 'leaf scorch', one of the most prevalent diseases of the time: the effect, however, was not simple but varied with the supply of nitrogen: an increase in the ratio N/K increased the amount of 'scorch' and *vice versa*. Different stocks and different scions differed in their sensitiveness to potash deficiency. These results were quickly utilized by the growers: hundreds of trees unproductive because of leaf scorch were restored to healthy growth by dressings of potash, and large areas of land deemed unsuitable for fruit could now be planted.

Another type of disorder manifested by intervenal necrosis of the leaves and early defoliation resulted from a low level of magnesium supply in relation to potassium; increase in the K/Mg ratio intensified the symptoms, lowering of the ratio reduced them; this was the first time a magnesium effect had been observed in Great Britain. These nutritional deficiencies were

[1] See p. 193.

reflected in the chemical composition of the ash of the leaves, and could therefore be revealed by chemical analysis of the folliage as more and more data accumulated from which a normal composition could be deduced. Wallace used this method largely in his surveys. The deficiencies could be conveniently remedied by spraying the leaves with a solution of the appropriate salt: this became common practice for remedying magnesium and manganese deficiencies. The diagnostic studies were later extended to the trace elements: they were summarized in a convenient form in 1943 in a handsomely illustrated volume.[1]

The soil surveys begun in 1923 by Wallace were greatly extended by D. A. Osmond, appointed in 1935, and they went on till the work was handed over to the National Soil Survey at Rothamsted in 1946. Osmond went with it and finally became Director of the whole organization. The Long Ashton surveys served the useful purpose of showing which soil factors were important in determining suitability for fruit growing, and the findings were confirmed by surveys in southeast England carried out by the East Malling staff, and elsewhere by the staffs of Cambridge and Reading Universities.

From the outset the insect and fungus pests of the various kinds of fruit were studied and remedial measures sought. The long sequence of observations revealed some interesting changes. The pests of 1920, aphides, apple suckers, apple blossom weevils, codling moths, and the caterpillars of winter moths and March moths were dealt with by the washes current at the time—soaps, quassia, nicotine, paraffin emulsions, lime and lime sulphur—applied by rather primitive spraying equipment. In 1921 a great advance was made. The washes in common use only partially destroyed the insect eggs. S.P. Wiltshire on a visit to Holland saw tar oils used as a winter spray which killed them completely. Lees tested them and confirmed their efficiency. The tar oils are of course an indefinite mixture: F. Tutin found that the active constituents were the high boiling hydrocarbon fractions, and with this knowledge an improved wash was made.

[1] T. Wallace. *The Diagnosis of Mineral Deficiencies in Plants*, a Colour Atlas and Guide. H.M.S.O. London, 1st Ed. 1943, Supplement, 1944, 2nd. ed., 1951, 3rd. ed. 1961.

The whole spraying technique was gradually improved and during the 1930's formulae combining insecticides and fungicides were devised which were among the best in use till the advent of the synthetic products. Spraying programmes were worked out and spraying machines and equipment greatly improved. Growers were thus able to keep pace with the increasing menace of pests and diseases: this was fortunate because the balance of the insect world was changing: treatments designed to cope with one lot of insects gave others the opportunity of developing. A new lot had developed by the 1930's including the apple saw fly and the capsid bug—this last especially interesting because up to the late 1920's it had apparently lived on willows, and then had turned over to apple trees. From 1943 the fruit tree red spider mite, hitherto of little account, became a serious pest for the particularly interesting reason that the very potent insecticide, DDT, first introduced into Britain in 1942, was coming into much wider use. It unfortunately killed insects that had preyed upon the mite but did not kill the mite itself, so that it was now able to multiply, which it did, especially in the Eastern Counties where it became a major pest. Fortunately it did not multiply so freely in the west. These new spraying methods, however, were used chiefly in orchards producing culinary or dessert fruits and only rarely in cider orchards as the value of the additional produce did not usually justify the cost of spraying.

Fungal pests were studied early, S. P. Wiltshire working on a Board of Agriculture scholarship during the summers of 1914 and 1915 studied the germination of spores of the destructive apple and pear scab, *Venturia inaequalis* and *V. pirina*. A succession of studies on these important pests followed, and by the 1930's R. W. Marsh and colleagues had worked out a scheme of control which was extended by H. Martin and others. Much work was done on the fungicidal value of sulphur in various combinations such as lime sulphur.

During the war years 1939–44 the programme of work was necessarily linked up with that of food production. Milk had become a central constituent of the national diet, especially for children and expectant mothers, but in the early days much of it had been over-pasteurized, thus destroying Vitamin C. ascorbic acid. Supplies of citrus fruits, the usual source of this essential substance, could not be relied upon; it was known, however, to occur in black currants and in rose-hips, but black currants were obtainable in much the larger quantity. They were found to contain from 100 to 400 mgms per 100 grams of fruit according to variety. Nitrogenous manuring decreased the percentage, but raised the yield of fruit so much that the total output per acre was increased. The outcome of the work on black currant juice was the marketing of *Ribena*, a commercial black currant juice product widely distributed during the war. Tomatoes also supplied Vitamin C. and they too differed in their content according to variety.

Studies already begun on fruit juices were further developed. Considerable attention had been given to apple juice. We lack the range of suitable varieties possessed by the Germans, but Bramleys Seedling proved an excellent source; it gave a product as good as the best German *Apfelsaft*.

Other fruit juices were studied as possible ways of utilizing gluts of fruit. They could be produced commercially but not from gluts alone: constant supplies of a standard quality were needed. It was a great disappointment that nothing could be done with the gluts of plums that periodically cause so much trouble in Worcestershire and other fruit districts, where the unwanted fruit falls to the ground and lies there rotting, even sometimes loading the atmosphere with its unpleasant smell. A more hopeful approach was to preserve the whole fruit with a dilute solution (0·15 per cent) of sulphur dioxide but this meant the provision of containers with a resistant lining. Much of this work found application after the war when fruit juice industries began to develop.[1]

Wallace's visual diagnostic tests of deficient nutrition of plants were applied to farm crops and proved very helpful to the County Advisors during the war in dealing with crops on ploughed-out old grassland much of which was deficient in one or other of the essential plant foods. The work on diseases and pests was also extended to farm crops during the period, and a temporary laboratory was established at Evesham for more rapid investigation of the problems of fruit and vegetable growers there.

[1] *Recent Advances in Fruit Juice Production;* V. L. S. Charley *et al., Commonwealth Ag. Bureaux (Fruit) Tech. Com.,* No. 21, 1950.

Much of the foregoing work reached its logical conclusion during the second post war period and must therefore be included here. Full advantage was taken of the new products and new methods resulting from the remarkable development of pure chemistry and of chemical technology during the second war and after.

The effects of the trace elements were studied in great detail. The sand culture method was used, elaborate precautions being taken to ensure as complete removal as possible of the elements under investigation so as to avoid vitiating the results by their accidental presence as impurities. The details have been set out by E. J. Hewitt,[1] The sand was purified by treatment with steam together with hydrochloric and oxalic acids, then with alkali. The large quantities of water required were obtained by treating clean rainwater with ion-exchange resins that absorb metallic ions to a high degree: the final content of copper, boron and zinc was about $0 \cdot 002$ parts per million, of manganese $0 \cdot 0001$ ad of molybdenum $0 \cdot 000008$ parts per million; of iron the quantities were higher. The nutrient salts had also to be highly purified. Delicate methods of assay were needed, and a biochemical procedure was adopted by D. J. D. Nicholas based on the fact that moulds also require these same trace elements, and their presence or absence in a solution can be detected by observing whether the moulds can or cannot grow. Specific strains of *Aspergillus niger* and *Penicillium glaucum* were used; they were grown on agar plates supplied with the appropriate culture solutions. The method was also used to detect deficiencies of trace elements in soils and to determine the amounts present in soil and in leaves where plants show deficiency symptoms and where they do not: also to determine their amounts in apple juices and ciders. This was the fullest investigation made in this country of the trace elements.

The effects of the various nutritive elements on the composition of the plants were also studied. The older analytical methods were commonly adequate for substances present in reasonable quantities, such as the fruit acids or the sugars, but they were often inconvenient or worse for the many highly

[1] E. J. Hewitt, Sand and Water Culture methods used in the study of Plant Nutrition. *Commonw. Bur. Hortic. Tech. Commun.* No. 22, 1952.

important constituents present in small amounts only. Paper chromatography was used by A. H. Williams for the examination of plant extracts. The effects of varying levels of molybdenum and manganese on the free amino acids of the leaves of brassicas were studied, particular attention being paid to cauliflower because of its susceptibility to molybdenum deficiency. The tannins or phenolics in different parts of the fruit trees, and in the fruits themselves, were studied and also the differences in phenolic constituents of cider apples and those suitable for dessert or culinary purposes, and of apple and pear trees. Pears, unlike apples, are not always grafted on stocks of their own species but may be grafted on quince stock: when this was done it was found that phenolic substances not common to the two species could not pass across the graft union. This curious inability is still a mystery: water, inorganic nutrients and some organic substances such as sugars pass easily. The same segregation occurred when apple scions were grafted on to pear stocks: phloridzin, the apple phenolic, was found only on the apple side, and arbutin, the pear phenolic, only on the pear side.

Some of the most interesting of the post war studies were connected with the auxins, organic substances formed in the plant in minute quantities which control many of its important activities. The initial discovery was made in Holland in 1935 at the Utrecht University by Kögl, Wendt and others: it was forthwith developed in the United States, particularly at the Boyce Thompson Institute, and for the next five years was a favourite theme in the leading plant physiological laboratories. The chemical pattern of the auxins was determined and a number of similar substances generally called hormones was prepared. Their potential number is almost indefinitely great, and each of those examined has some specific action on plants.

Hopes were aroused that hormones could be used to solve some of the fruit growers' long-standing problems: the strengthening of graft unions, the avoidance of frost damage to trees by prolonging winter dormancy, the induction of fruit buds, overcoming pollination difficulties by hormone-induced parthenocarpy, prevention of fruit drop and others. The possibilities were therefore studied at Long Ashton: the start was made in 1941 by T. Swarbrick. He showed that one of these hormones, α-naphthalene acetic acid, sprayed on to apple trees near harvest time, retarded the dehiscence which caused the apples and pears to fall, and kept them longer on the tree even in the strong southwesterly wind. This treatment proved so valuable to the growers that it became an established part of their practice. The same method could be used to reduce the June drop, but here there was less advantage: the drop is not necessarily bad for the grower: in a good year far more fruit may be set than the tree could ripen, and the drop may be simply the shedding of unwanted material: in a bad season, however, it may be desirable to retain more of the young fruits. The pre-harvest drop on the other hand is a real loss: the fruit has already been produced and the drop is sheer waste.

The reverse action, the encouragement of the early drop by hormones with a view to save the labour of thinning, was tested by L. C. Luckwill but not found satisfactory. The thinning was effected, but the remaining fruits were no larger than on the unthinned trees and the net result was a considerable loss of marketable fruit. Another hormone, 2-4-5- trichlorphenoxy-propionic acid, was shown to hasten maturity of Worcester Pearmain apples by about 12 days; it has also been used for ripening figs and stone fruits. Another hormone delayed ripening, making it possible to stagger the harvest. But in spite of much effort no hormone was found that would induce or prolong dormancy, or induce parthenocarpy—the production of fruit without the intervention of pollen from the male organ— in apple or plum trees, and the pollination troubles still remain unsolved. Hope need not be abandoned, however; the problem was solved for tomatoes and α-naphthoxyacetic acid came into regular use as a spray to induce setting of fruit in difficult conditions.

Other hormones retarded the sprouting of roots stored over winter: some of these were used by farmers and market gardeners for potatoes, carrots, beets and other crops. Special attention was given to maleic hydrazide which when sprayed on the leaves of the ripening crop before lifting inhibits the sprouting of the stored roots. Some special properties required further investigation: Darlington showed that it could change the chromosome number.

There have been no important new practical developments since about 1948 nor are any likely to come without much more fundamental knowledge of the hormones and their actions in the plant. Long Ashton's contribution has been a series of well conducted investigations by L. C. Luckwill on the auxins present in plants and fruits using as his experimental material cali-flower, blackcurrants and apples.

Wallace retired in 1947 and was succeeded by H. G. H. Kearns the entomologist who had joined the staff in 1931.[1]
In 1965 Wallace died at the age of seventy-three.

EAST MALLING RESEARCH STATION

While Hall was still at Wye he early organized conferences between groups of growers and the College staff and this custom was continued by his successors. In 1910 one was held with fruit growers, and although the Head of the Horticultural Department made the unhappy forecast that Cox's Orange Pippin and Ribston Pippin had had their day and should no longer be planted, other papers on fruit pests and diseases made the Conference a marked success. It convinced the growers that an experimental fruit farm was badly needed for Kent, and that the usefulness of the College in its advisory work would be limited without it.

There were already some fruit experiments on the college farm and as early as 1901 Hall had been able to demonstrate the beneficial effects of potash on the apple variety Bismarck, shown in particular by the longer retention of the leaves in autumn. The soil of the college farm, however, was less suitable for fruit than the lighter and deeper soils of the fruit-growing districts to the north and west. A more suitable site, a field of $22\frac{1}{2}$ acres, found at East Malling near Maidstone, was ac-quired by the Kent County Council in 1913 for use as a college out-station for fruit growing. It was called the Wye College Fruit Experiment Station, and was put in charge of R. Welling-ton, the College horticulturist and a former student. He started off with a sound programme of work based on 'problems met with in the actual culture or growth of fruit trees and bushes'.

[1] An excellent account of the history of the Long Ashton Station was prepared for its jubilee in 1953 under the editorship of T. Wallace and R. W. Marsh, the plant pathologist, which I found very helpful in preparing the above account.

The sorting and classification of rootstocks for apples, plums and pears was immediately begun as a necessary prelude to experiments concerned with pruning and manuring these fruits. Studies in 'running off' in black currants led to large numbers of black currant seedlings being raised, and experiments on pruning and manuring black currants and gooseberries were started. Wellington's high standard of work promised great success, but before he had progressed far the 1914–18 war broke out; he enlisted with the Yeomanry and before long was in France. The work was carried on by Jesse Amos, the farm manager and recorder, under Ronald George Hatton who was appointed Acting Director.

Amos had come from the botanical department at Wye where he had been assistant to S. T. Parkinson, the very kindly Professor of Botany under whom he acquired an extensive knowledge of systematic botany which, combined with his acute powers of observation and great ability as a grower, made him invaluable to the Station during those early years.

Hatton subsequently played so great a part in the development not only of the station but also of the subject that it is necessary to give some account of him. He was born in Hampstead in 1886; his father was a Barrister-at-Law of the Inner Temple and his mother a sister of Karl Pearson. His education began at Brighton College and Exeter School; he then proceeded to Balliol College, Oxford where he read Modern History, his tutor being the well-known A. L. Smith. He was expected to have a distinguished career, but unfortunately his health broke down, and in his Final Examinations, instead of the First Class anticipated, he attained only a Fourth Class.

Although his home was at Hampstead he had spent most of his holidays on his grandfather's farm and estate in Sleightholme Dale in the North Riding of Yorkshire. He had thought of being a Roman Catholic priest, but the state of his health indicated a more open-air life. He worked on the land for some years and learnt to know and admire the old generation of farm workers whom he described in a very successful little book, 'Folk of the Furrow'. Later, he was advised to see Malcolm J. R. Dunstan who had succeeded Hall as Principal of Wye College. He did so in 1912, and was at once accepted as a member of the College although he was then twenty-six years old and of course much above the average student age. Dunstan put him on to various problems particularly some of Wellington's, and he showed such ability in dealing with them that he was given charge of them when in 1914 war broke out and Wellington enlisted. At the end of the war Wellington decided not to return to Wye, and Hatton was therefore made Director of the Station, a post which he held during the whole of his working life.

He greatly developed the work on rootstocks. The importance lay in the fact that they determined many of the characters of the trees: whether they became very large or very small, good or poor croppers, early or late fruiters. He was fortunate in securing the interest of Professor V. H. Blackman who had the Chair of Botany at the Imperial College of Science and Technology, and who gave valuable help on the physiological side and generally in deciding what observations should be made. He suggested that the growth and form of the entire developing tree should be carefully studied as well as other details that would give as complete a picture as possible of the behaviour of the plant in its normal environment. He seconded one of his Staff, the late Dr R. C. Knight, to work on the problems of adventitious rooting and the effects of rootstock on the scion and vice versa. He gave much help with the physiological problems.

By about 1920 Hatton had classified the 'Paradise' apple rootstocks into sixteen distinct types, and plans were being made for planting the first large scale trials of several scion varieties worked on these stocks. Good progress had also been made with plum and quince rootstocks, with the grouping of existing varieties of black currants, and the raising of new seedlings. Much attention was paid to the solution of practical problems troublesome to the growers, and the successes achieved gave the Station a high reputation among them. This was shown by the Horticultural Trades Association quickly accepting the rootstock classifications, and asking for the speedy distribution of clonal material to nurserymen. Clonal methods of propagation by layering were standardized and great help was given to the industry by providing re-selected material of both rootstocks and soft fruit varieties true to type.

As the value of the Station's work became clearer it aroused more interest, and the important decision was taken of breaking the connection with Wye and making the Station independent. An organization known as the Kent Incorporated Society for Promoting Experiments in Horticulture was formed and took over the Station in 1921, managing it through a Governing Body composed of practical fruit growers, representatives of the County Councils of Kent, Sussex and Surrey, scientific bodies including the Royal Society, the University of London and later other Universities.

In 1923 extensive studies of the pests and diseases of fruit plants were begun and an entomologist, A. M. Massee, and a mycologist, R. V. Harris were added to the staff. Among the problems studied were the relationships of weather conditions and attacks by insect pests. Close studies of insect populations in orchards were made and sound guidance with spray programmes was broadcasted by Massee to growers. Pest control measures were continuously sought that would not disturb the predator balance. Virus diseases were closely studied. Strawberries and raspberries had been affected on so wide a scale as to imperil the important industries of growing them by the degeneration of commercial stocks of all important varieties. Clones of all the main varieties of tree and soft fruits were established and East Malling became the main source of healthy propagating material for the fruit growing industry of this country. Later the development of resistance to insecticides was studied. In association with the Research Institute of Plant Physiology of the Imperial College of Science, investigations were made into the factors influencing the phytotoxicity of spray materials, and on the role of plant hormones in propagation and abscission.

In attempting to find explanations for the observed rootstock-scion interactions a biochemist, William Roach from Rothamsted was added to the staff in 1927. He found that the rootstocks affected some of the scion minerals which, however, were not involved in the effects produced. Sensitive spectrographic methods of analysis requiring only a few milligrams of dried leaf material were used for diagnosing mineral deficiencies in plants, and during the 1939–45 war were widely applied in reclaiming 'marginal' agricultural land in Devon, Romney Marsh and elsewhere. The mineral composition of the various tissues and parts of fruit trees was later studied to determine which would provide the best indications of the nutritional status of the entire tree in relation to growth period and season.

The new knowledge of the relations of stock and scion not only revolutionized systems of commerical planting, but made possible more accurate field experiments. In 1928 a large apple manurial experiment including nitrogen, phosphate and potassium was planned factorially in randomized blocks and planted in 1930; it was the first field experiment on fruit to be so designed. It showed the importance of potassium for the growth of young trees, confirming Hall's earlier indications at Wye and Wallace's results at Long Ashton. Nitrogen was slow to show any results, while phosphate showed none at all during the whole period of the trial. Much later a grass sward treatment was superimposed on half the plots in the original plan. No good evidence could be obtained that organic manures were better for fruit plants than inorganic though it is generally acknowledged that organic manures may improve the physical conditions of the soil. Continued cultivation and suppression of weeds combined with the application of nothing but artificial fertilizers were found liable to cause unthriftiness in trees, apparently due in part to effects on aeration, drainage conditions and lack of humus.

Decreasing supplies, and eventually total lack of 'London dung' caused difficulties in maintaining soil fertility and good physical condition, and from the 1930's onwards efforts to overcome these troubles were made. The method finally adopted was to establish long term closely cut swards, the trees being mulched where necessary during establishment. These swards greatly influenced the mineral and water relationships, and the growth and productiveness of the trees, while notably improving the quality of the apples.

As at Rothamsted, Hatton wished to keep the experimental and observational data under competent statistical review and T. N. Hoblyn, a Rothamsted trained statistician, undertook this work.

Recognition of the importance of the Station's work to the country during the 1939–45 war made money for research work readily obtainable, and in 1946 the Ministry of Agriculture took over full responsibility for the salaries and maintenance of the whole research staff, and also the finances of the experimental farm. Shortly afterwards the Station came wholly within the care of the Agricultural Research Council.

Hatton's work was so esteemed by his fellow scientists that he was elected a Fellow of the Royal Society in 1944; to the regret of his many friends he retired in 1948. In the following year he was awarded the well earned distinction of knighthood. He had indeed served the Station and the subject well. He had started in 1914 with a staff of one plus $22\frac{1}{2}$ acres of land, when the fruit growing industry was in much confusion; many of the varieties were wrongly named and little was known of the relations of rootstocks and scions. When he left the staff numbered about 80 of whom 40 were graduates and the experimental farm was 360 acres in extent. His outstanding scientific contribution was, in the view of his contemporaries, his recognition of the fact that before exact experiments could be carried out in fruit culture, it was necessary to have pure lines of pedigree material. He therefore proceeded first of all to sort out the mixture of apple rootstocks, and then to determine rootstock effects with his selections. With black currants rootstocks were not involved, but identification of varieties was undertaken. Having finally got his pedigree materials he proceeded to examine their growth and cropping qualities in relation to environmental factors. The practical value of the work lay in the recognition of the value of standardized pedigree materials in fruit growing.

Hatton's successor, Francis Ralph Tubbs, took charge in 1949. He was in his forty-second year and had been educated at the Hackney Downs Secondary School, London and the Royal College of Science, South Kensington. Later he went to Ceylon and became Head of the Department of Plant Physiology at the Tea Research Station there. With the more ample resources made available at East Malling after the second world war he was naturally able to work on a much larger scale than had been possible for Hatton. One of the most interesting additions is a large underground root observation chamber which enables workers to study the growth of the root systems of a variety of trees planted alongside. The periodicity of root growth has been studied and the development of techniques using time-lapse films has made possible the close observation of the activities of the soil flora and fauna.

Much breeding of soft fruits especially raspberries, black currants and gooseberries has been done with the purpose of producing varieties resistant to diseases and pests, especially those capable of transporting virus diseases. This work, and much else and much more at the Station lies outside our period.

FOUNDING OF THE RESEARCH STATION
FOR GLASSHOUSE CROPS

The fact demonstrated at Rothamsted that partial sterilization increased crop yields attracted the attention of intensive growers in several parts of the country, but especially in the Lea Valley where a great glasshouse culture had developed, started by the Rochford family and much helped by some highly competent and very industrious Danes. The main crops were tomatoes and cucumbers with flowers, especially chrysanthemums, during the winter months. After a few years the soils lost much of their productiveness, and this could not be restored by the ordinary fertilizers. One of the growers, Mr W. B. Randall, referred the matter to Rothamsted in 1909 and sent along quantities of 'sick' soil; after sterilization it gave quite satisfactory crops. Demonstrations in glasshouses in different parts of the Valley were arranged and proved successful: other problems were found and the need for properly conducted scientific experiments was evident.

Rothamsted was asked to undertake these, but I strongly urged that a separate Station should be set up locally, easily accessible to the growers so that they could call in without difficulty to see the experiments and discuss their problems with the staff. The best of the growers with few exceptions accepted this view: H. O. Larsen, a Dane, deservedly held in the highest repute among them as a superb grower, a most attractive personality and a man of sterling character, and W. B. Randall, a remarkable English grower, took the lead. Grants were obtained from the County Councils of Essex, Hertfordshire and Middlesex; land and glasshouses were acquired at Cheshunt, and the station started work in 1914. It was badly affected by the War and for a time afterwards, owing to the unsuitability of the first Director, but he took another post in 1921 and was succeeded by W. F. Bewley of Rothamsted, who had already worked at the Station for two years as mycologist.

From the outset Bewley was a great success: he quickly apprehended the growers' problems, and with his entomological colleagues—Ll. Lloyd and then E. R. Speyer—found working solutions for them. Thousands of seedlings were annually destroyed by 'damping off': even 100,000 was no uncommon loss, and this caused the growers serious loss of precious time. Bewley found that it was caused by a fungus *Pythium*, and showed also that this could be killed by a mixture of ammonium carbonate and copper sulphate without harm to the seedlings. Speyer's most notable success was the destruction of a so-called White Fly (*Trialeurodes vaporariorum*) (West w.) which did much harm. Spraying was no help. Biological control was adopted: an avid insect parasite, *Encarsia formosa*, (Gahan) a chalcid, was found, bred in large numbers and supplied to the growers.

Apart from its value to the growers, the work of the Institute was of special interest to Rothamsted because some of the experiments at the two places were on similar subjects, but at Cheshunt the conditions were much more intensive than at Rothamsted, and this raised a number of problems.

The effects both of potassic and nitrogenous fertilizers under glasshouse conditions were greatly influenced by the amount of radiant energy received from the sun; when this was low, as at the beginning and end of the growing season, potassic fertilizers were much more effective in increasing growth and in hardening soft plants than when it was high. On the other hand, plants growing too hard in the middle of summer could be improved by applying enough nitrogen. So the tomato grower gave heavy dressings of sulphate of potash at the beginning and end of the crop growth when days were short and light intensity low; but reduced the potash in the summer when days were long and sunlight usually more intense, and applied increasing amounts of nitrogenous fertilizers. Another important effect of potassic fertilizer was to increase the resistance of the plant to diseases, especially those like streak, which are caused by bacteria. A curious and unexplained result was that glasshouse soils could be maintained in a healthy condition by digging into them as much fresh grass cuttings as possible.

Yields were far higher than on farms. A good grower in 1914 expected 30 tons of tomatoes and 100 tons of cucumbers per acre, quantities quite outside the range of possibility for the farmer.

Sterilization of the soil still remained essential right to the end, but the methods were much improved; steam, however, was still among the best agents, though formaldehyde was widely used. Valuable work was done on the control of diseases and pests, and Bewley brought the results together in books convenient for the growers to use, notably *Diseases of Glasshouse Plants*, 1923, and *Commercial Glasshouse Crops*, 1950, 1963.

As the industry expanded and moved to the sunnier climate of Sussex[1] so also did the Station, and in 1954 the new one was established at Rustington, Littlehampton, designed by Bewley, larger and better equipped than was possible at Cheshunt. He put it in good order, then retired in 1956 after 37 years of valuable service to the industry. During his Directorship both methods and yields had greatly improved. When he retired in 1956 a good tomato grower expected 50 to 60 tons per acre and 124 tons had been obtained: a considerable increase on the 30 tons of his early days. Engineers and others had contributed to the result, but the Institute undoubtedly played an important part.

He was succeeded by F. W. Toovey who brought in tropical experience that promised to be valuable.

[1] Yield of tomatoes depends on the number of hours of bright sunshine between April 1st and September 30th.

CHAPTER XIII

RESEARCH ON GRASS

THE DISCOVERY OF THE ENGLISH GRASSES

IT might well be that the first treatise on English grass husbandry was written by a Cistercian monk, for it was they who, following in the wake of the Normans, introduced or adopted the alternate system of husbandry which was long and widely practised, especially in the English western regions. An area of land was cultivated for several years, then sown down to grass, the seed being collected from hay ricks—as described by Columella, the well known Latin writer on agriculture (first century AD). Alternatively it might be left to tumble down to grass. There it would remain for several years regaining fertility: it would then be broken up for a further arable course. The Cistercians were more systematic: Franklin reports[1] that the monks at Coupar in 1400 followed five years of grass with two years of corn, then grass again—an early example of ley farming. The system remained unchanged till the seventeenth century when it was enriched by various leguminous and other crops introduced from Flanders and France including red and white clover, sainfoin (French grass or holy hay), lucerne, trefoil, vetches, lentils, tares, 'ray' (rye) grass and buckwheat. They were called 'artificial grasses', and those wild and self sown were 'natural grasses'. Blith (1648) described some of the 'artificial grasses 'treating them as arable crops. They were cultivated to some extent in the eastern counties and produced such good hay that northern farmers tried to get the import of their seed prohibited and none was as yet home-grown. Another objection was that they increased the returns

---

[1] T. Bedford Franklin, *British Grassland from the Earliest Times to the Present Day*, (Faber, 1933). The alternative system much practised in eastern England is described by C. S. and C. S. Orwin in *The Open Fields* (Oxford 1938).

from the poor land without any deduction of the customary easements, which was considered unfair by farmers on the better land.

The Royal Society's enquiry of 1664 elicited the information that clover seed was on sale in Exeter for 2d or 3d per lb. It was sown in October at the rate of 2 or 3 lb. of seed per acre with the oats, the last of the arable crops. The second season was the best: by the fourth the crop had nearly died out.

In 1669 John Worlidge, who generally styled himself 'J. W. Gent', of Petersfield, Hampshire, in his *Systema Agriculturae* praises these 'artificial grasses' but makes no mention of rye grass: he does this, however, in the third edition (1681) where he refers to a field of trefoil and 'ray grass' being cut for seed, as do later writers, and he praises the ray grass for its wide adaptability to different soils, its earliness, resistance to hard grazing, and persistence. Mixed with non-such clover it made a lasting pasture: as the clover died out native plants took its place. But the quality of the seed seemed to be falling, for later writers are less enthusiastic: Tim Nourse in 1700 (*Campania foelix*) describes it as 'a spiny bent sort of grass' which thrives best in cold wet land 'and is not so much in vogue as clover or St Foin'. But it was the only grass grown as a crop, the only one named, and it was still a foreign crop grown from imported seed,[1] though English grown seed was becoming more common. John Mortimer in the *Whole Art of Husbandry* (1707) relates how farmers would grow a crop of rye grass for hay, but before using it would thresh out the seed to secure the next year's crop. But there was still no question of the utilization of English grasses.

A striking change came in 1759 when Benjamin Stillingfleet in his *Miscellaneous Tracts relating to Natural History, Husbandry, etc.* gave English farmers a lively trouncing for their neglect of English grasses. 'It is wonderful to see', he wrote, 'how long mankind has neglected to make a proper advantage of plants of such importance, and which in almost every country are the chief food of cattle. The farmer for want of distinguishing and selecting grasses for seed, fills his pastures either with

---

[1] Although these writers did not seem aware of it rye grass was and had long been in England. Sir Edward Salisbury tells me it was found in Roman deposits at Verulam and he thinks it was probably the Red Darnel of Gerard's Herbal (1597).

weeds, or improper grasses, when by making a right choice, after some trials, he might be sure of the best grass, and in the greatest abundance that his land admits of. At present if a farmer wants to lay down his land to grass, what does he do? He either takes his seeds indiscriminately from his own foul hayrick, or sends to a neighbour for his supply. This is such a slovenly method of proceeding as one would think could not possibly prevail universally, yet this is the case as to all grasses except darnel grass (rye grass) and what is known in some few counties as Suffolk grass.'

Incidentally it must be mentioned that there were exceptions. Richard North, a nursery gardener and seedsman on the Lambeth side of Westminster bridge wrote also in 1759 in his booklet 'An account of the different kinds of grasses,' (i.e. leguminosae and rye grass) 'propagated in England for the improvement of corn and pasture lands' that some of the better farmers procure hay seed from fine, clean upland meadows. This, he wrote, contained the best kind of grasses and was invaluable for sowing pastures, lawns, walks, etc. Presumably the vendors of these seeds were among the objectors to the import of the foreign 'artificial grass' seed (v.p. 380).

Reverting to Stillingfleet: he knew the native grasses well and gives a list of ninety-five putting English names to some that had none. He notes the suitability or otherwise of some of them for stock, including meadow foxtail, widespread in the best meadows round London, and making the best London hay; sheep's fescue, found in the best sheep pastures in Hereford, Oxford, etc.; crested dogstail for parks, good for deer and perhaps sheep; annual meadow grass (Suffolk Grass); perennial darnel, well known and cultivated all over England. But he did not merely write about the grasses; he did something about them: he taught children to collect quantities of seed of some of the best sorts, 'the Creeping Bent, the Fire Bent, the Sheeps Fescue, the Crested Dogstail' and a few others. Unfortunately he was unable to complete his plans; he had intended to propagate these seeds by sowing the different kinds on separate beds, but could not. He thought perhaps a dozen species would be suitable and gave copper plates of the flowering heads of ten of them. But he emphasized that 'those grasses only which throw out many leaves from the root seem to be worth propagating for hay or pasture'—a fact which was later re-discovered at the Welsh Plant Breeding Station.

William Curtis working on similar lines a generation later was able to go much further. In his *Practical Observations of the British Grasses* (1798) he quotes with approval Stillingfleet's recommendation to sow properly selected grass seeds instead of hay rick sweepings; and goes on: 'Ray grass still continues to be the only grass whose seeds can be purchased for the purpose of laying down meadow and pasture land; and how inadequate that grass is for such a purpose is known to every farmer'. He undertook to remedy this by providing seed for six recommended species which should be sown as the following mixture: 1 pint each meadow foxtail and meadow fescue; $\frac{1}{2}$ pint each smooth stalked meadow grass and rough stalked meadow grass; $\frac{1}{2}$ pint each crested dogstail; sweet scented vernal; $\frac{1}{2}$ pint each Dutch clover and wild red clover or broad red. A packet of these mixed seeds could be bought at the Botanic nursery, Brompton, for 10s. 6d. The seeds were to be multiplied on the farm to produce the quantity needed for sowing.

A further advance was made by John Russell, 6th Duke of Bedford, at Woburn Abbey, who in 1813 published his *Experiments on the Produce and Nutritive Qualities of Different Grasses*, a small book packed with data but little discussion. Much of the work had been done by his gardener, George Sinclair. As already stated[1] Davy had tried to determine the nutritive values of the grasses by analysis of their dried aqueous extract, but the method proved unsuitable. Rye grass and cocksfoot were the two main pasture constituents; there was, however, it was stated, a choice of 215 other grasses.

The grasses under experiment were grown in beds 4 ft. square and the produce weighed at flowering, at ripening, and in some cases as aftermath. There are agricultural notes on all the species tested and a special note of grasses found abundantly in good pastures.

This small book was followed in 1816 by a much larger one under the name of George Sinclair, *Hortus Gramineus Woburnensis*, the first edition of which was a massive volume containing pressed specimens of plants; later editions were on a smaller

[1] P. 70.

scale. He repeated the statement that imported ray (rye) grass was till lately the only species used for making 'artificial pastures' and went on: 'there is no account of any other species of perennial grass being cultivated till about 40 years since when meadow cat's tail (*Phleum pratense*) was partially recommended'. The culture of cocksfoot (*Dactylis glomerata*) had been considerably extended, replacing ray grass in some districts, following the example and recommendation of Mr Coke of Norfolk. Sinclair described at length twenty-five species of grasses and clovers found in the best natural pastures, and recommended the following mixture for high yields, nutritive value, earliness, reproductive powers, ease of sowing the seed and permanence: rye grass, cocksfoot, meadow fescue, foxtail, rough stalked meadow grass, tall oat-like soft grass (*Holcus avenaceus*), timothy,[1] hard or smooth fescue, dogstail, *Poa nervata*, *Poa nemoralis*, *Poa angustifolia*, fiorin, rye grass, white clover, bush vetch (*V. sepum*), vernal grass, perennial red clover. On the Duke's farm the mixtures used included the first seven of these grasses, and the two clovers. Recipes for mixtures suited to different soil conditions are given and also for alternate husbandry which was still much practised; useful information was added about the relations of grasses to soils, laying down of land to grass, and the management of grassland. These Woburn Abbey observations and experiments provided a great fund of knowledge on grass land which has not been sufficiently recognized.

Looking back over these years it is clear that British grasses were almost unknown to British agriculturists till the middle of the eighteenth century when Stillingfleet discovered them and William Curtis somewhat later showed how to utilize them; the Woburn experiments then transferred the small scale experience to the large practical scale.

Nothing further of importance concerning grass appears to have been done till the middle of the century. The *Journal of the Royal Agricultural Society* has no important paper on the subject till its 14th volume in 1853, when J. T. Way, always a breaker of fresh ground, discussed the relative nutritive and

---

[1] The *Annual Register* for 1765 reports that timothy was imported from Virginia in 1763. It had a great reputation in America and Sinclair was told in 1815 that it was the best grass in Canada.

fattening properties of different natural and 'artificial' grasses—interesting as always but showing the limitations of the times. He stated for example that the mineral constituents of the grass had no nutritive value. In the following year (vol. 15) J. Buckman published an important paper on the Natural History and Agricultural Economy of British Grasses in which he estimated the proportions of the different species of plants in grasslands on different soils and under different management. The Rothamsted Park experiments on the manuring of permanent grassland for hay started in 1856; they are still continued. Two papers about them appeared in the Society's Journal for 1863. After the lapse of twenty-five years a mild controversy started in the Journal for 1888 when William Fream[1] reporting on the herbage of old grassland concluded that rye grass and white clover constituted the backbone of good pastures, while Carruthers, the Society's botanist, maintained (1890) that their quality depended more on the soil than on the vegetation. As often happens there was much truth on both sides.

In 1895, however, Carruthers and Voelcker started a much bigger series of grassland experiments on twenty-two sites in twelve different districts. Their first report appeared in the *Journal* for 1898 (vol. 59) and a second was issued two years later (vol. 61). The bad times of the 1880's and 1890's had stimulated an interest in grassland which the Society was prepared to encourage.

An interesting development by a Scottish landowner, Mr R. H. Elliot of Clifton Park, was described in the *Journal* for 1897 (vol. 58). Recognizing the desirability of deepening the soil by opening up and enriching the subsoil he used vigorous deep-rooting plants, not only grasses, but others acceptable to the farm animals, chicory, burnet, yarrow, sheep's parsley, etc. The roots penetrated into the subsoil and when the plant died they decomposed forming humus. A farmer, William Lamin, in 1944 wrote a glowing account of it in '*Thirty Years Farming on the Clifton Park System*' (Faber). It had enabled him to fix a blowing sand and convert it into a good foundation for succeeding crops.

The two advances of most importance for the development of grassland knowledge in the early twentieth century passed

[1] P. 182.

N

almost unnoticed at the time of their announcement. One was John Wrightson's discovery of the remarkable effectiveness of the new basic slag in improving the poor pastures of the north of England, which gave Somerville and Gilchrist the means of developing their grassland investigations already described. The other was the announcement from Cambridge of a method of estimating the percentages of the different species in the grassland flora which was far better than the old rough estimate by eye. As it developed it allowed the making up of far better pictures of the grasslands of Britain than had been possible before and proved very helpful in the improvements and reclamations that came later.

A certain amount of work was also done on the manuring of grassland. Early in the twentieth century A. D. Hall summarized the results so far obtained by the Cockle Park, Cambridge, and Essex workers. [1]Much botanical surveying was done in Scotland and a beginning was made at Cambridge with nutritional studies on modern lines. A good start had been made with seed-mixture problems but progress was limited by the fact that there was as yet no production of new varieties by breeding. This was accomplished after the First World War, and is one of the great triumphs of British agricultural science.

THE WELSH PLANT BREEDING STATION

The leading firms of British seedsmen have long sought to improve the cultivated grasses, but there was until 1919 no research station devoted to this purpose. The Cambridge Plant Breeding Station being situated on the drier side of Britain was more suited to the breeding of grain than of leaf crops, and the Welsh hill farmers working under a rainfall much higher than that of the eastern counties, soon found that varieties of crops produced in that region were of little help to them. This had been a handicap during the 1914–18 war when farmers were urged to intensify their output of food, and a great benefactor of the University College of Wales, Aberystwyth, Sir Laurence Philipps, later Lord Milford, gave £10,000 for the establishment of a Welsh Plant Breeding Station and an endowment of £1,000 a year for the first ten years. By great good fortune

[1] *Journ. Roy. Agric. Soc.*, 1903, Vol. 64.

the man eminently fitted for the Directorship was on the spot
and was duly appointed; he took up his duties in 1919 and held
the position till 1942, a period during which, largely through
his activities, the treatment of grassland was radically improved
resulting in a marked change in the face of the countryside of
Britain. The man was Reginald George Stapledon.

He was born on September 22, 1882, at Lakenham, Northam,
near Bideford, and came of a long line of North Devon landowners and farmers. His grandfather, James Stapledon of
Bideford had, like many others in the early nineteenth century,
broken away from the land and become a master-mariner; his
father, William (1829–1902), did likewise, sailing his own
barque from Appledore and including among other enterprises
much gun running to South America. He was capable and forceful, vehement in condemning the bad conditions under which
shipowners expected their crews to sail, very observant and
with an almost poetic appreciation of Nature—traits which re-
appeared markedly in young George. Shortly after the Suez
Canal was opened in 1869 he set up a shipping agency in Suez
and Port Said; it prospered and brought him also the friendship
of de Lesseps and the confidence of the canal community. All
this necessitated long absences from home and when finally he
returned he was smitten by a stroke which kept him bedridden
for some years before he died in 1902.

The outstanding influence of George's early days was his
mother, Mary, daughter of William Clibbett, the last builder
of wooden ships in Appledore, a man of pronounced literary
tastes and strong character who obstinately refused to abandon
wood for iron or to turn off his workpeople—and he died
penniless but owing nothing. She was very beautiful and very
independent minded; she had had little formal education and
was largely self taught; she was an enthusiastic admirer of
Darwin, Huxley, and other advanced thinkers of the time and
became an agnostic or free thinker as they were then called.
This in a small country town involved her in much social isolation which was made worse by the circumstance that she was
the sister of her husband's deceased wife: such marriages were
not approved by the strict in those days. George was devoted
to her and she to him; she had ample leisure, and like her
husband was a great lover of nature, fortunately also know-

ledgeable. She took George botanizing over Braunton Burrows, then floristically rich, and gave him a small garden where he grew flowers and fruit for her in friendly competition with the gardener who, like others of his tribe in those days, was somewhat of a poet and philospher. It was an idyllic childhood: he became and remained a keen gardener, and his familiarity with the famous golf course at Westward Ho! made him later a keen golfer. His happy relations with his mother lasted throughout her life; she died in 1928 at the age of 86, having lived long enough to see his early triumphs.

At the age of eight he went to the United Service College at Westward Ho!, a private school established by army officers for their sons, but he found the masters 'a drab lot' and although he remained there for ten years he was not conscious of deriving any benefit therefrom. He gained no distinctions and after he left in 1900 to go to Cambridge he had to spend a year with a crammer in London to make sure of passing the entrance examination.

In October 1901 he entered Emmanuel College and read geology, chemistry and botany for the Natural Sciences Tripos, but he developed no enthusiasm for any of these subjects. He was, of course, well off and under no compulsion to work hard, being intended for the family business; like others in those days he was there to develope poise and acquire the art of gracious living. He was mildly interested in geology, but not in chemistry or botany although he attended lectures by Marshall Ward and A. C. Seward, who was his tutor. He records that apart from a certain amount of golf and of botanizing he was somewhat bored and was not taken very seriously; indeed he relates that Seward treated him rather as a joke. In the Tripos he got a second class and went down in June 1904 undistinguished and not conscious of any marked influence of any of his teachers. Three months later he entered the family firm on the Suez Canal and was well trained in the keeping of detailed and accurate records, which proved invaluable to him in later years. But he was not happy; in fact he hated it; he retained only one pleasant memory: a holiday in the Lebanon where he did some geologizing.

After two years he decided he could stand it no longer; his grandiose ideas of business expansion were not encouraged, the climate did not suit him, he wanted to go back to Devon and grow fruit. Very wisely his father agreed: in 1907 he became a pupil on a large fruit farm in Kent. It was an interesting period. Wye College had for some thirteen years been making scientific studies of fruit problems and the best of the growers were showing a lively interest therein. Stapledon clearly felt the stirrings for he relates: 'it was there I suddenly came to life and realized that I was really a potential scientist'. He wrote for advice to his old college tutor, Professor Seward, who advised him to return to Cambridge and take the diploma course in agriculture. This he did in October 1908. The course then normally lasted two years, but as the first year was devoted mainly to the pure sciences which he had already taken in his Tripos he was allowed to proceed direct to the second year lectures. It was a youthful vigorous school doing much good scientific work. T. B. Wood, who had devotedly tended it since its small beginnings in 1894, had at long last in 1906 been appointed Professor of Agriculture, and was introducing modern concepts into the science of animal nutrition. R. H. Biffen under the stimulating influence of W. Bateson was applying Mendelian concepts to the breeding of wheat and had already produced the famous 'Little Joss', whilst F. H. A. Marshall was investigating animal reproduction. On the University Farm experiments on seed mixtures for grassland begun by T. H. Middleton were still being continued, as were S. S. Armstrong's pasture surveys.

But whatever may have been Stapledon's hopes and anticipations, none of this appealed to him. He was of course, much above the average student age, being now twenty-six, which would hamper student intercourse, though it did not prevent friendships with a few who afterwards rose to distinction. Others, however, found him 'very ordinary, with an annoying trick of arguing with anybody and propounding odd and often absurd theories to the senior people as well as criticizing their teaching methods', as one of them wrote. Looking back years afterwards he considered his time at Cambridge 'a rather colourless interlude'; forestry ('which I read as a bye-play') was the subject that most appealed to him; the reader was Dr Henry, an amusing and eccentric Irishman 'whose enthusiasm thrilled me', and he wrote 'I was much more deeply influenced by (him) . . . than by any other professor, teacher, or master under whom I had ever sat'. Excepting Dr Henry, he wrote, 'I made no inspiring contacts with my professors and teachers'. Neither at school nor at the university had formal class instruction seemed to do much for him; he felt he gained more from his mother's mode of self-education. He obtained his diploma in June, 1909, and left Cambridge, undistinguished and having apparently made as little impression as when he had gone down five years earlier.

But although he did not realize it at the time, Cambridge had given him two gifts of vital importance for his future work: its technique for analyzing botanically the herbage of a field, and an ecological outlook, which he may have acquired from Henry, as his first ecological references dealt with woodlands.

Immediately after leaving Cambridge he proceeded to the Royal Agricultural College at Cirencester, where he had been appointed Assistant in the Department of Natural History which included botany, zoology and geology. The head of the Department, J. R. Ainsworth Davies, who was also Principal of the College, had lectured on all three subjects (as was usual in his younger days) and wanted to split off botany: he accordingly gave it to Stapledon as a new department. Stapledon's first assignment was to examine the ground flora of the Forestry Department's experimental field, but he was quickly attracted to the field experiments of Edward Kinch, the Professor of Chemistry to whom, as he wrote, years afterwards, he owed the beginning of his interest in grassland.

Kinch was the outstanding figure on the staff at that time, and the type of man to whom Stapledon could certainly be drawn. He was a native of the region, born sixty-one years earlier at Faringdon only eighteen miles away, soaked in knowledge of country lore and much else—'ask Kinch' was usually the answer to a difficult question—a fascinating companion on a country walk, also a keen gardener. Mellowed by a great sorrow in his early days, when after a year of happy marriage he had lost his young wife, he was deeply interested in his students and young colleagues and always ready to help them. He had first come to the college in 1869 as assistant in the Chemical Department, then in 1876 he went to Japan as

Professor of Chemistry at the Imperial College of Agriculture, Komada, Tokyo. Westernization was only just beginning; he had known the old Japan and could talk about it. He had returned to Cirencester in 1881.

He was well versed in the Rothamsted investigations and had in 1888 started a repetition on a smaller scale of the park grass experiments on the manuring of permanent grass for hay.[1] No botanical analyses of the herbage, however, had been made and Kinch asked Stapledon to undertake this, which he did.

This was the beginning of Stapledon's association with grassland.

At Kinch's suggestion he widened the scope of his enquiries by analysing the herbage of other Cotswold pastures, using a modification of the Cambridge method for collecting the samples. Fortunately for him the two seasons in which he did this were sharply contrasted, 1910 being fairly normal whilst 1911 was exceptionally hot and dry. Each of the hay plots had developed its characteristic flora, as at Rothamsted, the species most favoured by the treatment having repressed those less favoured. The flora finally established remained unchanged so long as the conditions remained unchanged, but it shifted to a new equilibrium if the conditions altered.

Stapledon saw that these two factors, competition and the dominating effects of environment (including treatment) explained several well known observations. Competition affected not only components of the flora but also explained why poor grasslands carried far more species of plants than rich ones: nothing could grow very vigorously and therefore any plant arising from seed blown in had a chance of survival, whilst on the richer grassland the favoured species grew so vigorously that only equally vigorous intruders could hope to survive. Stapledon found some twenty to thirty species on the good grasslands but over sixty on the poor land.

But he was far more interested in the ecological problem, the effects of environment in determining the vegetation type. The first requirement was ability to classify the types and he thought he could do this if he had sufficient botanical analyses, the species in each case being classified in the usual ecological groups: dominant, sub-dominant, etc. In natural habitats there

[1] See p. 149.

was good correlation between association and environment; he wanted to find out whether it existed for grassland, an association created artificially and then for a period of years left undisturbed except by the grazing animal—the history of most of our permanent grassland. 'It only needs to be proved' he wrote, 'that the flora of an area is essentially a function of the environment, and that chance is not a serious disturbing factor, for ecology to become a very important subject . . . a knowledge of the one affords material for accurate deductions concerning the other'. Years later he expanded this theme in connection with his visit to Australia. In these associations he thought the weeds would be particularly useful as diagnostic agents.

The most important of these observations, however, was made in the hot dry season of 1911. There were heavy casualties among the sown grasses in the pasture, but unsown indigenous plants of the same species had survived much better. One grass in particular attracted his attention: hard fescue (*Festuca duriuscula*). 'It is probable', he wrote,[1] 'that if large amounts of seed from the endemic variety could be collected, results as satisfactory as those recently obtained by the use of wild Dutch (i.e. White) clover might be forthcoming.[2]

In 1912 C. Bryner Jones, Professor of Agriculture at the University College of Wales, Aberystwyth, received from the Board of Agriculture a grant for the appointment of a botanical advisor and he chose Stapledon. The main task was a botanical survey of Central Wales; this was expected to take several years. He had also to advise the farmers on botanical matters and to devote not more than 100 hours per session to teaching in college.

He proceeded energetically with the botanical survey. Fortunately, O. T. Jones, then Professor of Geology, and a group of students were making a geological survey of the region and Stapledon camped with them. He made long expeditions with them on foot into the hills collecting many sod samples which in the evenings he tore to pieces, identifying and counting the plants, then calculating the percentage that each species con-

---

[1] *J. Agric. Sci.*, 1912–13, Vol. 5, pp. 129–51.

[2] The reference is to Gilchrist's demonstration of the superiority of wild white clover over the cultivated varieties. See p. 249.

tributed to the total. Like some other biologists of his day he was not strong in mathematics, and his companions were sometimes amused at seeing him produce and use a multiplication table in those operations. These and his earlier analyses laid the foundation of his unrivalled knowledge of the herbage plants, and also provided for the first time a basis for the classification of grasslands that he had been seeking. His maps of the distribution of the vegetation types showed distinct correlation with the geological maps, the governing factor being apparently the water relations.

These expeditions brought him into contact with the Welsh farmers whom he soon learnt to like, and they liked him. But he found their agriculture deplorable. Oats were the chief crop, but the sorts grown, he declared, would be classed by most agriculturists as weeds. The other crops were also poor. Part of the trouble arose from the very poor quality of the seed supplied. He went thoroughly into this question and produced a scathing report on the local seed trade, which led to speedy improvement.

Many of the hill grazings were very poor, carrying no more than one sheep to the acre even in summer. He resolved to improve that, and in collaboration with Abel E. Jones he published in 1916 the first of a series of technical studies which continued throughout his working life.

In 1914 he became acquainted with an Honours Botany student, T. J. Jenkin, who quite independently of Stapledon's work had based his honours thesis on some interesting observations he had made on the changing flora of a sown pasture on his father's farm in Carmarthenshire. He had noticed the superiority of self sown indigenous *Festuca duriuscula* over the commercial variety and had suggested that it should be cultivated for farmers. As Stapledon in his 1913 paper had been thinking along the same lines (except that his suggestion was the collection of the wild seed) he proposed to Jenkin that they should join forces and produce a joint paper on indigenous plants in relation to habitat and sown species. This appeared in 1916, and is one of the most important on the subject.[1] The commercial foreign varieties may give better yields for a few years, but they are sooner or later ousted by the indigenous varieties; it is therefore better to start with these, or simply

[1] *J. Agric. Sc.*, Vol. 8, pp. 26–64, 1916.

N*

to make the conditions more favourable for them when they will more speedily develop of their own accord.

At first the war had not interfered with Stapledon's activities, but by the end of 1916 the food situation had called into existence the Food Production Department and Stapledon was required to take charge of the new Seed Testing Station associated therewith. After the war he gave this up and returned to Aberystwyth in 1919 as Director of the newly established Welsh Plant Breeding Station. He began by visiting Denmark and Sweden along with Biffen and a few others to see their well equipped stations for seed control and plant improvement, and he made some useful contacts, notably with Turesson, whose studies of the wild grasses and dicotyledons of Sweden had shown that one and the same species might be found in somewhat modified forms in different environments. This work was then attracting considerable attention among botanists.

Back at Aberystwyth he proceeded to build up his Staff. T. J. Jenkin became Senior Scientific Officer; the junior staff was built up from students as suitable ones appeared. He had the gift of detecting, attracting and holding prospective good research workers, and the Welsh hill farms from which the college drew a number of its students were—and still are—a prolific source of good human material.

The initial programme of work fell into two broad divisions: a search for possible new crops to diversify and enrich the rather meagre system of farming practised in Wales, and the improvement of crops already grown. The search for new crops yielded little result: none of those tried proved more useful than those already cultivated. On the other hand the efforts at crop improvement were highly successful. Three crop groups were investigated: grasses; clovers and lucerne; and cereals with some green fodder crops. The work on cereals was chiefly on oats, much the most important arable crop in Wales, occupying nearly half the cultivated land. The common varieties *Avena sativa* and *A. strigosa* were poor though reasonably tolerant of their conditions, but the station soon produced better varieties which have now superseded the old sorts. Clovers and grasses, however, were entirely novel subjects for plant breeders and new techniques were required. The methods suitable for cereals were not directly applicable to grasses because, while cereals are self fertilized, grasses in the main are cross fertilized, the pollen being usually carried by wind.

The first step was to make a collection of as many types of the wanted grasses and clovers as could be found. Both Stapledon and Jenkin travelled widely to survey grasslands, often taking small sample sods as they went. These were sent to Aberystwyth in boxes of sterilized soil, then transplanted in rows each of ten plants two feet apart. These were then divided into two sections: one was cut each year for hay and aftermath, the other was cut monthly to simulate the effect of the grazing animal. Observations were made on characters of agricultural importance: habits of growth (leafy or stemmy), length of growing season, time of flowering, winter hardiness, rate of mortality, susceptibility to disease; in selected cases the mineral constituents and nitrogen contents of the leaves were determined.

The collection became enormous and the number of observations colossal. In one investigation on red clover R.D. Williams made individual observations on ten different characters in 30,000 seedlings over a period of three years. Stapledon's training in recording in his father's counting house at Suez must have proved invaluable. It was of course, magnificent material for an ecologist; his paper, *Cocksfoot ecotypes in relation to the biotic factor*[1] is one of the classics of agricultural botany.

During the 1920's British agriculture was passing through long periods of depression. As usual, the part of the farm that suffered most was the grassland: much of it got into a deplorable state and improvement was desperately needed, particularly on the hill grazings. Two general methods were investigated. One, the ecological method, was to make the conditions as favourable as possible for the better herbage type so that it could readily develop. Given time this would come automatically, the indigenous varieties being wide spread. Wild white clover and a few of the grasses, notably rye grass, were the desirable basis and the requirements for clover satisfied the grasses. A dressing of phosphate, either basic slag or mineral phosphate and in some cases lime, together with a good harrowing, often sufficed. But the alternative method, to plough

[1] *J. Ecol.*, vol. 16, pp. 71–104, 1926.

up and reseed was quicker and better, and from the outset Stapledon had tried to devise suitable seed mixtures.

Unfortunately, early in 1926 he suffered a serious breakdown in health, and made the long sea voyage to Australia and New Zealand, staying there for some months. E. Bruce Levy was there seeking ways of improving the New Zealand grassland, mainly on ecological lines. Stapledon urged Levy to carry out extensive trials of agronomic strains of grasses and clovers. So successful were these that he was asked to send out one of his staff to develop them. He chose one of his ablest young colleagues, William Davies, who did such good work that later the University of New Zealand conferred upon him its honorary D.Sc. degree.

He then proceeded to Australia where he saw the various stages in the conversion of the native flora—the stable climax vegetation—into the unstable transient forms that dominated the countryside. A proper appreciation of the successional relationship of the different types of vegetation to each other and to the varied soil and climatic conditions would, he considered, facilitate the conversion of the natural vegetation into a more desirable type and indicate ways of maintaining it.

What impressed him most in this journey, however, was the enormous potential but unrealized value of the grasslands of Australia, New Zealand and such of the South African veld as he had seen during the ship's stay at Cape Town. None of these countries had a properly equipped grassland research station, and he recommended that one should be established on generous lines like the Svalöf Station in Sweden; also that in each country proper agrostological surveys should be made.

He returned to England much improved in health and found a lively interest in agricultural development both at home and in the Commonwealth. The Ministry of Agriculture's campaign for the improvement of grassland was in full progress, and he and J. A. Hanley, one of the most experienced Agricultural Advisors of the time, wrote *Grassland, its management and improvement*, which was well received.[1] Unfortunately the depression of the early 1930's disheartened farmers and they lost interest for a time.

Meanwhile some of the plants in the station's great collection

[1] Oxford University Press, 1927.

appeared sufficiently promising to justify extended farm trials and by 1930 some of the grasses, clover and oats were being tested throughout Britain.

Stapledon realized that selection alone would not provide the range of characters wanted; combinations of characters were required which could be obtained only by breeding. Fortunately the search for suitable techniques was successful after what he described as 'eleven years of trial and error' and the final results were published in a Station bulletin (1931). Following his usual practice he had allotted the grasses mostly to T. J. Jenkin, the clover to R. D. Williams, and kept cocksfoot (*Dactylis glomerata*) for himself. He chose cocksfoot because in the Aberystwyth region it occurred more commonly than any other grass in more or less well-defined ecotypes; it was also more highly self fertile than most of the other local grasses and, as one of the most persistently leafy grasses it had high agricultural value. It still appeared that the pure line technique was unsuitable, there being too much hetorozygosity. Recourse was therefore had to mass hydridization. About thirty desirable parents were selected from the vast collection, they were selfed, some 200 'quintessential plants' were selected from the progeny, but not emasculated, they were enclosed together in a small glasshouse in conditions intended to exclude foreign pollen, and at the proper time shaken by a simple mechanical device to ensure distribution of the pollen. In each generation there was re-selection, and non-conforming plants were rejected. The method was frankly empirical and subjective: 'largely selection and trial on what would now be termed poly-cross lines' a colleague described it.

Stapledon was not interested in genetics or cytology. At the outset he disclaimed any intention of aiming at genetical purity. This he considered might be necessary for crops like wheat that had to be processed but not for forage crops where the difference between higher and lower purity is chiefly a difference in weight per unit area rather than in quality. Many generations, he wrote, would be needed to attain complete genetic purity, whereas a 70 per cent purity could be attained much sooner and would represent a great advance on existing varieties of grasses. It was not that he was satisfied with 70 per cent purity: he was imbued with a deep sense of urgency, the pressing need to improve the grasslands of the country, especially in the hill districts, and as the new varieties were a great advance on those still in use he wanted to get them out to the farmers as quickly as possible. Like some other very successful plant breeders he had a clear vision of what he wanted to produce, and the artist's intuition to guide his choice of initial material.

The method is open to the objection that some degree of heterozygosity is inevitable, rendering the variety liable to instability: indeed at one time there was a blurring of the differences between certain varieties, but this was rectified by reconstructing them. His judgment had, however, been so good that his first strain of cocksfoot to be distributed, S26, developed from five plants found in a gorse brake in Devon and put on the market in 1937, still retains its popularity as do two later ones, S37 and S143.

While Stapledon was producing the cocksfoot varieties, T. J. Jenkin was working on perennial rye grass (Lolium perenne) timothy, and other grasses with equally successful results: some of his strains, especially S.23 rye grass, are still very popular. His technique, however, differed from that of Stapledon, being based on genetic principles,[1] as also was the technique of R. D. Williams who produced the very valuable S.100 white clover and S.123 red clover.

Considerable time elapses between the production of a new variety at a plant breeding station and the appearance of the seed on sale to farmers. For the market, of course, it must be produced in tons. Grasses being cross fertilized, with wind as the carrier of the pollen, special care has to be taken to avoid contamination during their multiplication. Anything from twelve to fifteen years may elapse between the first crossing and the marketing of the resulting new variety; for the two clovers just mentioned the interval had been seventeen years; from 1920 to 1937.

Stapledon did not wait for this final stage: having got sufficient seed of these better varieties of grasses and clovers for experimental purposes, he was anxious to organize a large scale demonstration combining all the methods of improvement of hill grazings that had proved effective in his numerous trials.

[1] Described in Station *Bull.*, No. 2, 1924.

He drew up an ambitious scheme estimated to cost £20,000, a large sum in those days and far beyond anything the Government would provide. He and the College Principal, H. Stewart Jones, sent a letter to The Times pointing out that large areas of grass in our country now regarded as inevitably derelict, could, by these new methods, become an asset of enormous importance, and appealed for funds to show the way. The letter was published on July 11, 1932; soon came the response by Sir Julien Cahn who generously offered £3,000 a year for seven years. A lease was taken of a hill farm near Devil's Bridge with grazings up to 1,350 ft. altitude, and some 2,000 acres of sheep walk up to 1,850 ft. altitude, much of the herbage being of the very poor molinia–nardus type. Molinia is the blue moor grass and is useful animal food, nardus is the white grass and was classed by Stapledon as one of the most worthless of hill plants. The customary procedure was to keep the sheep on these walks during summer but remove them during autumn and winter, selling those ready for market, transferring others to lower fields on the farm, and boarding out weaker lambs on lowland farms, a costly and often unprofitable business which Stapledon sought to obviate by producing more winter food on the upland farms besides making the summer grazing more profitable.

Moses Griffith, Agricultural Adviser for Merionethshire, was put in charge of the work; it began in March, 1933, and quickly yielded striking results which Stapledon intended should be seen, and they were. He had a wonderful gift of presentation. From the road one saw on the bleak hillside a great patch of green herbage dotted with sheep happily grazing, surrounded by the dark forsaken wild vegetation to which, however, they occasionally had recourse apparently in search of some nutrient not adequately provided by the plants shown. When Sir Julien's gift was exhausted the scheme was financed by the Ministry of Agriculture until 1947 after which it was included in the Ministry's experimental Hill Farm.

The information obtained had wide and lasting value, and with other work of the station staff has provided most of the techniques now employed by farmers for upland reclamation. By the irony of fate the grass varieties Stapledon produced did not turn out to be the most suitable for the purpose. The really pivotal grass is Jenkin's remarkable S.23 rye grass, which, according to P. T. Thomas, the Director of the Station in the 1960's, has been responsible for more grassland improvement on the hills, than all the others put together: notable examples are on the Kerry Dolfor hills and the Shropshire hills in the Bishop's Castle and Clun areas. Stapledon's influence and advice stimulated extensive reclamation during the last war, much of which still remains greatly improved.

Meanwhile the experimental plots at the Plant Breeding Station, always interesting to scientists, were becoming increasingly interesting to farmers and many came from far and wide to see them. As demonstrator Stapledon was unrivalled. He could hold his audience spellbound by his vivid descriptions and his amazingly infectious enthusiasm; on occasion the chara-banc due to take the party home would be kept waiting two hours or more because he was still willing to continue answering questions and elaborating. At Cahn Hill he would at times demonstrate mounted on a Welsh pony and armed with a trumpet-shaped megaphone: a striking unforgettable figure with his finely moulded features and great shock of hair; he must often have reminded his Welsh hearers of a warrior chieftain calling them to battle, and indeed it was a crusade he was leading; an end to the poverty of the hill farmers and a better life for them through more productive grassland.

Later on the Ministry of Agriculture, wishing to intensify the grassland improvement scheme, asked Stapledon in October 1938 to do a lecture tour of England and Wales and with William Davies and three assistants to make a detailed survey of the grasslands. His theme for the lectures was that the grass now treated as permanent should be regarded as a crop and made to play its part in the rotation. Instead of being left down indefinitely it should be ploughed up and followed by a highly productive sequence of arable crops, then the land laid down to grass again for a further period. 'Take the plough round the farm' was his new slogan, and ley farming became the new method—or rather a revival of the old alternate husbandry system as practised by the Cistercian monks in Norman and later times.

Meanwhile the grassland survey was becoming increasingly important, for war was threatening and if it should break out the survey would form the basis of the inevitable ploughing

up campaign to increase the area under corn. It was a remarkable undertaking and the most extensive yet made. More
than 9 million acres of permanent grassland were reported to
be 'a standing reproach', but 'fit for the plough'. Much of it
had been ploughed up and made productive in the first War,
but during the post-war depression had deteriorated or even
become derelict. When war broke out in September 1939 the
Ministry of Agriculture provided funds for a Grass Land Improvement Station at Drayton near Stratford-on-Avon on a
derelict 500 acre farm, most of it on heavy lower lias clay: 'the
epitome of all that was wrong with rural Britain', was Stapledon's description. Two other equally dispiriting farms were
included in this scheme, 1,300 acres of poor moorland in Staf-
fordshire, and 1,000 derelict acres in the Cotswolds. Stapledon
was in charge of all of these, and the changes he effected
attracted large parties of farmers; he also did much lecturing
to large farmer audiences besides retaining his post at Aberystwyth. He was fortunate in having William Davies' help, for
wartime difficulties about labour and transport had made the
combined tasks very heavy, greatly overtaxing his strength.

In 1942 he felt no longer justified in retaining the Directorship of the Plant Breeding Station in view of the long absences
necessitated by his work for the Ministry from 1938 onwards.
He therefore resigned the Directorship and his scientific work
ceased. He continued his demonstrations until the end of the
war in 1945 and then retired into private life broken in health
through years of overwork. He could not however, rest and
recoup. As with other scientific workers of those days, the
pre-war pension arrangements were quite inadequate to meet
the rising costs of post-war years and there followed a period
when he had to do some journalism. In 1947, however, Messrs.
Dunn's Farm Seeds of Salisbury invited him to become their
Scientific Adviser, and later, one of their Directors. This
brought him back to his favourite occupation in very congenial
circumstances. Dunn's were old friends, having been among
the first to recognize the importance of the station's work and
to distribute the new varieties of grass and clover seeds.

He was at first very happy, but soon began the pitiful tragedy
of his last years. His first breakdown in health which had sent
him on the voyage to New Zealand and Australia had been

followed by two others, one in 1928, the other in 1935, from which happily he had recovered, but now came the third more painful period. In 1952 he had a serious operation and from then till the end in 1960 he was rarely free from illness: angina, kidney trouble, bronchitis, Menières disease and then, greatest affliction of all, stone deafness for the last three years of his life. All communications with him had to be by writing. To the end, however, his mind remained unclouded, restless and critical as ever. His interest in agriculture waned, but was replaced by a wide range of others; among them poetry, philosophy, psychology, and education. He left twelve large note books full of comments and ideas on what he had read: these formed the subject of a book, *Human Ecology* written by R. Waller in Stapledon's name.

He died on September 6, 1960. Few men in his generation left a greater mark on the countryside of Britain than he did. Before he began his work grass had been the cinderella among crops: it could tolerate neglect and in bad times was the first to get it. When he began his crusade great stretches of permanent grass had a woebegone appearance, and produced only a fraction of what was possible; it was a thing apart from the cropped land. He made it possible to effect a complete integration in all but the drier eastern parts of the country, thus considerably changing the landscape of the farm and giving greatly increased yields of grass resulting in marked increases of milk and meat, and leaving the soil much improved for the succeeding arable crops.

His work on the reclamation of hill land showed how large areas of the $5\frac{1}{2}$ million acres of rough grazing in England and Wales could be made more productive if and when the need arises, it also enabled marginal land to be kept in cultivation when otherwise it might slip back and become derelict.

He recognized however, that the nation had other needs besides food—non-material needs he called them—and he felt strongly that the uplands should contribute to these. Moreover in his extensive travels through Britain he was, like many others in those days, sensitive to the beauty of the countryside, made painfully aware of the devastation then proceeding at an appalling rate following on the very heavy war-time losses of sons and fortunes sustained by the county families who had long been its custodians. In 1935 he wrote *The Land, Now and Tomorrow* telling of some of the atrocities he himself had seen, of the unnecessary village poverty due to the neglect of our agriculture, and in glowing terms setting forth what rural Britain could be like if changes now quite practicable were made. The complete sincerity of the book brought it a wonderful reception; repeated re-issues were called for, and it must have played an important part in stimulating public interest in the countryside.

He was not interested in college organizations as such or in faculty or senate meetings, indeed he seemed completely lacking any regard for academic procedure or regulations and was often rather a rebel, but a very likeable one. Nor did he take much interest in scientific societies except the Grassland Society of which he was one of the founders and its first President; its first congress was in 1937. 'Grass and grassland, and yet more grass and grassland', as he put it, was his main interest in work, and gardening, golf and later riding his relaxations. Yet he was no dull recluse: his love of the countryside, his vigorous enthusiasms for it, the visionary and poetic elements in his character with a touch of Peter Pan, his intense dislike of pretentiousness and injustice combined with his gift of racy description made him a good companion, popular alike with students and staff in the college and brought him a wide and varied circle of friends outside.

No account of Stapledon would be complete without including his wife Doris, only daughter of Thomas Wood Bourne and of Jessie Bourne. They were married in 1913, but having no children she devoted herself entirely to his work, which she equipped herself to follow: always, too, she sedulously guarded his uncertain health. They were inseparable companions. His extensive agricultural tours were almost invariably by car and she always drove. Towards the end he estimated that she must have driven him some 700,000 miles, often over very difficult track ways, to almost inaccessible places. In prefaces to his book he describes her variously as his dictionary, his ready reckoner, on occasion his Cahn Hill demonstrator. It is certain that without her aid he could never have achieved anything like as much as he did.[1]

[1] I sincerely thank the Royal Society for permission in preparing this chapter to make full use of the Biographical Memoir of Sir George Stapledon that I wrote for their Series in 1963.

Although he was not on the staff of the Plant Breeding Station, Thomas Wallace Fagan of the Department of Agricultural Chemistry rendered invaluable service by undertaking many chemical investigations. His papers were mostly published in the *Welsh Journal of Agriculture,* volumes 1 to 18, 1928 to 1945, and they were nothing like as well known as they deserved to be. He was the first in this country to deal comprehensively with the chemical composition of herbage plants, especially the variations with stage of maturity, ratio of stem to leaf, frequency of cutting, manuring, environment, and strain or species. He showed that the shorter the interval between two cuttings the richer the grass in protein and the lower in fibre content, but the weight of total produce fell off. Frequent cutting also tended to produce a more leafy herbage with a higher ratio of leaf to stem than less frequently cut herbage; and both leaf and stem contained more protein and less fibre than when the herbage was cut less frequently. Different species and even strains grown under similar conditions could vary considerably in their content of phosphoric acid and of lime, indigenous strains being richer than the commercial.[1] The clovers contained less phosphoric acid than either perennial or Italian rye grass or cocksfoot, but much more nitrogen and lime. Fagan was an indefatigable analyst and published details of the compositions of numerous wild pasture plants and of various species and strains of grasses at different stages of maturity. As a result of his work much more was known in the 1930's about the chemistry of grassland herbage than about that of arable crops. He made an interesting set of determinations of the recovery of nitrogen from nitrogenous fertilizers applied to pastures and found it was much higher than is usual for arable crops, being commonly of the order of 70 per cent instead of the customary 50 per cent. He took the view that nitrogenous fertilizers encouraged microbiological changes in the soil which increased the amount of soil nitrogen available to the plant. On the sward rich in clover, however, the recovery of nitrogen from fertilizers was negligible because of the harmful effect of the nitrogenous fertilizer on the clover.

His history was simple. From his school in Caernarvon he

[1] Many of the soils on the Welsh hill farms were low in phosphate and lime though generally well supplied with potash and nitrogen.

went to Denstone College in 1887 and remained there till 1895 when he won an exhibition to Caius College, Cambridge, where he took a First Class in the Science Tripos in Chemistry. After a short period at Abertillery Secondary School he went to University College, Bangor, in 1901 to study Agricultural Chemistry, and then went to Harper Adams College. In 1905 he transferred to a lectureship at the Agricultural Department of the University of Edinburgh and remained there for 14 years; he then passed on to Aberystwyth in 1919, the year in which the Plant Breeding Station was opened. From the outset he took the greatest interest in its work and was always extremely helpful to members of its staff. He was contemporary with Woodman of Cambridge who, however, was working on lowland grassland so that their work when it touched was complementary. His first paper was with H. Trevor Jones on the nutritive value of grasses as shown by their chemical composition and is typical both of his style and his thoroughness.[1] He was a quiet modest man, a good and likeable colleague. He never received the recognition that he had so thoroughly earned, but he had never sought it.

The directorship of the Welsh Plant Breeding Station passed in 1942 to Thomas James Jenkin who, as stated earlier, had already been managing it during Stapledon's enforced long absences. During the war the staff of the Institute had been scattered to provide advisory officers in the counties needing them: Jenkin had the task of keeping the Institute alive and restoring it to activity after the war. He was the first to apply modern genetic principles to the breeding of grasses on a large scale; he abandoned mass selection methods and based his results on the genetic qualities of individual plants. He devised the intricate selection and breeding techniques necessary for the work and was able to produce true breeding strains of leafy perennial grasses of great value. He investigated interspecific hybrids within the genus lolium with notable success, and later extended his researches to other interspecific and intergeneric hybrids among the grasses. He deserved fuller recognition than

[1] *Bull. Welsh Pl. Breed. Sta.*, Series H, 1924, No. 3, p. 85. Two other papers dealt with the effects of nitrogenous fertilizers on the chemical composition of the grasses, (*Bull.* No. 9, 1928 and No. 13, 1932) and another gave the chemical composition of eleven species and strains of grasses at different stages of maturity (*Welsh Jn. Agric.*, 1931, Vol. 7, p. 246).

he obtained. He retired in 1950 and was followed by E. T. Jones who held the directorship for eight difficult years of post war rehabilitation when it passed on to Percy Thomas.

Very considerable changes in farm practice had taken place in the meantime, and this necessitated changes in the work of the Institute. The earlier object had been to produce varieties genetically adapted to specific environmental conditions. The breeding material was therefore selected on an ecological basis. The new conditions required a different purpose: it was in the words of the Director 'to ensure efficient conversion of solar energy and soil nutrients into that kind of herbage needed by the animal for maximum production'. Progress to that end is not yet in the realm of history and is to be sought in the Annual Reports of the Institute.

The long standing problem of assessing and recording the utilized output of grassland grazed by livestock was taken up again in the 1950's and is still being debated. Knowing the numbers of grazing animals and days, and the number of pounds of starch equivalent required per day by a grazing animal for maintenance, putting on weight and milk production, the total number of pounds consumed over any given period can be calculated. The starch equivalents furnished by any supplementary foods are deducted and the resulting value is recalculated on an acreage basis.[1] The conversions involved in these calculations rest for the most part on the work of T. B. Wood and the Cambridge School on the scientific basis of rationing for animals.[2]

THE NEW GRASSLAND AGRONOMY.
THE HURLEY INSTITUTE

It was early realized that intensification of grassland management would raise many new problems that could not be studied at the Plant Breeding Station. Moreover the meteorological conditions at Aberystwyth differed considerably from those of great areas of English grassland, and it was therefore decided to establish a grassland station in England. Drayton near Stratford-on-Avon was used for a time after Stapledon left it

[1] *Journ. Brit. Grassl. Soc.*, 1955, Vol. 10, p. 67; also *ibid*, 1964. Vol. 19, p. 160.
[2] *Journ. Ag. Sci.*, 1928, vol. 18, p. 486.

in 1945, but it had unsatisfactory features and was given up when the Agricultural Research Council took over grassland research and in 1955 the work was finally transferred to Hurley near Maidenhead where some 600 acres of land rise from the 100 ft. level of the Thames Valley to a plateau at 300 ft. level. The soil is a clay with flints as at Rothamsted, the yield of natural grassland is below average, but the leys and improved pastures are highly productive[1]. The rainfall is about 25–26 inches, conditions not unlike those of much of eastern and central England.

The early history of a research station depends very much on the character and activities of its first Director, and here Hurley was particularly fortunate. William Davies from the Welsh Plant Breeding Station was chosen.

He was born in April 1899 and on both sides came of old Welsh farming families. At the time of his birth the family was living in Kensington where his father had a dairy and grocery business, but the children spent much of their time on Cardiganshire farms owned and worked by their mother's people. William's first schools were in Aberystwyth and Borth, but at the age of eleven he transferred to a London school. His father wanted him to enter the family business, but his ambition was to become a farmer, and his father giving way he returned to Cardiganshire for the purpose. But the First World War was on and it was difficult for a young man of mettle to keep out of the Army; he therefore duly enlisted. He was demobilized in 1919 and returned to his farm, but soon realized that he would not get far without some proper technical education. The University College of Wales at Aberystwyth was conducting suitable courses and William obtained a county grant enabling him to attend one of them. He showed such outstanding ability that he was offered a four year grant which enabled him to take an honours science course at the college. He chose botany as his chief subject and obtained a First Class in 1923.

Here he attracted the attention of Stapledon, who had a keen eye for a brilliant student. Stapledon brought him into his re-

---

[1] The leys yield 5,000 to 14,000 lb. of dry matter per acre depending on the treatment and the permanent grass when improved and heavily fertilized yields 4,000 to 6,000 lb. of dry matter per acre. About $6\frac{1}{2}$ lb. dry matter of first quality grass produces 1 lb. live weight gain in young beef cattle.

search team and started him off on some plant breeding, but soon transferred him to ecological problems for which he had a preference. He showed a marked ability at working independently and for a time was in charge of investigations on seed mixtures. He developed great capacity for surveying grasslands, detecting good points and weaknesses and suggesting improvements: for this purpose he was asked to visit New Zealand, Australia and the Falkland Islands besides taking an important part in the wartime surveys of British grasslands.

No hard and fast programme of work was imposed at Hurley, but a general intention that it should include the production of herbage, its utilization by farm animals, and its role in their nutrition. The place of leys in the arable rotation was studied and also hay and silage, which played an important part in the improved utilization of grass, but their feed value needed to be increased and the losses in conservation reduced. One of the early problems undertaken at Hurley was to lengthen the grazing season by manipulating strains and species of grasses and nitrogen supply. An interesting feature was the introduction of Mediterranean grasses. Unlike ours which are active leaf producers during the summer months and dormant during winter, they lie dormant during the arid summers of their native environments and produce leaf during winter. The indigenous tall fescues of Morocco and Algeria make outstanding growth during winter from October to March. The result of these investigations was to extend the grazing season from the usual four or five months to about nine months. Davies' ambition had been to make all-the-year grazing possible. He did not quite achieve that, but had got well started on the way. A result definitely attained was the production of grass of high digestibility—over 70 per cent—throughout the season and from season to season. This investigation involved the devising by Raymond and Tilley of an *in vitro* method of determining digestibility which gave reproducible results closely agreeing with those given by *in vivo* methods. Another important result was that much larger quantities of nitrogen could profitably be given to grassland than is customary: 400 lb. per acre properly used was highly profitable. This quantity exceeded those recommended by I.C.I. in the 1920's—which were then thought to be extravagantly high. Grass-fed beef became some 30 per cent cheaper to produce than the usual barley-fed beef: it was also considerably more palatable. 400 lb. per acre was not the limit: it was possible to go to 1,000 lb. per acre without injury even to lambs. These are among the definitely ascertained practical results which have been passed out to farmers and may therefore be said to have passed into history.

The investigations on digestion led to interesting results recalling some obtained at the Dairy Research Institute, Shinfield. The efficiency of utilization of 'digested' energy appears to depend on the balance of acetic to propionic acids produced during rumen fermentation. There are, however, some long standing problems still without satisfactory solutions. How much grass does a grazing animal consume in a day? T. B. Wood some sixty years ago tried to find a solution but without success. A chromium oxide technique was used by later workers (1964) for estimating the digestible organic matter intake by grazing animals, the faecal nitrogen index being used to estimate the digestibility of the organic matter eaten, but Davies was not altogether satisfied with either. How can the value of grass in a pasture or meadow be best assessed? The old method was to estimate the dry matter plus crude protein per acre and try to evaluate them. Search for a solution of this and other problems was not confined to the members of research stations but was undertaken by others also.

CHAPTER XIV

THE DAIRY RESEARCH
INSTITUTES

SHINFIELD

I N general agricultural science is not concerned with agri-cultural products once they have left the farm; accordingly much of the dairy research could be excluded in view of the fact that most of the milk produced on British farms is sent away almost immediately and the farmer has nothing more to do with it. This, however, is a comparatively recent develop-ment; up till the latter part of the nineteenth century it was mainly converted on the farm into butter or cheese for marketing, there being few facilities for the transit of liquid milk till re-frigeration became practicable. The early syllabuses for agri-cultural education usually included classes on butter or cheese-making for prospective dairymaids, and some continued to do so after the need for them had passed.[1]

Robert Warington included a chapter on the science of dairying in his *Chemistry of the Farm*, the leading British text-book on the subject during the period 1880 to 1900, and it has remained as part of the subject ever since. Townspeople had their milk supplied from cows kept in the back premises of a multitude of little milk shops and fed on roots and hay brought in by farmers; the soiled straw and manure was taken away for use on the farms. It could not be said that the standards of dairying were generally high: it was a woman's job, and a farmer very proud of his crops and his livestock would tolerate lower standards in the dairy.

The Continental chemists were ahead of ours in dealing with milk and it was 1874 before J. A. Wanklyn, a well known

---

[1] In the early 1900's I used to make a small batch of butter each month to keep my hand in.

pioneer analyst, published his *Milk Analysis. A practical treatise on the examination of milk and its derivatives, cream, butter and cheese;* the earliest on the subject in English that I have been able to find. Little interest seems to have been taken at the time, and there is no evidence that the government chemist concerned himself with it. Only one other edition was called for and that was not till 1886. In 1875, however, an Act was passed dealing with adulteration of foods including milk, and from that time onwards analysis of foods became more important.

The Aylesbury Dairy Company set up a laboratory for the analysis of milk, the first of its kind so far as I can discover; by 1881 Paul Vieth was in charge of it, making analyses on the grand scale and doing much for the development of the subject; he may be regarded as the second founder of the subject here. Unfortunately I have been unable to find out much about him. He was almost certainly German and came to this country in the 1870's at a time when a number of German intellectuals were doing the same. He was already a well-trained chemist with his Ph.D.; he joined the Chemical Society and in 1877 became a Fellow of the Institute of Chemistry. He not only made many analyses of milk and dairy products, including mares' milk, but did much research on them, publishing the results sometimes in English, sometimes in German chemical journals. He was a prolific writer. His first English paper was in the *Analyst* for 1883, but the most impressive was in the *Journal of the Royal Agricultural Society* for 1888 in which he assembled and discussed the results of the 82,746 analyses that had accumulated during the period 1881 to 1887. He wrote no book and only one small booklet: *Easy Methods for the Examination of Milk.* 1887. He was one of the first to design a lactometer and he worked out a polarimetric method for determining lactose in milk. In 1892 he resigned his post at Aylesbury and his Fellowship of the Institute of Chemistry and later went to Hameln, in Hanover. No more is known of him.

Of the younger men who continued the development of dairy chemistry the most distinguished was Henry Droop Richmond. He was born at Hampstead in 1867 and educated at University College School where he studied chemistry under Temple

Orme, and at Finsbury Technical College. He then became an assistant in Otto Hehner's analytical laboratory, and later went to Cairo as second chemist in the Khedivial laboratory. He left this in 1892 to succeed Vieth as Chief Chemist to the Aylesbury Dairy Company, and he further developed the work that had been done there. He published many papers in the *Analyst* dealing among other topics with the variations in the composition of milk and their relation to season and other features; about 1895 he elaborated a formula and slide rule for determining the total solids in milk, which in a modified form was still used in the 1960's. He was very interested in the statistical approach to the treatment of the analytical data.

One of his great services to the subject was to write a book *Dairy Chemistry, a practical handbook for dairy chemists*, first published in 1899 in which he collected much verified but scattered information on the subject and worked it up into a coherent whole. It long remained the standard treatise on the subject.[1] In the earlier editions he made many references to Vieth's work. In 1915, after twenty-three years of valuable service to dairy chemistry, he transferred to Boots Pure Drug Company in Nottingham, first to work on the production of casein foods and of glycerophosphates, later to become Chief Analyst. He was a very likeable man, helpful to his younger colleagues, conducting classes for them in Latin and higher mathematics and while his health allowed joining them in indoor and outdoor sports and in week-end walks. He bravely stuck to his work till his death in 1931 though he suffered much sickness during the last seven years.[2]

Returning to the main story: in 1888 the British Dairy Farmers Association set up the British Dairy Institute also at Aylesbury under guidance of F. J. Lloyd to provide practical and scientific education in dairying. Eight years later (1896) it moved to Reading because better science teaching was available there, and the college showed its interest by appointing representatives on its committee of management. Lloyd had for some years been investigating cheese problems on a cheese-making farm in Somerset financed by the Bath and West

---

[1] Its last edition, the fourth, revised by J. G. Davis and F. J. Macdonald was issued in 1953.

[2] A good obituary notice appeared in the *Analyst*, 1931, vol. 56, p. 700.

Society and aided by a grant from the Board of Agriculture; in his report to the Board in 1899 he pointed out among many other items of interest that while the problems of cheese making had hitherto been supposed to be mainly chemical his experiments had shown that they were largely bacteriological.

Later at Leeds University Department of Agriculture H. Ingle had begun milk studies about 1900 but he left for South Africa in 1906. He was succeeded by Charles Crowther whose work is described elsewhere.[1]

In 1907–8 Thomas Orr, a medical bacteriologist seeking the sources of bacterial contamination of milk in the East and West Ridings of Yorkshire, had traced them mostly to improperly cleaned utensils on the farm, to dirty udders, and careless retailers.[2]

With this and other information before him Hall had no hesitation in sending to the Board of Agriculture on September 30, 1911, a memorandum urging the establishment of a centre for dairy research and the suitability of Reading for its location. The Board agreed and expressed their willingness to provide two-thirds of the cost up to a limit of £2,500 per annum.

So it came about that the National Institute for Research in Dairying was established by the Development Commission in the autumn of 1912 at University College, Reading (later the University), and was given a grant of £1,510 to cover its first year's working. With these limited resources only two major appointments were possible; it was decided that one should be a chemist and the other a bacteriologist. They were to be part of the college staff and under the jurisdiction of the Dean of the Faculty of Agriculture and Horticulture, then Ronald Hart-Synnot, an Army officer who had resigned his commission after the South African war and during the period 1905–8 had very successfully taken the London University Degree Course at Wye College.

The first to be appointed was John Golding with the title of Research Chemist in Dairying. He was born in 1871 at Plaxtol, near Sevenoaks, and came of an old Kent family of landowners

[1] See p. 252.
[2] The early history of investigations on milk is set out by James Mackintosh in *Agriculture in the Twentieth Century*. (Essays presented to A. D. Hall) Oxford, 1939.

and farmers, but he wanted to break away from the family tradition and become a chemist. His chemical education, however, was quite unusual, and I have been unable to trace it completely. He would no doubt have had a good start at his school, the Queen Elizabeth Grammar School, Sevenoaks, and he studied for a period in a laboratory of the Pharmaceutical Society, Bloomsbury Square, at a time when it was loaned to Fellows of the Chemical Society for teaching purposes. According to his obituary notices he also studied chemistry for periods at Birkbeck College,[1] Finsbury Technical College and the Royal Agricultural College, Cirencester, but at none of these nor at Bloomsbury Square is there any record of him. College records, however, suffered considerably during the two World Wars. He spent some months in Voelcker's laboratory, and finally in 1893 he was helping Dymond in the Chemical Department of what is now the Essex Institute of Agriculture at a salary of £60 per annum, but he left in September of 1894 to take up an appointment as analyst and lecturer in agricultural chemistry at University College, Nottingham. In 1900 he became head of the Chemistry and Bacteriology Departments of the Midland Dairy Institute at Kegworth, Nottinghamshire.[2] Here he was very successful in detecting the causes of taints and disorders in milk and its products, and in showing how they could be avoided. In order to keep well abreast of modern movements in science he spent his long vacations in research laboratories in Switzerland, Germany and Denmark; he was working in Sorensen's laboratory in Copenhagen when he was appointed to the Dairying Institute.

Shortly afterwards Robert Stenhouse Williams was appointed Research Bacteriologist. He was born in 1871 at Liverpool, was at school there, and also commenced his medical studies, but he continued them in Edinburgh obtaining his medical qualification in 1896. He did not, however, set up in practice, but remained to take a higher degree in 1902. He then returned to Liverpool to work at the Institute of Comparative Pathology; later he became bacteriologist to the David Lewis'

---

[1] Birkbeck College records that he attended a course of lectures on electricity and on mathematics.

[2] Later transferred to Sutton Bonington and renamed the Midland Agricultural College. It is now part of the Nottingham University.

Northern Hospital and Lecturer in Public Health Bacteriology
in the University. For some years he was Assistant Physician
to the Stanley Hospital for Consumptives; he also held various
teaching posts. During this period he published several papers
on experimental and clinical pathology; he also spent a year at
the Pasteur Institute in Paris.

Two minor appointments completed the list: an assistant to
Golding, Elfrieda C. V. Cornish, who had a Development Commission Scholarship and was therefore no charge on the Institute funds, and W. A. Hoy as laboratory assistant to
Williams. Both spent all their working lives at the Institute.
Miss Cornish was later put on the Staff and married A. T. R.
Mattick, who joined the Institute in 1919 and spent his working
life there. Hoy turned out a treasure, with 'a long record of
successful research into some of the most awkward problems of
practical dairying', as Kay recorded. He rose to be an Experimental Officer. For lack of funds no appointment was possible
for dealing with problems of animal nutrition. Instead, James
Mackintosh, formerly at Wye, who was showing great promise
on the livestock side of the College Agricultural Department,
was appointed Advisor to the Institute while still holding his
college post. The Institute was not housed in the college, but
in an early Victorian abode, Summerbrook, formerly a girls'
private school, but then occupied by certain officials, the Institute's share being a room on the ground floor for Williams
and an attic for Golding. Work started here in the autumn of
1912 with, as Kay put it, 'two men and a boy', and a total
income of £1,610 for the year. Naturally little beyond exploratory work could be done at first and even this was soon
curtailed. The first World War broke out in August 1914. and
Golding early volunteered as a private: he was accepted in
spite of his forty-one years by declaring himself as 'apparently
thirty'—which was quite correct, for he was always younger
than his years and long retained his youthful zest and joy in life.
By a wise decision in France he was put in charge of the bath
and rehabilitation facilities at the base for men sent back for
rest after a period in the insect-infested trenches. He returned
to Reading in 1919, a Captain awarded a D.S.O. by the British
Government, and made a Chevalier of the old-established Order
of Agricultural Merit by the French.

Williams was not sufficiently robust for overseas duties; instead he gave his services to the medical authorities at home and was much employed for inoculations and other activities; he remained at the Institute, but could do little more than prepare for developments after the War. In 1916 a committee of the College Council was set up to supervise the Institute, there being as yet no Director: Williams could have served in that capacity, having not only a dominating personality, but, as Burgess records,[1] 'a sense of mission tempered by a keen sense of humour'. But he also held quasi-egalitarian views and was reluctant to accept a position of authority over his colleagues. Nevertheless, he was for all practical purposes the Director from the outset, and was widely regarded as such though unwilling to accept the title. This situation possessed certain difficulties, and in 1930 Williams' reluctance was overcome: after eighteen years he accepted the title and the *de facto* became *de jure*.

With end of the war in 1918 came the beginning of the main work of the Institute. The milk sold in the towns at that time was often very unsatisfactory. It was handled by a multitude of small purveyors, and not infrequently was dirty, infected with harmful bacteria and adulterated with water. Williams felt the need for a clean milk campaign, and with characteristic energy proceeded to make this the immediate purpose of the Institute. For this and other desirable objects the existing accommodation at Summerbrook was entirely inadequate. The Institute needed a dairy herd and a suitable farm closely linked with the rest of the establishment; it would have been unworkable to have the laboratories in Reading and the farm several miles away. Fortunately a very suitable farm and mansion at Shinfield, four miles from Reading, became available in September, 1918, and Williams started negotiations for its purchase. Fortunately also the war ended a few weeks later, and the problem of raising the necessary funds could be attacked.

The Government at that time and for some twenty years later would provide at most only one half of any capital sum required: the rest had to be obtained elsewhere. An Appeal Committee was set up with Viscount Elveden as Chairman: he and his lady rendered invaluable service to the Institute through-

[1] H. F. Burgess, *The National Institute for Research in Dairying, a Memoir,* 1963.

out its difficult years. As the work of the Institute developed, more and more expansion became necessary and much of the labour of collecting the money fell on Williams. This was also the position in the other Research Institutes. It was a bad arrangement, for the appeals had no emotional content, and research directors being ill equipped to deal with them wasted a good deal of time and energy to little purpose. The committee tried the experiment of employing a London appeals agency, but it collected little more than its cost, and the method was abandoned. To the end of his life Williams had the anxiety of this financial problem. Shinfield Manor House and farm were acquired in June, 1921, but a bank loan was needed: being guaranteed by Viscount Elveden it was granted. The work of converting the house into laboratories and offices was begun and complete possession was obtained in October, 1923.

James Mackintosh had already in 1919 been transferred from the College Staff to the Institute, and he proceeded to make the changes needed to convert the Home Farm into a research farm. He had been trained at the West of Scotland Agricultural College, Glasgow and the Dairy School, Kilmarnock, then appointed to the Staff at Wye College and later to Reading. He was an indefatigable worker and did not rigidly confine his activities to the Institute; his wide knowledge and sound judgment of farm animals and the ways in which they could best be reared were freely at the service of farmers and their organizations. It was an intellectual treat to hear him, as I once did at an agricultural show, as he sat at the centre of the Ring and using a loud speaker pointed out the good points and the weak points of the animals brought before him. He played an important part in building up the high reputation the Institute acquired among practical men. He remained at the Institute for the rest of his working life and retired in 1946 after 34 years of valuable service.

The Institute remained under the direct control of the College till 1921 when the College Council delegated the management to a separate governing Board, later a Delegacy. It was still an integral part of the University, a connection of which it has always been proud. It now consisted of three departments: bacteriology under Stenhouse Williams, chemistry under John Golding, and dairy husbandry under James Mackintosh. The

o

difference from the old organization was that all were closely integrated with the farm, the dairy herd and each other, and Kay felt quite justified in writing about 1921, the year when Shinfield became its new home: 'the name "National Institute for Research in Dairying" and the work of the Institute as an effective research organization essentially dates from this year.'[1]

While these developments were proceeding Williams was ceaselessly carrying on the clean milk campaign. He planned it on the large scale; he secured the interest of Wilfred Buckley, a wealthy and vigorous advocate of clean milk, and urged both the Board of Agriculture and the Ministry of Health to participate. He studied the sources of infection of milk by the tuberculosis bacilli and the means of preventing the spread of the disease, also the sources of other contamination of the milk as it travelled from the producer to the consumer. He worked out a programme of precautions to be taken, beginning with the cow and the milker and ending with the retailer, keeping it on such practical lines that it could easily be adopted by farmers. The old cow sheds at Shinfield were very typical: dark, dirty and ill-ventilated. Williams showed that at very little cost they could be given concrete floors, efficient lighting, drainage and ventilation. Hitherto the life of a cow in the herd had been uneconomically short; it could now be lengthened. Even in the hottest weather clean milk could be produced if the milker's hands, the cow's udder and the utensils were scrupulously clean and sterile, and he showed how these conditions could be obtained in practice. Farmers who adopted these methods found that retailers took their milk more readily: it kept longer and did not turn sour, then a common cause of wastage.

Another aim was to free the country of bovine tuberculosis. This was not achieved in Williams' time, though it has been since. He knew, of course, that pasteurizing the milk would free it from harmful organisms, but he had the feeling, although no proof, for vitamins had not yet been discovered, that fresh milk contained valuable health-giving substances that would be destroyed by heat. He regretted that so little research had been done on this question: it could not be studied at the time but was taken up later. Meanwhile, he did not oppose pasteurization,

[1] *Proc. Roy. Soc*, 1951, Vol. 138, pp. 17–31,

but preferred to ensure that fresh unheated milk should be a safe drink.

In 1920 the first clean milk competition was held. It was in Essex where, as already stated, the traditional wheat growing had largely given place to milk production. Williams and Mackintosh were the judges. It was very successful and led the Board of Agriculture to encourage similar competitions in other counties and to establish an advisory service for dairy bacteriology. The Campaign occupied almost all of Williams' time, but he managed to publish a few scientific papers dealing with the viability of the bovine tubercle bacilli and the causes of discolouration in cheese, then a source of considerable loss.

As already stated, Golding returned to the Institute in August, 1919, and entered enthusiastically into the clean milk campaign for which his wide analytical experience was a great asset. The problems were many and varied. He devised a test for the serious and wide spread cattle disease, mastitis, and studied the fat soluble and other vitamins in cows' milk. The utilization of whey, then being produced in large quantities, was attracting much attention and Golding studied its nutritive value for pigs—the favourite agents for consuming food not quite suitable for human beings. He also investigated the nutritive value of raw and of heated milk. He improved the methods for the standard analysis of milk, making them both more rapid and more accurate. It can fairly be claimed that he played an important part in laying the foundations of the more refined chemical techniques now used by milk investigators.

Another who joined the staff on demobilization in 1919 was Alexander T. R. Mattick, a former Reading agricultural student who had taken a London degree. He came first as voluntary assistant to Stenhouse Williams and was later appointed to the Institute's staff. For many years he made intensive studies of the *Streptococci*, a group of organisms specially important in milk production. His investigations included their taxonomy, serology, ecology, bacteriophage relationships, and their production of antibiotics. Some of them, particularly *Strep. agalactiae*, were responsible for a bovine mastitis already mentioned, which had hitherto almost defied treatment and had caused considerable losses to milk producers. The treatment Mattick and his colleagues recommended was to infuse the udder with a solution of penicillin. He also used, experimentally, a powerful antibiotic discovered by Hirsch and himself, and named by him 'nisin', which was produced by a Group N streptococcus frequently present in raw milk. This antibiotic was shown to destroy a wide variety of organisms, not only streptococci and staphylococci, which also caused a mastitis, but also tubercle bacilli. It is now widely used in commercial cheese-making to prevent the development of certain deleterious bacteria. It was studied chemically by N. J. Berridge who prepared sufficient to crystallize for examination. It contained alanine, valine, leucine, isoleucine and the unusual amino acids crystathionine and lanthionine. It appeared to be a mixture of at least two fairly large polypeptides.

H. R. Whitehead discovered in New Zealand in 1935 that bacteriophages were often responsible for serious delay in the process of cheese-making. These very interesting entities, studied at Rothamsted as destroyers of important soil organisms, were found by White to destroy the lactic streptococci used as 'starters' in cheese manufacture before they could produce from the lactose of the milk the lactic acid needed in the early stages. This finding was confirmed and extended both in theory and practice by Mattick and his colleagues with great benefit to the British cheese-making industry.

In 1930 Golding's staff was greatly stengthened when S. K. Kon came to Shinfield from the laboratory of Professor J. C. Drummond on a five year grant from Viscount Elvedon to assist with the investigations on the biochemistry of nutrition. He did this so successfully that he was permanently appointed in charge of that section of the work.

In February of 1932 there came the first great break in the history of the station. Stenhouse Williams had been ailing for some time, but with characteristic courage he continued his work at the Institute and even accepted an invitation to Northern Ireland to help with the dairy industry there. On the journey back he was taken ill in the train and at London was sent to University College Hospital; within a few hours he was dead. 'A beloved and greatly revered chief', his Secretary, H. F. Burgess, described him, and it was no exaggeration. He was devoted to his staff and was greatly distressed when in 1931 the Treasury had ordered salary cuts which he knew some of them could not afford: quietly out of his own resources he effected some amelioration. Though struggling always with the Institute's burden of debt he had kept alive his vision of the organization he wanted to establish, although stern necessity had compelled a postponement of the scientific investigations he felt it should be making. He had, however, taken a leading part in ensuring an abundant supply of clean pure milk for the nation. A building to house his extensive collection of books on dairying and allied subjects was erected in 1934 to constitute a memorial library to him; it remained in charge of Miss D. Knight under whose care the collection had originally been. It has been greatly developed in subsequent years to form what has been well called 'a crowning glory of the Institute' and it can now be counted as one of the most important dairy science and technology libraries in the world.

It was nearly a year before the new Director took charge and in the meantime the Institute was managed by a staff committee with Mackintosh as Chairman.

The new Director, Herbert Davenport Kay, arrived on January 1, 1933, He came immediately from Toronto University where he had been Professor of Biochemistry and had already won a high reputation. He was born in 1893 at Heaton Chapel in Lancashire, the son of John and Ellen Kay (née Davenport). According to family tradition their ancestors included John Kay of Bury, Lancashire, who in the 1740's had invented the flying shuttle. He was educated at the Manchester Grammar School, Manchester University, Gonville & Caius College, Cambridge, and the University of Freiburg (Baden). He served in the army during the whole of the First World War, first as an infantry officer. He was wounded in the Somme fighting of 1916 and twice mentioned in dispatches; later he was in the Gas Service, finally Chemical Adviser at General Headquarters of the Home Forces. He was awarded the O.B.E. (Mil.). For six years after demobilization in 1919 he held research and teaching posts in biochemistry successively in the Physiology Department of Leeds University, the Lister Institute, London, and as a Beit Memorial Fellow under Gowland Hopkins at Cambridge. He then in 1925 became biochemist to the Medical Unit of London Hospital for the next four years, and in 1929 was appointed Associate Professor and later Professor in Biochemistry at Toronto University where he remained till the end of 1932. That ended his wanderings: he remained at Shinfield as Director for twenty-five years, retiring on age limit in 1958, the year in which he was sixty-five.

It was no easy task that he had undertaken at Shinfield. The economic and social conditions of the nation had been profoundly altered by the war, and a new policy for the Institute was essential. The advisory work among farmers, so important in pre-war days, was being taken over by the county organizers and later by a special advisory service of the Ministry of Agriculture. The Milk Marketing Board set up in 1933 was beginning to play an important part in maintaining continuity of the benefits conferred by the clean milk campaign. On the other hand important advances in the sciences basic to agricultural science were being rapidly made, new techniques and appliances were being devised with bewildering speed, and it was imperative that the Agricultural Research Institutes should be able to take full advantage of them. Kay realized this, and saw that it required additional keen young workers, well trained in their subject and research-minded: within a short time he appointed no less than eleven new members of this type to his staff.

More and better laboratory accommodation was urgently needed. Unfortunately the war had so exhausted the resources of the Nation that financial stringency was still the position in the early 1930's. On the recommendation of the May Committee of 1931 the Government had cut all grants to research institutes, including salary grants, and for some time fears for the future caused considerable anxiety: G. L. Peskett, head of the small Physiology Department set up in 1930, left because of the uncertainty and went back to his medical studies. Nothing is worse for a research organization than a feeling of uncertainty. The cuts were still on when Kay took charge. But he persevered: the new restrictions had not necessitated actual dismissals as was happening in industry, and this gave sufficient feeling of security to enable the staff to get on with their work. The problems abounded. The whole dairy industry 'depends on the efficient functioning of the bovine mammary gland', wrote Kay, 'but in 1933 next to nothing was known about the physiology of lactation, the hormonal control of mammary activity, the physiology of the "let down" of milk, the peculiarities of ruminant digestion. Little was known about the environmental factors affecting not only milk yield but also the compositional quality and, therefore, the nutritive value of the milk.'

All these were scientific problems within the ambit of the Institute and all were studied in due course. Kay himself was able to participate in the laboratory work during his first six years until the outbreak of the second World War gave him other duties: during that time he studied the phosphorus compounds and phosphatases of milk, blood, and with Folley, the mammary gland. He showed with Graham that alkaline phosphatase in milk is completely destroyed by heat at a temperature slightly above that at which the tubercle organism—the most resistant of the possible pathogens—was killed and therefore its complete absence in pasteurized milk proves that the operation had been properly carried out. This test has been adopted on a world wide scale. The process of pasteurization has been improved: a higher temperature is used for a shorter time—not less than 161° F. for at least fifteen seconds —in place of the older 145°–150° F. for 30 minutes: used in conjunction with the phosphatase test this has proved entirely satisfactory. He had previously shown that blood phosphatase was of diagnostic value in certain types of bone disease. He had also studied the proteins of egg yolk and their biological relationships, showing among other things that certain types of acquired immunity are transmitted from hen to chick *via* one of the egg yolk proteins. He worked with Graham on the synthesis of milk constituents by the mammary gland. The importance of these and other investigations was recognized in 1945 by his election as Fellow of the Royal Society.

Kon continued his important investigations on the nutritional value of milk for human consumption. Contrary to Williams' fears he and Stephen Bartlett showed that this was only to a negligible extent affected by pasteurization carried out by holding the milk for thirty minutes between 145° and 150° F. or for fifteen seconds at 161° F. Trials in schools in the mid-1930's done jointly with the Rowett Research Institute and the Ministry of Health showed that properly pasteurized milk and clean raw milk had strictly comparable effects in improving growth and health in children. The need for pasteurization was shown in an experiment in which eleven calves were fed for six

months on commercial raw milk and eleven on pasteurized from
the same bulk. At the end of the experiment the tuberculin test
was applied: eight of those fed on raw milk reacted positively but
only one of those fed on pasteurized milk. Condensing and drying caused small but appreciable losses, but sterilization of the
milk was rather more drastic and destroyed some 30 per cent
of the vitamin B_1 (thiamine). Kon and R. G. Booth showed, however, that ordinary daylight and especially sunlight fairly rapidly
destroyed vitamin C (ascorbic acid) and some of the riboflavin
in milk. During these investigations Kon considerably improved
the methods of assaying the B vitamins, including B_{12}, in milk
and milk products. Another interesting result obtained by Kon and
his colleagues was that the biological value of bread or potato
protein is considerably increased when milk and cheese proteins
are consumed with them. They showed also that the site in the
cow's body where the plant pigment carotene is transformed
into vitamin A, one of the most important milk constituents, is
the wall of the intestine and not the liver as previously supposed. Other studies included the significance of colostrum in the
calf's diet and the effects of wartime diet on human milk. These
investigations extended over a number of years and Kon was
still working in 1964.

A young chemist, Sydney John Folley, a temporary research
assistant in the physiology department, appointed in 1932 for
one year only, had, by 1933 shown himself so competent that
Kay asked him to stay on permanently, a decision that he
abundantly justified.

Folley was born in 1906 in Swindon where his paternal
ancestors had been associated with the railway engineering
works almost from the beginning. From the Secondary school
there he went in 1924 with a county scholarship (not easily
obtained in those days) to the Chemistry School of the University of Manchester where he studied under two distinguished
Professors, Arthur Lapworth and Robert Robinson. In 1928,
having become interested in biology and wishing to participate
in the application of chemistry to biological research, he transferred to the Physiology Department under H. S. Raper; in
1931 he became Assistant Lecturer in biochemistry at Liverpool
University, and from there moved on to the small Physiology
Department at Shinfield in 1932 where for a few years he

worked with Kay on the phosphatase of the mammary gland and on the effect of thyroxine on milk secretion.

This thyroxine investigation had been brought by Kay from Canada in 1933. While still there, he and an outstanding Ph.D. student, W. R. Graham, Jun., had in 1931 begun studies of the effects on milk production of thyroxine supplied as dried thyroid gland fed by mouth. In Shinfield the problem was further studied in collaboration with Graham, Folley, Paul White, K. L. Blaxter and others. The final results in 1943 showed that sub-cutaneous injection of thyroxine or small dietary supplements of iodinated casein (which contained thyroxine) increased both milk yield, percentage of butterfat and other constituents in the milk of cows past the peak of lactation: increases up to 20 per cent in yield were readily obtained; unfortunately the response did not persist for more than about two months. Implantation of L—thyroxine tablets was later shown to produce similar results.

Folley's interest in endocrinology was further aroused by reading A. S. Parkes' book *The Internal Secretions of the Ovary*, and he became engaged in important investigations on the endocrine control of mammary growth and function. Great interest was aroused by his work in conjunction with Helen Scott Watson and A. C. Bottomley on the artificial induction of oestrus and rapid growth of the udder followed by a considerable period of lactation in virgin goats and heifers which were brought about by the injection of a synthetic chemical, diethyl-stilboestrol. Farmers were astounded when they learned that the mere insertion of a factory-made tablet under the skin of such an animal would cause it to produce milk just as if it had been made pregnant by a male.

As in animal production, so in milk production, hormones from the posterior pituitary gland play an important part. One of these, oxytocin, is responsible for increasing the pressure in the udder at the time of milking: the 'let down' of milk. The hormone is reflexly liberated by stimulating the teats by hand milking or machine milking, or even in some cows by other stimuli associated by the animal with milking, such as rattling the cans, and it is carried to the udder in the bloodstream. Foot and F. H. Dodd further showed that usually only about a half of the secreted fat present in the udder is withdrawn at a normal

o*

milking, but most of the rest may be obtained as a thin cream by intravenous administration of a small dose of posterior pituitary extract.

The biochemistry of milk formation in the udder was studied at Shinfield from 1933 onwards and among other interesting results it was found, using sodium acetate labelled with radio-active ^{14}C, that a considerable portion of the fatty acids secreted in the milk fat is synthesized in the gland from acetate circulating in the blood.

Much work was done on the composition of milk and the causes of its variation. Investigations were made to discover the causes of fall in the yield of milk and its percentage of non-fatty solids during the late winter months; in some cases the drop in this percentage was from $8 \cdot 8$ to about $8 \cdot 2$ with consequent reduction in nutritive value; the loss was mainly in the casein. Similar falls in yield and composition were brought about by Bartlett and S. J. Rowland by reducing either the energy content or the protein content of the cow's food. Both yield and non-fatty solids were restored when the cows went out to grass in spring or when they were given oestrone. In seeking the cause of this Bartlett and G. S. Pope found small quantities of oestrogenic substances in the young herbage, especially the clover, which would have afforded an attractive explanation of the improvement, but further investigation failed to show that they had any significant effect. Springtime is not always a better season for all lactating cows; some are liable to suffer from hypomagnesaemia, and a number of these may die from 'grass tetany'. The causes of these serious and widespread metabolic diseases were studied by Rook and Rowland, and practical methods were devised for their prevention.

In 1937 John Golding retired after twenty-five years of devoted service to the Institute as head of the Chemical Department. He had intended ultimately to return to his ancestral home at Plaxtol, where he would set up a laboratory and continue his investigations; but first he and his wife wished to travel leisurely. They spent nearly a year touring in South Africa. Before he could complete his plans, however, the second World War broke out; some of the agricultural staff of the university were called off to help with the food production programme, and Golding volunteered to serve as lecturer in agricultural chemistry. He never lived to carry out his plans for Plaxtol, but died in harness in 1943 before the war had ended. Agricultural science thus lost one of its most attractive personalities; kindly, generous and modest, giving always of his best to his work.

In 1937 George William Scott-Blair succeeded Golding as head of the Chemical Department, and was later transferred to the headship of a new Physics Department where he and his colleagues began a vigorous attack on the physics of milk and milk products. He came from the Physics Department at Rothamsted where he had worked since 1925. He was born in 1902 and educated at Charterhouse and Trinity College, Oxford. He brought with him to Shinfield a new science, rheology, the study of plastic materials, which he began to apply to some of the cheese problems, especially those relating to the assessment of the correct time for 'pitching' the cheese curd and to measurement of the so-called 'body' of the cheese. The fundamental measurements included the extent of indentation of the cheese by a loaded sphere, of resistance to cutting with a wire and to penetration by loaded needles and cutters of the cork borer type. Breaking tests such as were used for many plastics were also made. With increasing development of the subject much more use was made of it, and it proved a valuable addition to the Institute's resources. Scott-Blair soon broke new ground by devising tests on uterine secretions to show whether a cow is on heat or not, and when she is pregnant. The biochemistry of these secretions has since been intensively studied by R. A. Gibbons.

Of the numerous other investigations prior to 1955 space allows the mention of only a few. A. S. Foot, S. Bartlett, C. C. Balch and others in studies of ruminant digestion showed that the available caloric content ('energy') of the diet was more important in relation to milk compositional quality than high protein; the rise in non-fatty solids during spring grazing was largely due to the increase in energy content of the diet at that time. Low fat percentage in milk was usually associated with a diet defective in roughage which lowered acetic acid production in the rumen. Addition of sodium acetate to the food increased the fat percentage. They noted that bovine saliva was markedly alkaline and secreted in quantities of the order of 130 litres ($26\frac{1}{2}$ gallons) per day.

S. K. Kon, S. Y. Thompson, J. W. G. Porter and others studied and measured the production of B vitamins and isolated B_{12} and other cobalt-containing relatives.

At least two naturally occurring antibiotics ('lactenins') were found in milk and it was shown that young chickens and piglets grow faster if antibiotics were added to their diet: probably due to destruction of toxic intestinal micro-organisms such as *Cl. welchii*. Members of the Physiology and Radiobiochemistry Departments studied the synthesis of fat, lactose and protein by the alveolar cell of the mammary gland using either radioactive or heavy isotopes. The relations of mammary enzymes of cells and sub-cellular structures to protein synthesis and of mammary arginase and phosphatase to milk formation were also investigated. There was an interesting demonstration in the Physiology Department that the administration of pregnant mares' blood serum produced multiple ovulation and foetuses in cows.

In 1942 an experimental centre for artificial insemination of dairy cows was set up and immediately proved so successful that it had to be greatly extended; in 1949 nearly 21,000 cows were served, and over 50,000 in 1958.

In addition to the scientific work numerous investigations of technological and farming interest have been successfully carried out, and when Kay retired in 1958 he was able to leave the Institute in a far larger, more vigorous and flourishing form than he had found it.

RESEARCH ON DAIRYING IN SCOTLAND; THE HANNAH

The south western region of Scotland has long been famous for milk production: the special milk breed of cattle evolved there, the Ayrshires, are known all over the world. Its dairy school, which was for many years at Kilmarnock but is now part of the West of Scotland Agricultural College, Auchincruive, Ayr, is also widely known, having trained a long succession of experts who have helped generations of farmers over the problems of milk production. In addition to its Dairy School, the West of Scotland Agricultural College has also a Dairy Research Department concerned chiefly with problems arising out of the daily work of the milk producer, and with problems that arise also in the transport, distribution and processing of milk. Until 1928, however, there was little in the way of basic scientific research related to dairying and in particular no research institute corresponding to that at Shinfield which was founded some fifteen years earlier. The need for an Institute in Scotland was pointed out by the Development Commissioners in their eighteenth Report, and the Secretary of State for Scotland in 1927 appointed a committee of management to establish one. Fortunately in the same year the late John M. Hannah, Esq. of Girvan Mains in Ayrshire, offered the estate of Auchincruive for purposes of promoting agricultural education and research. The larger part of the estate went to the West of Scotland Agricultural College, and the adjoining farm of Kirkhill was offered and accepted as the site of the new research station. The Development Commissioners made a capital grant of £15,000 for the building and equipping of the new laboratories, the modification of the farm buildings and the stock of the farm. Money went much further then than it does now: the grant would be the equivalent of about £60,000 today (1965). The new station was named the Hannah Dairy Research Institute to commemorate Mr Hannah's gift.

The work of the Institute did not have to wait its building. Temporary accommodation was provided in the Institute of Physiology in the University of Glasgow and work began there in 1928 under Professor E. P. Cathcart, the well known physiologist, as Interim Director, with a very small staff that grew in time to four other graduates and three honorary workers. The best known of the group was the physiologist Norman Charles Wright, who had for a short time been on the staff of the Institute at Shinfield. Later additional accommodation was obtained in Ayr and it became possible to increase the staff and take control of the farm of Kirkhill.

Meanwhile the Institute was being built, work on it had begun in November 1929, and it was formally opened in April 1931 by the Secretary of State for Scotland, then the Rt. Hon. William Adamson.

Cathcart relinquished the directorship in 1930 and Norman Wright was appointed thereto and remained in charge for the next 18 years. He was then thirty years old, and had been educated first at Reading University College and then at Christ

Church, Oxford. After graduating at Oxford he did research at Cambridge, where he was a member of Caius College, and later at Cornell University, U.S.A. For a time he had worked under Golding in the Chemistry Department at Shinfield, where he had good opportunities of seeing the kind of work a dairy research institute could and should do. Wright, working with W. L. Little, a veterinary surgeon, on the calcium level in cows' blood had shown that this was below normal in animals suffering from milk fever, a serious disease to which high yielders were liable after calving, and the more serious the attack the lower the calcium level. The trouble was cured by slow intravenous injections of calcium chloride solutions, and this laid the foundation for the modern treatment of injecting with calcium borogluconate.

The programme of investigations at the Hannah Institute was very wide. As at Shinfield it fell into two broad classes: biological research and technical research. Only the biological research will be dealt with here; it included the production and management of grass and home-grown feeding stuffs, the nutrition of dairy cattle at all stages of their lives, including the protein requirements of lactating cows and the relative values for milk production of the nitrogenous constituents of different feedingstuffs, problems associated with the secretion of milk, and the eradication or control of bovine diseases. The technical problems not treated here were concerned with the improvement of the bacteriological quality of milk by the most effective methods of sterilizing the dairy utensils and of cooling the milk on the farm, with the pasteurizing and sterilizing of milk, and the manufacture and properties of condensed milk and dried milk products. So much work had been done and continued to be done at Shinfield and elsewhere on problems connected with cheese- and butter-making that it was decided not to include research on these products in the programme of the new institute.

One of the earliest scientific papers published was by L. A. Allen in the *Journal of Dairy Research* in 1931[1] on the mineral constituents and citric acid content of milk. Another by him in the same year had a wide and homely interest in a region where bread and cakes alike were home made: it was on the role of milk constituents in bread making, and was published in the

[1] Vol. 3, pp. 1–51.

Journal of the Royal Technical College, Glasgow. This was followed by a group of papers by Janet H. Blackwood in the *Biochemical Journal* for 1932 on the absorption of milk precursors by the mammary gland, including the relation of blood sugar absorption to lactose secretion, and the relation of amino acid secretion to protein synthesis: the lactose paper was jointly with J. D. Stirling.

In the following year the same two authors issued a bulletin on the nutritive properties of milk in relation to pasteurization. Norman Wright and S. Morris in 1933 commenced a long series of comparisons of the nutritive values for milk production of proteins from various sources: beans, linseed and meat meal in the first series; blood meal, pea meal, decorticated groundnut cake in a second series; and grass of various origins—spring growth, autumn growth, conserved by drying and as silage.[1] Morris also made a series of investigations on the influence of the pituitary gland on parturition which he reported in the *Journal of Obstetrics and Gynaecology* for 1933. Janet Blackwood continued her investigations on the absorption of the milk precursors by the mammary gland, in the course of which she studied the relation between the amount of blood sugar absorbed and the amount of lactose secreted, and between the amino acid absorption and protein secretion. She also studied the phosphorus metabolism of the mammary gland, and certain aspects of its fat metabolism and dealt with various physico-chemical aspects of milk secretion: these papers appeared in the *Biochemical Journal* during 1933 and 1934.

The investigations on the nutritive value of proteins from various sources were followed by others by J. C. D. Hutchinson and S. Morris on the digestibility of these proteins in the ruminant in certain conditions. The first, published in 1936, dealt with endogenous nitrogen excretion on a low nitrogen diet and in starvation; and the second, also in 1936, with nitrogen excretion following a prolonged fast. Fasting and realimentation in the ruminant were studied, especially the calcium and phosphorus metabolism, during both conditions. Questions of immediate practical interest received considerable attention: on the technical side, for example, faults in canned cream were

[1] The results were published in Vols. 4 to 7 of the *Journal of Dairy Research* (1933–6).

causing trouble and the reasons for them were investigated around 1938.

In 1936 J. A. B. Smith, a Lecturer in Biochemistry at Liverpool University, who had published several papers on fats and problems relating to fat metabolism, was appointed to the staff of the Institute. His first work was concerned with the relationship between dietary fat, labelled with iodine, and the fat as secreted in the milk, and also with the effect of inanition on the yield and composition of milk fat. Reports of this work were published in the *Biochemical Journal*. Three papers by Norman Wright and Morris were soon to became of great topical interest: they appeared in 1939, the year when the second World War broke out, and dealt with feeding standards for farm animals to supply their various requirements: dry matter, energy, protein, both as to quantity and quality, minerals and vitamins. As these were intended for the guidance of farmers they were published in the Ministry's journal *Agriculture*, while the scientific papers were in the appropriate scientific journals. S. Morris and S. Ray investigated the effects of high temperature of drying and of season on the nutritive value of grass proteins. At this time also J. A. B. Smith and N. N. Dastur studied the secretion of milk fat and included work on the effect of thyroxine on the blood lipids and on the composition of the milk fat (1940).

During the second World War a number of subjects of great importance at the time were investigated. The shortage of feeding stuffs led to a search for partial substitutes for protein. Urea, which could have been obtained in large quantities, was studied by R. M. Pearson and J. A. B. Smith in a series of investigations on protein breakdown and synthesis and on the utilization of non-protein nitrogen in the bovine rumen. Problems associated with the storage of dried milk were studied, and an important report on the subject was issued jointly by workers at Shinfield and at the Hannah Institute.[1] The deterioration of stored feeding stuffs caused by moulds under various degrees of dampness was a source of much anxiety; it was investigated by D. Snow and others. The effects of sulphanilamide, sulphonamide, propamidine and other bacteriostatic drugs on the growth of moulds on feeding stuffs were

[1] *J. Dairy Research*, 1945, Vol. 14, pp. 116–150.

studied. During this period Norman Wright published useful guidance to farmers in meeting difficulties that arose out of war conditions.

R. Waite joined the staff in 1939 and made an extensive study of the factors affecting the chemical composition and therefore the nutritive value of cow's milk. He and his associates studied the chemistry of grass, and did much to elucidate the nature of the large and complex nitrogen-free extractives fraction which is of great importance in the nutrition of ruminants.

Ever since the early 1930's Norman Wright had been actively interested in the improvement of grassland, and during the 10 years 1940–1950, at his instigation the Institute made an extensive study of the extent to which a dairy farm such as Kirkhill could be made self-sufficient in feeding stuffs. This involved much work on the management, efficient utilization and conservation of grass, and after the war W. Holmes, the able agriculturalist then in charge of the farm and later Professor of Agriculture at Wye, was immediately responsible for this work to which he made a most valuable contribution. He published several papers in scientific journals, and also other articles that were of immediate assistance to farmers on the use of nitrogenous fertilizers in grassland management, on controlled grazing and on the use of conserved grassland products as winter feeds for the dairy herd.

Meanwhile (1945) Smith was continuing his work on the role of the microflora of the alimentary tract in the nutrition of ruminants, and he and E. C. Owen, who had come to the Hannah Institute in 1939 from the Rowett Research Institute, Aberdeen, published the results of their work on the possibility of using urea as a partial substitute for protein in the diet of lactating cows. Owen aslo advanced and extended the Institute's earlier studies on the metabolism of lactating cows, dealing particularly with nitrogen, calcium and phosphorus.

A young physiologist, J. D. Findlay, appointed in 1942 and his colleagues built up a department of physiology in which long-term basic studies have been made of the effect of climate on the physiology of cattle with special reference to heat tolerance and acclimatization. An excellent climatic laboratory was provided for the study of this subject and much work has been published on it by Findlay and his colleagues.

K. L. Blaxter joined the staff of the Institute in 1948 and in the next three years he and W. A. Wood made important investigations on the nutrition of the young Ayrshire calf, including the metabolism of the calf during starvation and subsequent realimentation. Later, between the years 1954 and 1964, Blaxter did distinguished work on the energy metabolism of ruminants, a subject little studied since the days of Kellner in Germany and Armsby in the U.S.A., work which brought him the Thomas Baxter Prize in 1960 and the Royal Agricultural Society's Research Medal in 1964. In the meantime E. C. Owen and his colleagues had made an extensive investigation into the composition of human milk, including the usual determinations of total solids, fat, nitrogen and phosphorus and in addition a number of substances of more recent interest; aneurin, nicotinic acid, vitamin A, carotene and carotenoids. They also discussed the correlation of the phosphatase content of milk with the partition of phosphorus and with the content of phosphorylated aneurin. Owen later studied other vitamins of milk and riboflavin in milk, also its metabolism in the ruminant, and its related enzyme, xanthine oxidase, in milk.

In 1948 Norman Wright was appointed Chief Scientific Adviser to the Minister of Food and resigned the directorship of the Institute, which he had held for 18 years. It had been a period of useful work well done which had given the Institute a solid foundation for further development. The Institute had started its work in Ayr in 1930 with five graduates on the staff and three honorary workers. By 1950 the graduate staff exceeded twenty. He was succeeded by James Andrew Buchan Smith who had been on the staff for the period 1936–1946 but had then transferred to Glasgow University as Lecturer in Biochemistry. On Wright's retirement he accepted the invitation to return to the Institute as its Director. As a former student of Norman Haworth and E. L. Hirst at Birmingham and of A. C. Chibnall in London and the practical experience gained in six years of lecturing on biochemistry at Liverpool and Glasgow he was able further to strengthen the biochemical activities of the Institute while his earlier ten years service gave him an invaluable knowledge of the inner details of its working.

It had for some time been realized that research in agricultural science was changing its character and requiring more and more team work and therefore larger staffs and more and better accommodation. Both were provided, and the new laboratories were opened in April, 1951.

CHAPTER XV

WEED AND SOIL STUDIES

WITH Daubeny's death research in agricultural science ceased for a long time at Oxford University, and only the Sibthorpe lectures remained as fragments of agricultural teaching. As already stated, Sibthorpe's endowment was to be used primarily for the publication of his magnum opus, Flora Graeca, and only the meagre residue was available for the Sibthorpian Chair of Rural Economy. At first this was to be held by the Sherardian Professor of Botany, and the duties were to read one public lecture each term and to appropriate part of his garden for the cultivation of plants used in agriculture and the arts. The two chairs were separated by statute in 1882: owing to the smallness of the endowment a visiting professorship only was allotted to agriculture, and twelve lectures annually were to be delivered. Gilbert was the first holder of this new post and he held it from 1884 till 1890. It was left vacant till 1894, when Warington was appointed: his length of tenure does not seem to be recorded.

The arrangement was inadequate for the needs of the subject, and in 1907 St John's College supplemented the Sibthorpian endowment sufficiently to provide for a full-time Professor. Somerville (afterwards Sir William) had already been appointed in 1906. He held the post till 1925. He did no research work of consequence, but he took a poor downland farm and greatly improved it by dressing it well with basic slag, as others were doing elsewhere.

He was followed by a well-known agriculturist, James Scott Watson (later Sir James) who stayed till 1944. He was research minded, and although, as he relates, there were in his days neither the funds, the facilities, nor the time for research he and his staff managed to do some interesting sheep feeding experiments. The quantity of food required for provision of maintenance energy was found to be considerably less than Wood had shown to be needed by cattle. In general, young sheep appeared to utilize food more efficiently than cattle could do at the same stage of growth. Over quite a wide range the surrounding temperature, cold in particular, had little effect on their rate of growth or of fattening. This was in sharp contrast with the effect of environmental temperature on young cattle, which was of considerable importance.

Scott Watson took a useful step in 1932 in setting up a readership in soil science with its own laboratories in a separate building close to the school of Rural Economy, and in appointing to it C. G. T. Morison of Christchurch who, after working with Hall at Rothamsted on the coagulation of clay suspensions with calcium compounds, had been appointed Demonstrator in Agricultural Chemistry by Somerville in 1909 and promoted to a readership in 1923. Morison gave a special turn to the work by making a soil survey of the Dinka district of the Sudan with J. M. Stubbs.[1] He also surveyed part of Tanganyika. He collected typical profiles about four feet deep and kept them properly mounted in the laboratory for teaching purposes. His assistant, G. R. Clarke wrote a very useful book, *The Study of the Soil in the Field*, first issued in 1936, and the fifth edition in 1965.

Morison retired in 1948 and was followed by E. Walter Russell from Rothamsted. He continued the work on soil cultivation, particularly ploughing and subsoiling on which he had been engaged; he also studied the effect of humus on the properties of hydrated iron and aluminium oxides present in the soil, particularly their absorption of phosphate. In co-operation with the plant physiologist, R. Scott Russell (no connection), work was done on the relation between phosphate uptake by various plants and the level of the isotopically exchangeable pool of phosphate in the soil.[2] With L. T. Evans he studied the absorption of humic and fulvic acids by clays (1959).

Walter Russell left in 1955 to become Director of the East African Agricultural and Forestry Research Organization with

[1] Published in *Sudan Notes and Records*, Vol. 21.
[2] *Journ. Soil Sci.*, 1957, Vol. 8, p. 248, and 1958, Vol. 9, p. 101 (with P. G. Marais).

headquarters at Muguga, Kenya. R. K. Schofield was then appointed Reader and continued investigations he had begun at Rothamsted. Then by a particularly sad tragedy he was struck down by a severe attack of cancer and died in 1962, a grievous loss for British soil science of which he had long been one of the brightest ornaments. He was followed by Philip H. Nye, whose work lies outside our period.

Scott Watson resigned in 1944, and it was decided that his successor should be a scientist. Geoffrey E. Blackman, then lecturer in Botany at the Imperial College of Science, South Kensington, was appointed. He was son of Professor V. H. Blackman and nephew of F. F. Blackman, both very distinguished botanists. Since 1941 he had with a small team been investigating new methods of weed control and the possibility of introducing new crops, especially oil seeds. The war was on: we had to grow foods that we had previously imported from Europe: the acreage of onions, for example, had to be raised from 800 to 25,000. The weed problem was serious: it was, however, lessened by 1943 by pre-emergent spraying with sulphuric acid. Weed control in a number of other crops, especially cereals, was studied, using nitrophenols, copper salts and phenoxyacetic acid, particularly 2,4-D and MCPA. As the team expanded more crops were studied.[1]

When Blackman came to Oxford in 1945 the Agricultural Research Council and the university agreed that the team should accompany him and the work continue. It fell into two divisions: the study of new herbicides, and investigations of the factors controlling selectivity and the nature of herbicidal action. By 1950 the research programme had been defined: studies of the retention of the spray by the shoot, penetration into the shoot, transport within the plant, localized accumulation and action in the cell. When the herbicides were applied to the soil, uptake by the roots and penetration and transport to the shoot had also to be studied.[2] E. K. Woodford was an early member of the team and soon became its Assistant Director. As the work increased a new body, the Weed Research Organization, was formed in 1960, and the development work—examination of new herbicides, etc.—was transferred to a new site at Begbroke, six miles

---

[1] J. Roy. Ag. Soc. Eng., 1945, Vol. 306, p. 137.
[2] Discussed in Science Progress, No. 152, October 1950.

north of Oxford; but the fundamental aspects continued to be studied at the university. The subject developed considerably and in order to get a proper view it is necessary to go back earlier in its history.

Weeds must always have been a source of trouble, but the old writers say little about them. Neither the Greek nor the Latin languages had a word for weeds in spite of their rich vocabularies; one result is that we have no name for the new and growing branch of science concerned with them. Cultivation was the only method of dealing with them in the early days, and when sufficiently well done it was fully adequate; control seemed complete, and there was nothing more to be learned about them. 'There is perhaps no object the nature of which is so well understood', wrote John Buckman, the well-known Professor of Botany at the Royal Agricultural College, Cirencester, in 1855. Indeed, he saw some educational value in weeds; he emphasized the farmer's need for knowledge of their 'nature and habit' which botanists could give and which he urged farmers to acquire.

Weeds have several advantages over the sown crops. They are native plants, survivors by natural selection over a long range of seasons because of their close adaptation to their surroundings. They have colossal power of reproduction. A wheat plant may produce 60 seeds, but the poppy, as Sir Edward Salisbury has shown, produces an average of 17,000, indeed he found one monster producing 480,000, fortunately not all viable in any one year.

Agricultural research on weeds was begun at Rothamsted in 1905 by Winifred Brenchley as already recorded, and one of her early results showed the remarkable power of survival of their seeds once they get into the soil: numbers of arable weed seeds still remained viable after thirty years of burial under grass. So long as cultivation remained the only way of destroying them difficulties were bound to arise.

An entirely new method was started about 1885: destruction by chemical means. It originated accidentally and appropriately enough in France. Copper sulphate was much used in the vineyards for making the Bordeaux mixture used to protect the vines against phytophthera, and the sticky nasty-looking

material was sprayed on to the grapes to make them distasteful to the village boys who would otherwise have stolen them.
It was observed that a dilute sulphate solution did little damage
to some wheat plants on which it fell, but killed the broad-
leaved weeds growing with them. This suggested an easier
and cheaper method of weed destruction than cultivation and it
came into use in France. It was demonstrated near Chelmsford
by Strawson in 1898 and taken up by the Agricultural Institutes. Sulphuric acid was also used, with proper precautions.
At the end of the First World War (1918) a number of possible
substances became available in quantity, including sodium
chlorate and perchlorate: by 1920 the world of inorganic substances had been pretty well explored for effective herbicides,
but only about half a dozen had emerged as useful. Copper
sulphate was by far the best; its disadvantage was the large
amount of water required: 50 gallons of a 3 per cent solution
per acre, which meant $4\frac{1}{2}$ tons of water for a 20 acre field.

A great change came in the 1920's when a highly efficient
chemical industry was developed in this country, thanks to the
energy of Alfred Mond, Clavering Fison, Jesse Boot and a few
others. For the first time it became capable of producing on a
large scale the most complex compounds, organic and inorganic, in any desired state of purity. Complex materials like
dye stuffs were being manufactured and outlets were sought for
the intermediate products or substances that could be prepared
from them. This new manufacturing system required a highly
organized and very efficient research service. Imperial Chemical
Industries was established in 1926; in the following year it set
up its research station at Jealott's Hill, and within a few years
started weed control research. The staff had access to an indefinitely large number of substances, organic and inorganic,
which the factories could produce. In 1937 an associated company, Plant Protection Ltd., was established at Fernhurst in
Sussex with considerable acreage of land for experiment.
Fison's Pest Control Research Station was set up at Chesterford
Park, Essex; May and Baker Ltd. and Shell Ltd. also proceeded
to make control agents.

The first weedkillers made by the new chemical industry were
derivatives of benzene. This is not itself effective, but some of
the enormous number of its derivatives are very poisonous to

plants. One of the first to be manufactured was dinitrocresol, called DNOC for short; the names are too long to be used in full and contractions are always used instead. It reached us in 1948 from France, where it had been used since 1933. This was a great advance on sulphate of copper, needing only 6 to 10 lb. per acre instead of the 15 lb. of the copper salt and above all no water. It killed many of the weeds of cereal crops but not the weed grasses, wild oats, black bent, etc. and it could not be used for leguminous crops nor for cereals undersown with clovers. Later on, a close relative called dinoseb[1] proved more effective, only 1 lb. per acre being needed. This was started in California in 1945 and was tested at Oxford by Blackman and by Dr Ripper of Pest Control and came into use in the early 1950's. This and DNOC are contact herbicides causing death of the cells in the neighbourhood of the chemical on the leaf.

Later came the growth regulator herbicides, MCPA and others which move within the plant and can affect tissues remote from the point of application: general effects in contrast to the localized action of the contact herbicides. They were discovered independently at Jealott's Hill and Rothamsted during the second World War when research was permitted but publication of important results forbidden, communication to the Agricultural Research Council or other official body alone being permitted.

At Jealott's Hill study of the growth-promoting substances had started in 1936 with investigations of their effects on the rooting of cuttings; they were extended to discover the effects of ranges of concentration of β indolylacetic acid and α naphthylacetic acid on seedling growth and on the growth of established plants. Beneficial effects were confined to low concentrations, higher ones were harmful but in different degrees on different plants. It was expected, therefore, that higher concentrations would show selective phytocidal action. Experiments in August, 1940, on a field of oats weedy with yellow charlock showed this was so: 25 lb. per acre of α naphthylacetic acid killed the charlock but only slightly and temporarily affected the oats. As this substance was too costly for general use, an enviably long list of carefully chosen related compounds was tested in November, 1941, and 2-methyl-4-chlorophenoxy-

[1] 2-4-dinitro-6-sec.butylphenol.

acetic acid was found to be most active in destroying cereal weeds without damage to the cereals themselves. In November, 1942, all this knowledge about selective weedkillers was communicated to the Secretary of the Agricultural Research Council.

Meanwhile, as that body knew already, the same end had been achieved at Rothamsted by entirely different methods. This work had been begun in November, 1941, fifteen months after that at Jealott's Hill, and, as at Jealott's Hill, it followed naturally from investigations that had been going on for some years previously. Reference has already been made to the curling of the roots of clover brought about by a hormone β indolylacetic acid secreted by the root.[1] Experiments made in test tubes with red clover and lucerne on an agar medium and also on sterilized soil showed that both this and α naphthylacetic acid produced marked deformation of the root hairs, but also both were toxic to germination and subsequent growth at dilutions up to one in ten millions. Mustard was a little less sensitive and could tolerate up to one part per million, but wheat was much less sensitive and was affected only at ten parts per million. This high toxicity range suggested the possibility of using such compounds for controlling plant growth. In unsterilized soil, however, neither compound proved toxic, both apparently being decomposed by soil micro-organisms. Chlorine atoms were therefore introduced into the ring for the purpose of making them resistant to breakdown. Tests were made in October, 1942, of the comparative toxicity in agar and unsterilized soil of 2-4-dichlorphenoxy acetic acid and a few related compounds. The dichlor-compound proved much the most toxic of all those tested, and retained its toxicity in unsterilized soil. Clover and sugar beet were scarcely affected by it, even at one part per million, wheat not at all till ten parts per million were used. The action was most strikingly shown on the stunting of the root, which thereupon was taken as a measure of the toxic effects of different substances. Experiments to discover the effect of rain in leaching out the hormone showed that a quantity of water equivalent to 1·4 inches of rain produced an effect that was just significant, while even the equivalent of 5·6 inches of rain failed to remove all the toxic effects.

These results were communicated to the Agricultural Re-

[1] See p. 310.

search Council who arranged a meeting of the Jealott's Hill and Rothamsted workers and also Professor G. E. Blackman of Oxford University. From then on there was co-operation and interchange of knowledge. After the war both the Jealott's Hill and the Rothamsted staffs wrote letters to *Nature* describing what they had done, from which the above account was taken; they were published on April 28, 1945.[1]

When munitions were no longer needed, I.C.I. undertook the manufacture of both the dichlor- and the methylchlor-compounds and put them up in forms suitable for use by farmers: inconveniently long names were shortened to 2-4-D and MCPA respectively.[2] The latter was more popular in Great Britain and the 2-4-D in Canada and the United States; it became indeed a valuable export commodity. The 2-4-D had the advantage of destroying more weeds, but the MCPA was safer, particularly on spring oats. 1 lb. per acre of either sufficed. Both proved popular with growers, and in the 1950's many thousands of acres were sprayed with them: in Britain and various European countries great areas of cereals, grass and other crops; most of Canada's cereals and small seeds; vast areas in the United States and increasingly large areas in Australia. Many experiments had shown their value in Africa. However, neither substance dealt with all weeds, and there were cases where the elimination of some gave those left untouched a better opportunity to develop and build up a formidable population. The wide use of 2-4-D greatly reduced many broad-leaved annual weeds, but left a field for wild grasses and the resistant broad-leaved weeds which not infrequently created a new problem more difficult than the old one. These difficulties were met by searching for new herbicides. The method was still trial and error; even in the 1960's it was not possible to write down a formula that would certainly be an improvement on the older compounds. In 1952 is was estimated that out of every 2,000 substances tested in the United States only one could find use in agriculture and some half million dollars had to be expended on it before it could be marketed. But the method works. It not

---

[1] A fuller account of the Jealott's Hill work was given by W. G. Templeman and W. A. Sexton in *Proc. Roy. Soc.* (1946), Vol. 133 B, pp. 300–313.

[2] 2-4-D is 2-4-dichlorophenoxy acetic acid and MCPA is 2-methyl-4-chloro-phenoxy acetic acid.

only produces results; if persisted in long enough it gives a great body of attested facts which may help in tracing relations between chemical constitutions and herbicidal actions.

In 1947 a research unit of the Agricultural Research Council was set up at Wye College under Ralph Louis Wain to deal with plant growth substances and systemic fungicides. He had studied chemistry at Sheffield University and done useful work on copper fungicides at Long Ashton: in particular he had shown that toxic concentrations of copper can arise from bordeaux mixture only under the influence of excretions from the fungal spores themselves. Amino acids in the spore exudate were the main agents involved. Among other plant growth studies was an investigation to discover whether plants can, like animals, break down fatty acids by β oxidation, i.e. splitting off and oxidation of the α C and COOH, and conversion of the β CH$_2$ into COOH. It was shown that some plants could do this by means of an enzyme but not all. Wain saw that this could be used for producing selective herbicides. Butyric derivatives of MCPA[1] and 2-4-D[2] were not themselves poisonous to plants or small animals so far as was known, but if the plant possessed the β oxidase enzyme system, this would convert the relatively harmless butyric compound into the highly poisonous acetic acid derivative and the plant would thus, as Wain put it, commit suicide. Cereals and various other farm crops, clovers, lucerne, certain vegetables did not possess the necessary enzyme, and consequently did not suffer; creeping thistle and a number of pernicious weeds did possess it and consequently perished. (1955).

The oxidation of the butyric group of atoms takes a little time, consequently the destruction of the weeds is slower than when the acetic acid herbicides are used, but the advantage of being able to use them on clover and certain vegetables more than outweighs this. Moreover, they can be applied early to cereals since they do not produce the deformed heads liable to result from early application of the acetic acid herbicides.

The butyric herbicides rapidly increased in popularity and by 1964 were being manufactured not only in Great Britain but also in Japan and South America.

[1] 4-(4-chloro-2-methylphenoxy) butyric acid.
[2] 4-(2-4-dichlorophenoxy) butyric acid.

It may seem strange that so many of these potent herbicides are derivatives of the plant growth hormone indolylacetic acid. That substance also would be harmful in large quantities, but most plants possess an enzyme system that would destroy any harmful excess. But it cannot function against these man-made derivatives and plants have no protection against them.

Some public anxiety has been felt about the growing use of chemicals as weedkillers. They have been accused of killing birds and other small animals. Apart from DNOC, dinoseb (DNBP) and endothal modern weedkillers are relatively harmless to animal life. Sodium arsenite formerly used to some extent is poisonous, but it has been withdrawn from agricultural use. DNOC has almost gone out of use, dinoseb has a limited use for peas and endothal for sugar beet. But by far the greatest part of the spraying is done with modern harmless substances. The benefits of the herbicides have, however, been undeniable. Great tracts of the chalk regions which in June used to be yellow with charlock and scarlet with poppies are now vivid green, while meadows once gay with flowers have also become uniformly green. But crop yields have increased so that the nation has gained in farm produce what it has lost in natural beauty. Insecticides on the other hand are poisonous, and have caused the death of birds and other small animals.

In 1954 a survey by B. M. Church showed that in the arable regions of eastern England between a quarter and a half of the cereal fields examined were treated with herbicides, but in the grass regions the proportion was much lower. About 80 per cent of the fields surveyed had received MCPA; most of the rest had had 2-4-D or DNOC. Three years later it was estimated that over the whole world 100 million acres had been sprayed.

The older books on agriculture often included descriptions of the soils of districts dealt with, but really full accounts were not possible till sound methods had been evolved for the analysis of soils. The older methods of Davy and Augustus Voelcker and some of the Continental chemists have been described and the improvements introduced by Daubeny and Dyer; the latter's use of dilute acid for extracting potash and phosphate remained in use for many years, and indeed in a modified form still survives. Difficulties arose from the complexity of the action.

E. J. Russell and J. A. Prescott showed that it consisted in two parts: a direct extraction by the acid of the substances it could dissolve, and an absorption of some of these same substances by some of the soil constituents that remained undissolved. The direct action was the same for all soils and solvents tested; it probably gave a true measure of the available material. Resorption was averted by doing the extraction in a diffusion apparatus, which would be unsuitable for ordinary analytical practice. Instead, a great variety of solvents has come into use: the Commonwealth Soil Bureau in 1950 listed some fifty of them used in Great Britain, Western Europe and the United States, for each of which something could be said. Citric and acetic were the favourite acids in various dilutions or associations, but others were used also. No less than six different solvents were used in Great Britain, making comparisons impossible.

In addition to the chemical analysis of soil Davy had instituted a mechanical analysis to show the relative proportions of coarser and finer particles. It fell out of use during the nineteenth century, but was revived in an entirely different form in the late 1890's and early 1900's by Hall at Wye, Wood at Cambridge and C. M. Luxmoore at Reading—the first in the modern period to publish an extensive survey.[1]

It was a very thorough piece of work which deserved more attention than it received. One hundred soils were analyzed mechanically and chemically including determinations of soda, magnesia, iron and aluminium oxides, as well as Dyer's available phosphate and potash; also the specific gravity of the soil material and the soil in tilth as well as the porosity of the soil in tilth. The fractions adopted in the mechanical analysis were the same as in the United States. Unfortunately the work came at the end of Luxmore's term at Reading and he finished the writing up after he retired to Yorkshire in 1906. He was followed by John Percival, the botanist, who was not interested in soil surveys and let the matter drop.

The idea of making surveys came to us from the United States Department of Agriculture where they had been made for many years—one of Maryland was done in 1860 and was very

[1] *The Soils of Dorset, a Report on their Mechanical and Chemical composition and on their Physical Properties.*

helpful during that period of renewed activity. The new soil analysis including the Dyer improvement and the mechanical analysis usually provided good advice for farmers. The idea of making local soil surveys gradually spread: Hall in 1894 began collecting data for one of Kent, Surrey and Sussex which he and I completed; T. B. Wood shortly afterwards set his students on to local surveys of interesting districts and L. F. Newman on to survey the light soils of Norfolk. Before long the question arose of the basis on which the survey should be conducted. The geology was so clear cut in our three counties that Hall and I accepted it as our basis. But in the Eastern counties the position was very different; there was so much drift that Wood found the solid geology unhelpful; this same difficulty arose in Shropshire where he had set one of his students, Gilbert Wooding Robinson, to make a soil survey. Later (1912) Robinson was appointed Advisory Agricultural Chemist to North Wales by the Board of Agriculture and was housed in University College, Bangor, though the work formed no part of the college activities. It was a particularly happy arrangement for him as the staff was a small cultured group with whom he found friendship easy. He was very wisely left to find his own work, so he decided to undertake a soil survey of his region. Being almost single-handed he was compelled to simplify the tedious procedure of the current methods, and having a very ingenious mind his experiments in simplification opened up problems which he handed over to his students or junior colleagues for further investigation. In the mechanical analysis of soils it is necessary to remove the organic matter if much is present: Robinson found that this could be done by treatment with hydrogen peroxide, and in the course of the work realized that the treatment could be so modified as to fractionate the organic matter, separating the 'humus' from the yet undecomposed material. The subject was followed up by G. W. McLean who showed that 70 to 80 per cent of the soil organic matter was easily oxidizable and had a C/N ratio of about 10 and might be regarded as a fairly definite complex; about 10 to 15 per cent was less easily oxidizable and contained no nitrogen (he regarded it as chiefly lignin); the remainder contained nitrogen and was still less oxidizable. These results are consistent with Page's view (p. 293). Organic chemistry was not, however, sufficiently far advanced to allow the investigation to be carried further.

Rice Williams studied the colloidal properties of organic and inorganic constituents of the soil. He found that, weight for weight, organic colloids contributed eight times as much to the base-exchange capacity of the soil as did the clay colloids, but that the clay was, nevertheless, the more important, owing to its higher percentage in the soil.

Robinson found it impossible to classify the soils on a geological basis; if two or more different formations had similar lithological characters they might produce similar soils. The palaeozoic silt loam, the most wide-spread type in North Wales, could arise from Cambrian, Ordovician or Silurian rocks. He then tried soil texture as the basis of classification. This meant making a mechanical analysis of the soil samples. This was an extremely slow and tedious process, but he greatly improved it, making it much more rapid without loss of accuracy. He attempted to classify the soils on the basis of the resulting figures but without success. The Continental soil scientists had been struggling with the same problems, and before the first World War had set up the International Society of Soil Science with the purpose among others of securing uniformity of technique and nomenclature in the surveying and ultimately the production of a soil map of Europe. One of its first achievements was to secure the adoption of an international method of mechanical analysis in which Robinson played a great part.

Meanwhile, the other advisory chemists were making soil surveys, each adopting his own methods. Sir Thomas Middleton of the Development Commission (which was finding the money) justified this on the grounds that the whole object of the survey was to help the advisory officers, and they must therefore decide how it was to be carried out. Two difficulties arose. The geological maps of that time did not usually show the drifts and were therefore unhelpful, and it was physically impossible to make the standard determinations on the large number of soils that the surveyors were expected to deal with. Fortunately the American soil surveyors had learnt to acquire great facility in rapidly mapping large tracts of country on the basis of soil texture estimated simply by feeling a sample between finger and thumb, and the results came out in the same order as when the full mechanical analysis was made. The British surveyors learnt to do the same thing and the classification problem of soil surveys might have been solved on those lines, except that no one likes purely subjective tests.

There was already in existence, however, a more fundamental basis for soil classification depending not on the texture or the source of the original material but on the formation processes and the fact that the rain washes the decomposition products vertically downwards to depths depending on their solubility and the nature of the underlying material. The profile of the soil dug down to its base showed these changes and constituted a sound and entirely objective basis for classification. The method had been devised by the Russian, V. V. Dokuchaev (1883) and developed by Sibirtzev; it was announced in this country by N. M. Tulaikov[1] but attracted little attention at the time here. Later in 1908 K. D. Glinka described its developed form in a book which Stremme translated into German in 1914, and C. F. Marbut, head of the United States Soil Survey, translated this into English. He was so satisfied with the method that he adopted it as the basis of the survey.

W. G. Ogg of the Aberdeen College of Agriculture was working with the American survey at that time (1919) and on his return proposed that a Soil Survey of Scotland should be made on the genetic basis. He began it, but left for Cambridge. On returning in 1924, he recommended that the survey should be on the profile basis, and in 1925 in collaboration with J. O. Veatch of Michigan and J. B. Simpson made specimen surveys of areas in East Lothian and exhibited the maps at a meeting of soil surveyors in Edinburgh in the autumn of that year. This is the first explicit mention of soil surveying being carried out in this country on the profile basis. Robinson also had suggested in 1924 that profile studies of soils should be made by the Geological Survey, as somewhat later did C. G. T. Morison. There was some confusion as to what was meant, but it was cleared up in July, 1926, when the International Society of Soil Science held a field meeting in Hungary where various soils were inspected and classified on the basis of their profiles; this had been arranged in order to further the uniformity of technique and nomenclature which the Society desired to achieve.

[1] *J. Agric. Sci.*, 1908, Vol. 3, p. 80.

P

Ogg attended this meeting and on returning arranged for the detailed instructions to be circulated amongst those making soil surveys. For a time both texture and profile methods were used; both were tested at Harper Adams Agricultural College in 1926 and Wykeham near Scarborough in 1927, but at the field meeting at Bagley Wood, Oxford, in September 1928 only the profile method was used and it has been adopted ever since.

A committee of the Soil Surveyors was formed in 1930 to co-ordinate and unify technique and classification. Robinson as the recognized and very efficient leader was appointed chairman and Morley Davies secretary. Reading University serves as an example; a soil survey of Berkshire was made in 1931 by N. H. Pizer, and one of Buckinghamshire by M. S. Temple. Both were on the extensive lines adopted by Hall and Russell as were various other surveys at that time. They were followed by a survey of the eastern portion of the Vale of White Horse made in 1934 on intensive lines by Dr F. F. Kay, a graduate in horticulture of Reading University (1927–1932). She was one of the most ingenious-minded of the soil surveyors of her time, and introduced some new features. Instead of the two depth samples, 0–9 inches and 9–18 inches of the older methods, she went down to 4 feet unless prevented by rock. The chemical and physical characteristics of the various sectors of the profile constituted the basis of classification into series, together with the geology, mode of formation, colour as measured by Ridgeway's coloured standards, topography and drainage: not, however, texture. The various series were recorded in colour on the six-inch Ordnance Survey maps. In 1936 she made a detailed survey on the same lines of the soils of the newly acquired University farm at Sonning-on-Thomas. A third survey, also of a limited area, the strawberry district of south Hampshire, was published in 1939 and a new departure was announced. The soils were classified into genetical groups, six in all: brown earths, podzols, gley, calcareous, organic and undifferentiated alluvium; these were shown in colour on the map. The basis was as agreed by the general body of the surveyors: Dr Kay got them to agree to the groups being mapped in colours uniformly throughout the whole country, each series having its own colour.

Up to this stage Rothamsted had taken little part in Soil

Survey work, it being under the county agricultural committees, and the Rothamsted staff concerned with soils were so heavily engaged that it was not possible for them to undertake anything else. Some of E. M. Crowther's work at Rothamsted, however, threw useful light on the difficult phosphate group in the soil. Reference has been made to the long series of field experiments on the manuring of sugar beet carried out on suitable farms from 1933 to 1949 for the Committee on Sugar Beet Education and Research in collaboration with the agriculturists of the seventeen sugar beet factories then operating in Britain. It was the largest series of outside field experiments carried out from Rothamsted. Crowther was in general charge and as usual he put the scheme on a broad basis. His purpose was to compare the effects of certain fertilizers on crop yield on different soils over a wide range of conditions. Nothing as extensive had been done before. The experiments showed some of the limitations of the methods of soil analysis. For phosphate determination the citric acid method was fairly good for calcareous soils, but unsatisfactory for acid soils; for these, acetic acid proved much better. He found it essential to standardize rigidly the technique both of extraction and of analysis: rough uncritical methods could be seriously misleading. Small scale pot tests were designed for testing available nutrients, especially phosphates.

An Indian worker, M. O. Ghani (1941–44), studied the organic phosphorus compounds in soil. About three quarters of the phosphorus in farmyard manure was inorganic, mostly easily water soluble; in poultry manure, however, much of it was in the form of phytin.

In 1939 the soil survey became a national undertaking under Robinson at Bangor. It remained in abeyance throughout the war (1939–45), but in 1946 it was transferred to Rothamsted and put under Alexander Muir who had followed Ogg from the Macaulay Soil Institute in Aberdeen. He was well fitted for the post having spent the two years 1928–30 in Russia studying the new soil survey methods. Accommodation was provided for Muir and the Ministry gave the necessary grant for staff. It was obviously best for the survey to be conducted at the same institution as the soil research work, and the arrangement worked very satisfactorily. Robinson was appointed Chairman of the Soil Research Board, and in various other ways continued his interest in the survey until his death in 1950 at the early age of sixty-two. He was a great loss to the small group of British soil scientists, one of the most scholarly of them with an unusual knowledge of languages including Welsh, Greek and Latin. With all this he was singularly modest and an attractive personality. He published little, but his influence was considerable and was a potent factor in securing the unanimous acceptance of the profile method of soil mapping. There was every reason why we should adopt the international method and none why we should stand out.

The change in method of conducting the survey was accompanied by a change in its purpose. The object of the older surveys where the soil was divided into two layers, surface and subsoil, 6–9 inches and 9–18 inches in depth respectively, had been to help the farmers by informing them of their requirement of lime, fertilizers, etc. The object of the Russian surveys by the profile method was to study a natural object, the soil. The connection with the farmer gradually weakened and became little closer than the old geological survey had been.

MODERN SOIL RESEARCH IN SCOTLAND.
THE MACAULAY INSTITUTE

The pioneer of modern soil research in Scotland was James Hendrick, Professor of Agriculture in the University and Director of Research in the North of Scotland Agricultural College, Aberdeen. He covered a wide range of subjects: liming, manuring, composition and feeding value of pastures and feeding stuffs, much of it connected with advisory work for farmers but also bringing out new facts of scientific importance. His most important work was in connection with his lysimeters already described and the series *Studies of a Scottish Drift Soil*, the northern granitic soil of Craibstone, widespread and of much agricultural importance. These were published in collaboration with George Newlands and others over the period 1916 to 1926. The lysimeters had been set up in 1914 with the purpose of discovering the losses of fertilizer constituents caused by rainfall from soils manured and cropped in the usual way of farm practice. The losses of phosphate and potash were low, as could have been expected, but so also were those of nitrogen, which was contrary to expectation. On the other hand the losses of bases, lime etc. were high.[1]

Newlands' mineralogical studies of the soils were the first of their kind in Britain and were later followed by remarkable developments at the Macaulay Institute. Meanwhile both the Edinburgh and the Glasgow Colleges had started making geological studies and soil surveys: the Edinburgh College had made a remarkable field-to-field acidity survey covering some 100,000 acres. Farmers were also advised on manurial requirements of their soils and on the improvement of hill pasture. Nutrition problems arising from mineral deficiencies in soils were studied in co-operation with the Scottish Animal Diseases Research Association, especially the malnutrition of mountain sheep.

The most important development in connection with soil research in Scotland was, however, the establishment of the Macaulay Institute in 1930. Its foundation reads almost like an act of piety. A wealthy Canadian, President of the Sun Life Insurance Co. of Canada, born in Canada to which his father had emigrated as a young man, remembering that his ancestors had come from the poverty-stricken island of Lewis, resolved to do something to improve its condition. He was Thomas Bassett Macaulay, of the Macaulays of Uig in Lewis, to which family Macaulay the historian also belonged. Lewis was then a bleak and barren region, only about $2\frac{1}{2}$ per cent of the land being cultivated; the farmers were almost all crofters with holdings from 2 to 5 acres and sharing a stretch of land for grazing. The soil is mostly peat lacking all the elements of fertility; some nitrogen and potash could be supplied from waste fish and seaweed, also lime from shell sand, but there were no means of supplying phosphates of which the soil stood in desperate need. There had been much reclamation of soils of this kind in the late eighteenth century, but it had come to an end, and Mr Macaulay wanted to see it started again.

In June 1928 he wrote to the Department of Agriculture for Scotland inviting co-operation in his schemes for improving the

[1] *Trans. Highland Agric. Soc. of Scotland*, 1921, vol. 30, pp. 56–79, and 1930, vol. 42, pp. 1–27.

agriculture of Lewis. The Department agreed, and sent William Gammie Ogg and W. G. Coles on a tour of Sweden and other northern European countries where similar soils were being effectively reclaimed by modern methods. Their report was sent to Mr Macaulay, and after studying it he decided to establish a demonstration farm on peat land in Lewis, with Ogg as Director, to show the crofters how it could be improved. To this Ogg demurred: he did not wish to confine his interests to marginal land or to live in Lewis. Mr Macaulay thereupon agreed to put the scheme on a broader basis; while endowing the farm he would also set up on the mainland an experimental station for the study of soils and soil-plant relationships provided the Government would maintain it. This offer was accepted.

The farm was duly established: 147 acres of moorland, with peat varying from 3 to 20 feet in depth, were acquired for this purpose, properly drained and manured. Dressings of basic slag, shell sand and fish refuse enabled good crops of hay, silage, potatoes and vegetables to be grown and also hedges and shelter belts. It continued to function as a demonstration farm until the outbreak of war in 1939 when it was let as a commercial farm. After the war it was handed over to the Stornoway Trustees, and in collaboration with the North of Scotland College of Agriculture the relatively costly full-scale reclamation schemes were replaced by more economic and feasible improvements of rough grazings by surface seeding and other operations: during the ten years 1955 to 1964 some 6,000 acres had been improved. It is in this direction that the change has occurred: the area of cultivated land does not seem to have increased, but the grazing value of a large area of peat land has markedly improved.

Aberdeen being the dominant centre for soil research was chosen as the site of the new Institute. Ogg was asked to find a suitable place which he did just outside Aberdeen at Craigiebuckler: a mansion with 50 acres of land. This was duly converted into an experiment station with the purpose of widely based studies of soils and soil-plant relationships. Ogg was appointed Director. He was in his thirty-ninth year and had been one of Hendrick's best students at Aberdeen University; he then studied at Christ's College, Cambridge. He had already taken an active part in soil surveying as described elsewhere.[1] Work started at the Institute in 1930. It was divided into five sections: (1) soil fertility under Alexander Boyd Stewart, (2) pedology and soil surveying under Alexander Muir with mineralogy under R. Hart. (3) soil organic matter and peat under I. M. Robertson and later G. K. Fraser; this included peat reclamation in Lewis and in Lanarkshire, (4) lysimeter studies under H. D. Welsh: the Institute having taken over Hendricks' apparatus, and (5) spectrographic analysis under Robert Lyell Mitchell, a research student from the Universities of Edinburgh and Aberdeen who came in 1931 at the age of twenty-one, having learned the instrument under Wiegner and Lundegardh. They were a very competent group. Stewart became Director in 1958; Muir was early put in charge of the Soil Survey of Scotland and in 1946 became Director of the Soil Survey of England and Wales; and Mitchell did good work by greatly widening the range of use of spectrochemical methods with such valuable results that he was in 1962 awarded the Research Gold Medal of the Royal Agricultural Society of England.

For the first five years the published papers dealt mainly with the reclamation of peat land and descriptions of the soils of Scotland. In 1933 a disease called 'pining' attacking the sheep attracted attention: it had occurred also in New Zealand in the 1920's in a region of very poor volcanic soil. The agricultural officer seeing the first lot of afflicted animals said in a jocular way: 'They look as if they needed a dose of Parrish's food'— a popular proprietary article described as a syrup of phosphates and iron. The farmer knew that phosphate was needed and had supplied it, but iron was a new idea. He bought some crude iron salts (low grade ferrous sulphate) and this effected a cure. The same remedy was applied in the Moredun Institute experiments with equally good results. Lack of iron was therefore announced as the cause of the trouble and a supply of iron salts was the remedy. But it was found in New Zealand that the good farmers who bought higher grade ferrous sulphate had less success than those who used the low grade material, which suggested that the curative agent was not the iron but one of the accompanying impurities. Investigations showed that it was cobalt: this and parallel work in Australia was confirmed at the

[1] See p. 449.

Moredun Institute and in 1941 a paper jointly with the Macaulay Institute appeared showing how the cobalt could be supplied.[1]

In the early 1940's work was started on the changes in the organic matter effected during the decomposition of compost heaps. The first flame emission spectrographic apparatus had been installed in 1935 and Mitchell had used it for the analysis of soils. In 1940 he described how the trace elements were determined by its means. Three years later came an account by E. G. Williams and A. B. Stewart of the fixation of phosphate by an acid soil and the course of its recovery by growing crops: a problem much studied by E. M. Crowther on the neutral soil of Rothamsted.

The Soil Survey of Scotland continued steadily over the whole period. It was and still is on a profile basis, and profile samples are analyzed for acidity, exchangeable cations, carbon, nitrogen and phosphorus. The sand fraction reflects the parent material and the clay reflects the product of weathering. The clay minerals were studied in detail by X ray diffraction techniques, differential thermal analysis and other methods.

In 1943 I retired from Rothamsted on age limit (seventy for the older directors because the meagre salaries of early years would have given them pitifully small pensions had they gone at sixty-five, the modern retiring age) and was succeeded by W. S. Ogg (later Sir William). As the war was still on he continued to serve as Honorary Director of the Macaulay Institute till 1945 when it ended. D. N. McArthur was then appointed and he held the post till 1958. He was succeeded by A. B. Stewart who had earlier worked at the Institute, but had left in 1954 to become Professor of Agriculture in the University of Aberdeen and was now in his 54th year. He had been educated at Robert Gordon's College, Aberdeen, University of Aberdeen, and finally the Zürich Polytechnic under Wiegner.

Work still followed the same lines, but the greater scope of analytical methods resulting from new appliances such as the infra-red and ultra-violet recording spectrophotometers allowed of a widening and steadily increasing refinement in results: Mitchell stated in 1963 that the lower limit of detection of trace elements was around one part per thousand million. From

[1] J. Stewart (Animal Diseases Research Association) R. L. Mitchell and A. B. Stewart, *Empire Jl. of Expt. Agric.*, Vol. 9, p. 145.

1946 onwards much work was done by D. M. C. MacEwan, G. F. Walker and colleagues on the complexes of clay and organic matter and on clay minerals, which indeed may be regarded as the Macaulay speciality as no other agricultural research institute is as well known in connection with them or is better equipped for studying them.

Soil organic matter continued to be studied in all stages from its formation from complex constituents of plants to its destruction by living organisms in the soil, special attention being given to humic acids and the water soluble polysaccharide fraction. The latter was found to contain small quantities of methylated sugars. The relation between plant lignin and humic acids pointed out by Page and Norman[1] was further investigated. Plant constituents were studied by chromatographic and other methods, and in order to minimize metabolic changes in the interval between collection and extraction this latter process was and still is done rapidly in a small laboratory maintained at $4°$ C. The uptake of the different nutrients and their various relationships have been studied: among other interesting results the ratios of phosphorus to iron and potassium to calcium in plant leaves were found always to vary in the same way. Similarly the phosphorus-iron and manganese-iron ratios were closely correlated. So also interrelationships were found between organic acids and mineral elements in plant leaves, as for example between malic acid and calcium in mustard leaves.

Three important groups of soil micro-organisms—bacteria, fungi and actinomycetes—have been studied, particularly their decomposition of soil organic matter, and what was at the time almost a new subject, their rather complex relations with the roots of plants. Certain groups received special attention, particularly bacteria capable of making phosphate and organo-phosphates more readily available to plants. The surprising discovery was made that certain bacteria and fungi living on rock surfaces and weathered stones can attack mineral silicates. Fungi that break down lignin in the soil have also been studied, the products being identified by ultra-violet and infra-red spectroscopy.

In addition to the research and soil surveying activities a considerable amount of advisory work has always been done,

[1] See p. 294.

P*

involving in the 1960's the analysis of some 12,000 soil samples annually; numerous field experiments connected therewith were and still are made on outside farms.[1]

[1] I am indebted to Sir William Ogg and to Dr A. B. Stewart, the present Director, for much help in preparing the above account to whom I wish to express my sincere thanks.

CHAPTER XVI

RESEARCH AT THE COLLEGES

INDIVIDUAL AND UNOFFICIAL
RESEARCH ORGANIZATIONS

THE increasing complexity and costliness of scientific research has changed the type of work the colleges can undertake and moved it rather in the direction of carrying new ideas and techniques out on to actual working farms where modifications and developments may increase their efficiency.

The Harper Adams Agricultural College was founded in 1901 and the first Principal was P. Hedworth Foulkes under whom its activities were almost entirely educational. He was very interested in poultry and built up a strong and widely known poultry department. He retired in 1922 at the age of fifty-two and lived to be ninety-five. Charles Crowther was the next Principal as already reported, and he brought with him research problems on which he had already been engaged, notably the nutrition of the pig: and did much useful work thereon. He also further developed the poultry side, and in 1926 the National Poultry Institute was established there; it rather widened its scope by including rabbits among its subjects. F. J. Dudley joined the staff in the same year, and M. Temperton in 1939; both were still active in the 1960's. While much of their work was mainly of technological importance a number of interesting scientific problems were studied, among others the effects on poultry of Vitamin A, and the biological activities of the xanthophylls of grass.

W. Morley Davies, one of Wood's students, joined the staff in 1922 as Advisory Chemist and in that capacity had to deal with a number of subjects. In the season of 1920–21 he had measured the draw-bar pull under different conditions of ploughing. The relation between draft and depth of ploughing was linear, the net draft per square inch tended to increase in value with increasing depth. The relation between draft and width of furrow was also linear, the net draft per square inch in some cases increased, in others decreased with increasing width.[1] In 1927 he and F. J. Dudley started experiments on the growth of sugar beet then being encouraged as a new crop in the eastern counties: it was shown to be promising in the midlands also. Other problems studied as being of practical importance over much of the country included liming and soil acidity in the West Midlands during the 1930's, also the comparison of three different methods of making silage and studies of the manganese deficiency problems associated with sugar beet growing.[2] He did useful work for the Soil Survey: he was in charge of the Wem region and at first (1926–30) tried a textural classification, then finding it inadequate used the soil series basis which became generally adopted. In association with G. Owen full chemical analyses were made of the various horizons of soils, among others a brown earth and a podzol, providing information of a kind often difficult to obtain.[3]

The Seale-Hayne Agricultural College, Newton Abbot, Devon, was endowed by the Rt. Hon. Charles Seale-Hayne and opened soon after the first World War. Development was slow for some time but an interesting set of observations by A. Beaumont of the microclimate within the potato crop over the eleven years 1929–39 led to the formulation of a rule which when further developed facilitated the forecasting of attacks of potato blight.

Another useful activity was the breeding by Frank Horne of cauliflowers as food for young lambs. This was still being continued in the 1960's. A larger scheme was started when Henry Ian Moore was appointed Principal in 1948 and raised the general level of the college. He was in his forty-third year, had been educated at the Universities of Leeds and of Cambridge, and had been Reader in Crop Husbandry at Leeds University, but during the war and later he

[1] *J. Agric. Sci.*, 1924, Vol. 14, p. 370.
[2] *Annals Applied Biol.*, 1939, Vol. 26, p. 385.
[3] *Emp. J. Expt. Ag.*, 1934 and 1935.

served as Chief Cropping Officer to the West Riding War Agricultural Committee. While at Leeds he did useful research work on the sugar beet crop and on grassland improvement by ploughing and direct re-seeding. At Seale-Hayne College he started investigations on the improvement in production and utilization of the grass crop by unusual practices such as zero grazing and self-feeding of silage, together with organic irrigation and intensive lamb production. Intensive series of field trials are carried out with numerous farm crops particularly with varieties of grass.

THE UNOFFICIAL RESEARCH STATIONS

The great development of the fertilizer and feeding stuffs industries necessitated the establishment of individual research stations to deal with matters arising out of manufacturing problems and especially with those concerned with new developments that they hoped to bring about. From the outset it was recognized that this would involve some purely scientific work, and it was wisely and generously announced that results of this kind should be made available to all scientific workers.

THE OLYMPIA AGRICULTURAL RESEARCH DEPARTMENT, OFFCHURCH, NEAR LEAMINGTON

This was the first of the unofficial stations to be established: it was purely agricultural although of industrial origin. It was set up in 1919 by Lord Manton, who, as Joseph Watson, had built up the Olympia Oil and Cake Co. of Selby, then sold his interests and acquired some farming estates with a view to practising large scale agriculture, with centralized direction and control. It went under the name of the Olympia Agricultural Company Ltd. He realized that scientific help would be needed for the scale on which he proposed to work and felt a moral obligation to contribute to the general body of agricultural science. The Director, Charles Crowther, had a free hand and an able staff including H. Hunter and C. T. Gimingham. In its first Report issued in 1921 it was stated to have 'the dual purpose of furnishing scientific advice in connection with the operations of the Company and of conducting scientific agricultural research for the benefit not only of the Company but of British agriculture in general'. The Staff had a free hand and generous resources; the whole enterprize was most promising. Lord Manton supplied the funds, and intended to make permanent provision for the continuance of the work, but most unfortunately he was accidentally killed in the hunting field before he had done so, and in its third year the work had to cease.

The Principalship of Harper Adams Agricultural College fell vacant at the time, and Crowther accepted it and remained for 22 years raising the College to a higher level than it had ever previously attained, but still finding time for research.

I.C.I. RESEARCH STATION,
JEALOTT'S HILL, BRACKNELL

As already stated[1] Imperial Chemical Industries started their research station at Jealott's Hill in 1928. It had excellent laboratories and a farm of some 500 acres which was later much extended; its staff included men of high scientific repute. Its first Director was the brilliant and versatile Frederic Keeble and some of the juniors later rose to important positions elsewhere; Geoffrey Blackman became Professor of Agriculture at Oxford University, while Martin Jones held the corresponding position at King's College, Newcastle. The practical and scientific experiments have always been open for scientists and farmers to see, and the results have been published in the usual scientific and technical journals.

Keeble paid particular attention to grassland. He began with methods of improving permanent pasture and conserving mown grass particularly by ensiling and artificial drying. A drier was devised that was widely used by farmers. Much work was done on the effects of heavy nitrogenous manuring. The amount of protein producible by the grazing animals was raised from the usual seven or eight cwt. per acre to one ton per acre. Nitrogenous manuring heavier than usual was known to be practicable but the operational details needed by farmers had not been

[1] See p. 440.

worked out. This was done, and a number of farmers tried the new methods from 1946 onwards. The heavy dressings gave fifty per cent or more of milk per acre at lower food costs and nearly doubled their farm income per acre.

Later much work was done on leys and on seeds mixtures designed to extend the grazing season. Martin Jones made important studies on sheep grazing, some of the most interesting yet done. Their purpose was essentially practical, but they were done on a fuller scale than had previously been possible, and they brought out much useful information for agricultural scientists. A troublesome problem concerning some 20,000 acres of Somerset pastures that had defeated previous investigators was satisfactorily solved. The pastures concerned were on the heavy clay of the lower lias formation and caused harmful, sometimes fatal scouring in the cattle: a trouble called 'teart'. Only ruminants were affected, and recently calved milking cows suffered most. No remedy was known: ordinary soil analysis afforded no indication. Three Jealott's Hill workers, W. S. Ferguson, A. H. Lewis and S. J. Watson began a more searching spectrographic examination in 1936 and found appreciable quantities of molybdenum in the teart herbage but only minute amounts, if any, in the healthy herbage. Direct experiment showed that administration of small doses of molybdenum salts to healthy animals caused the teart symptoms to appear. Small doses of copper sulphate proved an effective remedy.[1]

Investigations by A. H. Lewis, J. Proctor, A. E. M. Hood and A. J. Low showed the effects of a growing crop, especially grass, on the soil. In a five year rotation on an old arable sandy loam, two years of ley and three years arable just about maintained the nitrogen content of the soil at its original value, $0 \cdot 16$ per cent, while in a four year rotation with three years of arable and only one year of ley there was a slight fall. Soil from old grassland had more pore space than that from continuous arable land and a higher percentage of soil aggregates more than 3 mm. in diameter.

Reference has already been made[2] to the discovery of hormonal selective herbicides at Jealott's Hill during the second

---

[1] First account in *Nature*, 1938, Vol. 141, p. 353; later a fuller account in *Journ. Agric. Sc.*, 1943, Vol. 33, pp. 44–51. W. S. Ferguson, A. H. Lewis.

[2] P. 441.

World War. This may be regarded as the most important achievement of the Station up to that time.

At the adjoining Hawthorndale Laboratories, started in 1936, valuable work has been done in testing large numbers of chemicals (some 10,000 by 1953) for controlling plant pests and diseases. At another associated station, Butterwick Research Laboratories, Welwyn, Herts, studies have been made by F. W. Brian and colleagues on antibiotics and other products of metabolism of soil and other organisms. These are too recent to be included here. The scientific results obtained at these stations are published in the usual journals and the work is freely shown to other scientists working on similar lines.

Good work on the control of plant diseases and pests has also been done by the associated organization, Plant Protection, Ltd. at Fernhurst, Sussex.

Later, and too recently for inclusion here, two large and important research stations were set up by Fison's Ltd., one at Levington, Ipswich, and the other at Chesterford Park, Saffron Walden, Essex. An equally important one by Shell, Ltd. has been established at Sittingbourne, Kent.

THE ASSOCIATION OF APPLIED BIOLOGISTS

Research workers in agricultural science never banded themselves into a Society as chemists, geologists and others had done. Those who were biologists, however, had the advantage that they fitted in very well with the Association of Applied Biologists founded in 1904 by an active group of workers prominent among whom was Walter Collinge, a vigorous and sturdy individualist who started the *Journal of Economic Biology*, and carried it on at his personal cost until the Association was able to accept responsibility. This Association included all branches of biology, and its members were therefore in a more fortunate position than the agricultural chemists and physicists who in the early days had not the same opportunities of meeting workers in rather different branches of their subject.

Problems for the Association had been piling up for many years. The Rev. M. J. Berkeley, writing in Morton's *Encyclopedia of Agriculture* in 1855, had expressed the need quite clearly. In dealing with plant diseases he complained that the 'vegetable anatomist' as he called him, spent too much time indoors and too little in the field; in consequence, 'though he may be able to describe with great accuracy and precision the various morbid appearances presented by any particular case, it is not likely that he should have any good general view of the subject. Vegetable pathology, therefore, presents us with little more than a mass of facts of greater or less moment, out of which a clear and lucid system is still to be framed.'

As the preceding pages show, little was done for the next forty years, when a serious start was made at Cambridge and Wye by Hall and Wood, Percival and Biffen, Theobald and others. All were men of wide interests, naturalists in the old sense of the word with wide knowledge of anything in Nature. It was expected of a biologist that he should know something or everything about all living things; when H. H. King went out from Wye to the Sudan in 1900 as Government Entomologist, he found that his charges included hyenas and baboons.

These pioneers had to advise farmers and gardeners how to deal with pests, and a number of washes had already been discovered empirically: such as lime, soft soap, paraffin, sulphur, lead arsenate, quassia and tobacco extract but each grower had to make up his own mixture; there were no proprietary articles and no properly tested procedure. All sorts of mistakes were made: at times, in preparing Bordeaux mixture ferrous sulphate would be used instead of copper sulphate, because the trade name of the impure commercial ferrous salt was 'copperas'. H. H. Cousins at Wye had standardized the paraffin wash and had improved it in the 1890's, but little more was done for the next fifteen or twenty years.

By 1904, when the Association was founded, much empirical knowledge accumulated by farmers and gardeners had been sorted out, tested and reduced to order; some scientific account of the conditions necessary for healthy plant growth had been drawn up, and also descriptions of the common insect and fungus pests. Little, however, was known of the mode of action of either pests or washes.

In the early 1900's the small band of agricultural entomologists and mycologists had concerned themselves mainly with the systematics and morphology of the insects and fungi concerned, but from about 1907 onwards they developed the study of the life histories and the mode of life of the organisms. Collinge had emphasized the need for these in a lecture given at Bristol and printed in the second volume of the *Journal*. The need was widely recognized, but the workers were too few and their resources too slender to enable them to get far; there were as yet no state grants for agricultural research, the work was mainly done by teachers in their spare time or by amateurs.

In 1910, however, grants from the Development Commission became available and staffs were increased, but only for a time: the 1914 war broke out and held up research for the next five years. The Association of Applied Biologists suffered as did others, but was resuscitated by a devoted band of enthusiasts including W. B. Brierley of Rothamsted.

In the post-war era a new subject was introduced, mathematical statistics, which has profoundly modified the subsequent investigations. Whenever an investigation yields a series of figures there is always the probability that proper statistical treatment will extract more information than can be obtained by mere inspection. This was the case with H. F. Barnes' studies of the fluctuations in the number of wheat blossom midges, of C. G. Johnson's studies of the bean aphis fluctuations, of R. W. Howe's of the Pest Infestation Laboratory of the rates of increase and decrease of insect populations. These new methods, however, called for greater accuracy in the customary observations and for new ones that could carry investigations further than was previously possible. The customary weather observations no longer sufficed in crop growth studies: where, for example, the relations of an insect and a crop are concerned, the ordinary weather data were insufficient; the micro-climate within the crop as studied by Beaumont had to be the basis. Statistical methods have been increasingly used in applied biology from about 1946 onwards to its great advantage. Applied Biology is, however, essentially a field subject, and the observational method remains as its solid basis. A. M. Massee's forecasts at East Malling of insect attacks based on observed changes in insect populations which he broadcasted to Kentish fruit growers, proved very useful.

Towards the end of our period the number of possibilities began to open out with the rapid developments in organic and bio-chemistry. The chemical control of changes during the growth of plants was much more fully understood; the natural growth-promoting substance was isolated and identified in Holland, but the work was taken up vigorously by R. L. Wain and others in this country and new types of control of plant growth were developed: one of the first was T. Swarbrick's control of pre-harvest drop of fruit, now successfully and widely adopted.

NEOVITALISM

In 1941 Sir Albert Howard published *An Agricultural Testament*, in which he put forward a conception of plant growth and management wholly different from that hitherto held in the western countries. Starting from the fact that in natural conditions the death of one generation of plants furnishes food for the next, he argued that this 'wheel of life' as he called it, adopting a Buddhist phrase, was Nature's way, and if we departed from it we did so at our peril. This theme was further developed in his *Farming and Gardening for Health and Disease* (1945). He recognized the need of supplementing the soil resources, but maintained that this could be done only with materials that had been part of or associated with living plants or animals and retained some vital principle essential to health. These neovitalist ideas would probably have attracted little attention but for a deduction that artificial fertilizers being entirely mineral were not proper nutrients; they lacked the vital principle which alone could ensure complete health to the plant and the consumer. Instances were given of human beings and animals living on compost-fed products remaining healthy while others living on foods grown with the aid of artificial fertilizers were always liable to disease. He had already while at Indore in collaboration with Y. D. Wad studied composts and described them in a joint book, *The Waste Products of Agriculture: Their Utilization as Humus* (1934). It was not a new subject in the East, composts having been known from very ancient times, but they were not extensively used in the West. The Soil Association was formed to propagate the ideas and they attracted much attention in the press. At first the fertilizer manufacturers were somewhat perturbed, and in 1944 they asked the Royal Society of Arts to appoint an impartial authoritative committee which would issue a statement of the properties of artificial fertilizers. It soon appeared, however, that farmers had not been influenced by the propaganda. They had to obtain high yields in order to remain solvent, and they knew that they could never make the hundreds of tons of compost annually required to give even moderate crop increases. So they continued to use artificials as before.

The controversy had the effect of causing agricultural scientists to re-examine the effect of artificial fertilizers and inducing gardeners to make more and better composts.

The ideas received wider attention from the fact that both Howard and especially his wife were well-known Cambridge botanists who from 1905 had worked together at Pusa for nearly twenty years, producing valuable new wheats for India. They described their work in two books: *Wheat in India, its Production, Varieties and Improvement*, (1909), and a general summary *Corn Production in India*, (1929). Unfortunately, she died in 1930. Howard left India in 1931. Prominent among Howard's supporters were Lady Eve Balfour, a most persuasive propagandist, and Lady Louise Howard whose book *Earth's Green Mantle* (1947) is very interesting. There was also a Wiltshire farmer, Friend Sykes, who ran his farm on Howard's lines and claimed marked success including the better taste which he declared he could detect in the compost-grown crops. Scientists could find no evidence whatsoever of the alleged ill effects of artificial fertilizers properly used, and they were quite unable to accept the advice to use only composts. Gardeners, however, are using more, now that town horse manure has disappeared but they also use artificials.

Before closing this history it is necessary to add more about A. D. Hall who had played so great a part in founding and supporting the Agricultural Research Institutes and generally fostering the development of agricultural science. By 1922 he had adapted himself to the Civil Service although temperamentally unsuited to it, but he did not wish to remain in it, and when in 1926 William Bateson, head of the John Innes Horticultural Institution at Merton, died, Hall was offered the post and accepted it, the change to take effect in 1927 when he would have served ten years in the Ministry and become entitled to a small pension, still continuing, however, as Chief Scientific Adviser to the Ministry at a small retaining fee. He remained at Merton for twelve years, built a chemical laboratory where the colouring material of flowers could be investigated, completed his studies of the tulip begun at Wye and always continued, recorded them in his *Book of the Tulip* (1929) and *The Genus Tulipa* (1940), and established summer courses in genetics and cytology. He likewise studied the apple tree and with M. B. Crane wrote a short book, *The Apple*. He became a member of the Agricultural Research Council on its inception in 1931 and remained so till 1939. In 1917 he became a trustee of the Lord Wandsworth Trust which included two large boarding schools for children of 'agricultural labourers': he became more and more interested in its work. In 1939 he retired from the John Innes Institution, and on the outbreak of war, in the words of H. E. Dale,[1] 'offered his services to the Ministry of Agriculture, and received a refusal couched in terms which were intended to be polite but owing to a "clerical inadvertence" were in fact almost offensive'. He was appointed resident Trustee and Acting Principal of the Lord Wandsworth College at Long Sutton; in 1939 he went to live there and did splendid work with the boys. In 1940 and 1941 he wrote *Reconstruction and the Land* with many interruptions but with feelings of deadly earnestness, firmly believing that a definite plan was essential for successful agriculture. He knew that some of his views were unpopular, but he held fast to what he believed to be true and would not deviate from it for the sake of public support.

Scarcely had he finished his book when his health began to fail, although no specific complaint could be found. Gradually he got worse, and finally the trouble was diagnosed as internal cancer, inoperable. During the night of July fourth, 1942, he suddenly collapsed and died early on the morning of the 5th, thirteen days after his seventy-eighth birthday.

As the designer of the system of Agricultural Research Institutes and of the scholarship method of staffing them in the early days of what now seem to have been very meagre resources he was the constant helper of the small group who in the 1900's and 1910's were beginning the new agricultural research described in the preceding chapters. He was our clearest

[1] *Daniel Hall, Pioneer in Agriculture*, (1956).

thinker, most versatile and interesting writer, and a most attractive personality. More important: he steadily held to the course he believed to be right, and would not be deflected by fear of unpopularity. He was a born pioneer and saw clearly the end he wished to attain, but in striving to do so there was no unkindness to others engaged on similar lines. Those who had worked with him had great admiration and affection for him. He and T. B. Wood stand out as the greatest figures in the remarkable outburst of agricultural science during the early years of the present century.

CHAPTER XVII

CHANGES AND TRENDS IN AGRICULTURAL SCIENCE

THE foregoing pages show that agricultural science has passed through four stages during the past three hundred years and is now entering its fifth. The first, by far the longest, ran from the latter part of the sixteenth century when it was started by Francis Bacon to the end of the eighteenth century. It was entirely individual enterprise. A scientist would be attracted to some particular problem and would study it extensively. The work was done without payment, but the workers were enthusiastic, deeply interested and firm believers in its importance; they called themselves 'philosophers'—lovers of knowledge— and to gain it was their reward; but when they gave up an investigation it stopped, and there were no means of continuing it unless other enthusiasts took it up. Usually it simply lay in abeyance until its importance was recognized and that particular subject came to life again. As might be expected, progress was erratic and little in the nature of a coherent body of science emerged. Such as it was, the information related almost entirely to soil and plant growth, and it was limited by the circumstance that chemistry had not yet taken its modern form. Many facts were recorded, but they were isolated and their connection with each other was rarely perceived. There were books on agriculture, and some writers like Jethro Tull included speculations of a scientific nature, but few except Evelyn's *Terra* could make any claim to be regarded as scientific. There was no attempt to relate the results of observations to the problems of actual farming.

The second period began towards the end of the eighteenth century when modern chemistry was emerging largely as the result of research by Lavoisier, a Frenchman; Berzelius, a Swede; and others. With this a sound basis was gradually formed for the development of agricultural science. Humphrey Davy at the beginning of the nineteenth century was the first Englishman to put together the knowledge of chemical and physical aspects of soils and plant growth, and deliver it in the form of an annual course of lectures at the Royal Institution. Later (1813) these were published and the book had a wide circulation; it was several times revised in successive editions because, as Davy explained, the subject was being so rapidly developed. Its striking new feature was that it was becoming associated with actual farming, and agricultural societies were springing up through which farmers were beginning to formulate their problems and to expect help in solving them. Davy was anxious that science should help practice, and he offered soil analysis as a promising way of doing this; details of the analytical methods were printed and circulated to chemists so that they could undertake the work for farmers without difficulty.

Judging by the methods Davy advocated it is difficult to see what guidance a farmer could have been given on the basis of the results. However, help was given, and the chemist early became an essential member of an agricultural society's staff. Later, a botanist and an entomologist were added. Their purpose was to protect the members against faulty products and fraud, to conduct field experiments with lime and manures, to analyse soils with the purpose of advising farmers as to their manurial needs, and to help in coping with pests and diseases. Provided the scientist had sufficient local knowledge he could give a farmer useful advice.

There was a dull stage after Davy's time but a second vigorous stage during the 1850's to the 1880's when Daubeny, Lawes and Gilbert, and Augustus Voelcker were at their best, greatly advancing both agricultural science and its application to the problems of practical farming. The introduction of artificial fertilizers in the 1840's made a clear field for analytical chemists who alone could tell whether the material offered by the salesman was what it purported to be, whether it would be likely to do what was expected of it and whether it was worth the price asked.

During this second period agricultural science developed considerably, but it was mainly development for use rather than for discovery.

The third period began in the late 1880's and early 1890's when Oxford University and others, recognizing the necessity for a much wider diffusion of knowledge, started University Extension Lectures in the counties, and these, strengthened by the Technical Education Acts of 1889 and 1890, led to the development of more systematic educational activities than had hitherto been usual. Wye College was the direct outcome of the extension efforts in Kent, Surrey and Sussex; in certain other counties also permanent provision was made for agricultural education. Teachers soon found the need for text books on their respective subjects, and the initial production and maintenance of these books in reliable form required considerable search, often amounting to definite research. R. Warington's *Chemistry of the Farm* and W. Fream's book on agriculture were already in existence: Percival's *Agricultural Botany*, Theobald's *Textbook of Agricultural Zoology*, and Hall's *The Soil* greatly enriched the collection. Many of the teachers were so fully occupied that they could do little to break new ground, but a few, notably at Wye, Cambridge and Newcastle made investigations to improve the subject for which they were responsible. This was a new type of research: institutional in general although it was personal and voluntary in character. Often the investigation arose out of some problem submitted by farmers and not infrequently it ceased when a working solution had been found, but in some instances there had been distinct additions to scientific knowledge.

This was the beginning of professional research and the close of the earlier amateur stage which ended with the death of Spencer Pickering in 1920. No great progress could be made, for none of the Institutions had money to spare for research. The Board of Agriculture made a sharp distinction between education: the promulgation of existing knowledge, and research: the search for new knowledge. While they would provide funds for education they gave nothing for research beyond occasional small grants for dealing with specific practical problems. Nevertheless, a small but devoted band of workers kept alive the spirit of research, and it was continued at Rothamsted and Cambridge. Rothamsted had its own income of some £2,500 a year which Hall, first and one of the most successful of the beggars for agricultural science, was gradually augmenting, and at Cambridge a keen group of lecturers carried on their researches voluntarily after their hours of lecturing and demonstrating were done. At both centres the work was mostly the search for knowledge of underlying principles rather than attempts to solve practical problems as the Agricultural Societies were trying to do. Both, however, were severely restricted by lack of funds which hampered them in many ways: skilled assistants had usually to be obtained by capturing a promising student with a scholarship; costly apparatus like a good microscope had to wait the advent of a wealthy patron, and travel to other countries to discuss problems with workers on one's own subject had to be done somewhat after the manner of a mediaeval scholar. Delivery of one or more lectures at the first centre reached would provide board and lodging and a sufficient fee to cover the cost of the journey to the next centre where useful discussions and agreeable lodging could be obtained. I have done much pleasant and very valuable travel in the United States in this way in early days. Farmers were, however, suffering from a severe depression during much of this time, the result of unrestricted importation of foods at prices against which they could not compete. Farmers and landowners in many parts of the country became so impoverished that they could no longer maintain land or farm buildings in proper condition. Food was obtained so easily and cheaply from abroad that advanced politicians were throwing doubt on the need for agriculture, and a high agricultural official privately expressed his opinion that British agriculture was dead. Science and practice were so closely linked that if the practice lost its importance so would the science, and both were in low repute in the early days of this century: indeed agricultural science was hardly respectable among British scientists in general. The Chemical Society harboured agricultural chemistry and the Linnean Society recognized agricultural botany, but the situation was well expressed by the distinguished professor of pure chemistry who, in 1900, assured me that 'people in our position do not apply for posts at agricultural institutions'. The United States Department of Agriculture, however, helped us with their publications, for which we were grateful.

The fourth period began in 1909 when Mr Lloyd George, then Chancellor of the Exchequer, firmly believed that the parlous condition into which the rural districts had been brought during the long years of depression could be rectified; the remedies included among other things a much greater development of agricultural science. Accordingly, he set up the Development Commission to achieve this end and to foster its application for raising the standard of agricultural production. As agriculture could not employ the entire rural population the Commission was also to improve other rural industries thereby revivifying the countryside and raising its standard of life. A new type of research institute was to be created and a new profession: the full-time paid investigator in agricultural science.

It was at the outset decided that agricultural science should not be treated as a whole and centred at one large institute, but should be broken up into its various divisions, each with separate provisions for research. The year 1912 when the new arrangements began to function is one of the great landmarks of agricultural science. For the first time research became a full-time occupation at salaries sufficient to attract competent young scientists who wished to break away from the standard course and open up new subjects. Time showed that the official scheme was very good and worked remarkably well. It had, however, some weaknesses. Capital grants needed for construction of new laboratories were contingent on one half of the money needed being raised by the Institution, which meant in practice the Director. This was a new task for which directors had not been trained, and while some proved to be very successful beggars there was much loss of time and energy. Also the sums available for travelling were so small that visits to other research stations and attendance at scientific conferences were often impossible unless funds could be obtained from outside. No Agricultural Science Society was ever formed, and the only occasions when its practitioners could meet to discuss scientific problems were at meetings of the British Association or the Agricultural Education Association. The cause of the trouble was, of course, the inadequacy of the total grant. The Board of Agriculture officials were sympathetic and helpful: they included men who were scholars and gentlemen—to use a phrase much in favour in those days—like H. E. Dale, a notable Greek scholar, who after retirement was invited by the publishers to edit a new edition of Plato's Republic. But they could not increase the grants. There were other difficulties also, but the early days of the period were dominated by the feeling of youth: the application of modern chemistry had given the subject a new look, and the workers were mainly young people adventurous enough to break away from the conventional careers of the time in search of something new.

Progress was slow, all branches of the subject were at the elementary stage and the workers were few, but they could understand each other. There was much contact with actual farming: field experiments, soil analysis and manurial recipes based thereon, visits to farms to attempt diagnosis of causes of crop failure, and much empirical knowledge of soils and crops was gained thereby. Like many of my colleagues I profited greatly by periodic visits to good farms and careful examination with the very competent farmer of his difficulties. By the end of this period the problem of improving the nutrition of plants was well advanced and much progress had been made with the more difficult problems of improving the physical conditions in which the plant lives: its relation to the supply of air and water to the roots, and the problems of improving and retaining the crumb structure of the soil.

In 1927 there came a great change. Up till then travel overseas had been very difficult for English research workers. The Institutes had no funds for the purpose and salaries allowed no margin. The result was a certain narrowness of outlook and a loss of the stimulus that would have been gained by visits to well equipped overseas Institutes and discussion with people dealing with problems similar to our own. The first International Soil Science Congress was organized in the United States by Jacob Lipman and his colleagues at New Jersey. The Ministry of Agriculture provided funds enabling a small group to go from this country. It was a marvellous undertaking, the first of its kind, which assembled soil scientists from many lands, and when the paper reading was over took them on a month's tour of the United States and Canada to see the soils under the brilliant guidance of C. F. Marbut, one of the ablest soil scientists of those days. We met for the first time men we had long known by name, and some abiding friendships were formed which gave us much pleasure.

We returned home with greatly widened interests, determined to keep in touch with the work of overseas colleagues. This was greatly facilitated when, as one of the results of a Commonwealth conference held, also in 1927, our Government in 1929 set up a group of agricultural information bureaux, including one dealing with soils and fertilizers which, first under A. F. Joseph, and since 1931 under Graham V. Jacks, has quietly and unostentatiously rendered great service to many agricultural scientists in many countries. Abstracts of all important papers are issued, and periodical statements of the present position of developing subjects; specific enquiries are also dealt with.

Perhaps the most far-reaching change in scientific procedure during this period was the introduction of statistical methods for the examination of experimental data which necessitated discussion of the design of the experiment with a competent statistician to ensure that full advantage could be taken of statistical help. This interjection of mathematics into the biological sciences was not welcomed by some of the older biologists. Bateson's view was widely held among them—'The imposing correlation tables into which the modern Procrustes fits his rows of unanalysed data are no substitute for the common sieve of a trained judgment', he declared in his address to the Zoological Section of the British Association in 1904.

The agricultural research stations frequently acted as Advisory Centres until 1946 when the National Advisory Service was set up. That broke the link between farmers and many of the research workers, especially on the soil and plant side. It was agreed that the scientist should get on with his research, and any results likely to help the farmers should be picked out by the advisory officers and transmitted to them. The break had started in a small way in the 1930's when the soil surveyors began to hear about soil surveys in Russia. The International Soil Science Society, impressed by the value of its first International Soil Congress held in the United States in 1927, had organized a second to be held in 1930 in Russia. There the marked difference was seen between soil surveys in Russia and those in other countries. Usually, as in England, the purpose of the soil survey had been to help the farmers and their advisers. In Russia, however, the new soil scientists used it as a means of studying the soil as a natural object dissociated altogether from agriculture. This appealed to the English soil surveyors and a break began.

This breaking of the connection between farmers and the research institutes has raised a new problem: how best to pass on research results to farmers. This has been much discussed particularly by the members of the Agricultural Education Association. One difficulty is that farmers in general are not great readers: in a survey made in 1963 by *The Farmers Weekly* more than half the farmers (53 per cent) read agricultural literature only up to three hours per week and only 13 per cent read for more than five hours, 4 per cent did not read at all, 60 per cent had no books on agriculture and only 9 per cent had 9 or more—37 per cent depended on the agricultural press. The larger the farm and the younger the farmer the more reading was done.

During the second World War (1939–45) the Research Institutes were allowed to retain their staffs, but in fact they devoted most of their energies to food production. There had been enormous engineering developments during the twenty-one years of peace, and the National Farmers Union which started in 1908 had greatly helped the National Advisory Officers in raising the standard of farming. The result was a record production of food at home and a wide realization of the importance of developing a highly efficient agriculture which it was recognized would necessitate a much higher development of agricultural science. When the war ended in 1945 a new and entirely different epoch, the fifth, began.

There were important changes in this fifth period. The link between the Research Stations was no longer the Ministry of Agriculture but the Agricultural Research Council, which was far better suited for the purpose and more acceptable to the research workers. A factor in its favour was that it had much more money at its disposal and was able to make grants beyond the wildest dreams of the directors of the 1920's and '30's. Another important change was in the character of the research. The simple problems lying on the surface had been solved and a good foundation laid in all the branches of agricultural science covered by the research institutes. The most complex problems could now be dealt with, but they required treatment different from that which had sufficed for the earlier and simpler stages. No longer could one man with one trained assistant and a boy or girl to wash up hope to achieve important discoveries; a team of workers was needed under a gifted leader who could envisage and dissect the problem, and pick out the persons best able to tackle the different sections. This has raised difficulties of attribution when the time comes for publication. A study of growing fruit trees may go on for years occupying several generations of investigators. A problem on plant breeding may similarly outlast those who started to deal with it. Many of the important problems refuse to fit comfortably into the divisions of science that it has suited mankind to establish: Whitehead's 'seamless robe of knowledge' is not a mere piece of philosophical imagery but a fact of Nature which often requires the services of a group of workers. The method of attribution varies. Some investigators attach a number of names to the paper, placing them in alphabetical order, including the leaders, This is very generous but is apt to lead to confusion when, for example, the paper is quoted as by 'Allen *et al*', Allen being an unknown junior whose part was not specially distinguished. Others put the leader's name first, for which much can be said, as it keeps the leader's papers together. But the number of participants may become unmanageable, and at some of the Institutes, e.g. modern East Malling and the Scottish Plant Breeding Station, attribution to the Department is preferred rather than to individuals. The difficulty does not arise when, as commonly happens, the problem can be resolved into parts each of which can be studied by a small group. Hitherto the young scientist's prospects of better appointment elsewhere have not infrequently been improved by a show of good scientific papers in his name.

Laboratory technique became more refined and more complex, and the apparatus needed was much more costly and elaborate than in earlier days. When soil micro-organisms were first studied at Rothamsted a microscope costing about £15 was something to be rather proud of. Rothamsted's electron microscope in the late 1950's cost some £10,000 and later models were still more costly. These elaborate appliances needed specially trained attendants to look after them. Chemical investigations in particular required complex and expensive spectrographic and other apparatus, and the growing use of statistical methods called for so much calculation that a very costly computer had to be set up at Rothamsted to do the work for Rothamsted and for other Stations needing help. The number of scientists engaged in an agricultural research institute might easily exceed 100 while the numbers of skilled assistants might be larger.

The expenditure increased enormously. The first grant for 'agricultural experiments and research' had been £425 for the year 1909–10 by the Board of Agriculture, but there was no certainty of continuance. Mr Lloyd George made better and more continuous provision in 1909, and there was a steady increase in later years. The Agricultural Research Council continued the good work more rapidly: for the year 1953–54, one of the latest years considered in this history, its expenditure on research amounted to £3·6 million, and was still rising; by 1959–60 it amounted to £6 million. This is of course the modern difficulty: the need for more and more public money owing to the continuously increasing cost of modern research work, and, at the same time, the virtual impossibility of explaining the work even to farmers, still less to administrators and the general public. Attempts to overcome this have called into existence a new profession: special scientific journalism with the purpose of giving accounts to the public that will maintain the requisite interest.

Obviously where so much public money is being used there must be some means of assuring the Government that it is wisely spent on the purpose intended and that this is still in the national interest. The Agricultural Research Council has served this purpose well: its constitution and flexible methods keep it in touch both with research developments and current agricultural problems, and it will continue to enjoy the confidence of all parties so long as scientists and agriculturists of high standing continue to serve on it. The only fear is that Committee work may increase so much that scientists of the kind needed may no longer be able to afford the time required. Fortunately there is no present fear of this.

In addition to the public expenditure large sums are given by various Trusts and other Foundations towards the purchase of very costly appliances: by skilful financial arrangements they can apparently go on doing this indefinitely.[1]

The result of all this effort has been a prodigious increase in scientific knowledge which finds expression in a colossal number of scientific papers published annually. No one person can read many of them and the various Commonwealth Information Bureaux render splendid service by publishing summaries giving the main points of the work done. The presentation of the subject is often difficult, especially when it includes new ideas and phenomena never before observed which cannot be expressed or described by existing words: new ones often derived from ancient Greek have to be made up to express them. As Greek is rarely studied by modern scientists the name itself conveys no meaning but is merely an additional burden on the memory. Not infrequently the new factor for the sake of brevity is expressed by a letter: e.g. 'the A value', and the new name is soon used without an explanatory reminder. Worse still, the writing is sometimes bad, turgid, lacking in clarity, and tedious and wearisome to read. I have often felt that an author was not doing justice to himself or his subject and would have done much better if Quiller Couch's *Art of Writing* and Fowler's *King's English* had been compulsory studies in his last year's course.

These difficulties are not confined to agricultural science: they occur in other subjects also; the usual result is that each branch of each subject tends to become a sort of closed shop having only tenuous relations with other groups, having also its own language that few outsiders can understand.

Increasing efforts are being made to overcome this tendency to isolation. The soils group banded themselves together to form the British Soil Science Society in 1947; by the end of the year it had 127 members, by 1962 there were some 400. In 1949 it issued the first number of its *Journal of Soil Science* which has consistently maintained its high standard. The biologists have had for many years the Association of Applied Biologists, and all the agricultural sciences were or could be represented in the Agricultural Education Association. These bodies periodically organize joint conferences, joint meetings for discussions

---

[1] The secretary of one of them once told me, 'we started with £1 million, we gave away £1 million, we still have £1 million'.

of border-line subjects, and visits to other Institutes. The annual meeting of the British Association for the Advancement of Science affords the best opportunity for meeting workers in other branches of science.

Agricultural scientists have a responsibility from which the pure scientists are free. They have larger grants of public monies than most other scientific workers because in the past many of the results of their research work were so clearly marked in the field or the cattle stalls that its immense value for food production was obvious. The need for increasing this is constantly being emphasized by statesmen, medical men, social workers, politicians and others, and its achievement by a further development of agricultural science seems so obvious that requests for higher grants have been very favourably treated. Never before has there been anything approaching this generosity. Even more remarkable has been the complete absence of pressure on the research workers to produce results for the adornment of a Minister's speech. It would be affectation to pretend that this is due to any interest in agricultural science as such: it is certainly the hope that agriculture itself will thereby become more efficient. The modern research workers in agricultural science are in the dilemma that they are no longer familiar with the problems of the farming community, while their science is becoming so difficult that it can no longer be fully understood by farmers or indeed by any but specialized experts. It would be most unfortunate if contact between farmers and research workers should be lost, but there are difficulties in maintaining it. They are less for the research groups than for the farmers: periodical addresses by the Advisory Officers would keep them informed and they might well be able to offer some useful help. It would be more difficult to inform the farmers about the research work because the method would depend so much on what was offered, but here also the Advisory Officer could probably find the best way. Fortunately British agriculture has a good Press which periodically sets out some of the results of the scientists' labours in language that farmers can follow.

Looking back over the history of the relations of science and practice in agriculture the results are seen to have arrived in two stages. In the first the scientist has done little more than explaining the observations of the practical man and accounting for the exceptions that he observes. This may suggest improvements in his practice and it certainly adds to the interest of the work. In the second stage the scientist proceeds direct to the study of the soil, the plant or the animal, or the relations of one with the other. The purpose is to gain knowledge: whether useful or not is quite immaterial. The whole body of knowledge thus gained constitutes a subject which has repeatedly proved its value in dealing with apparently insoluble problems and in showing the way to the greater production of food which is fast becoming one of the world's greatest needs.

Britain's ever increasing population and steadily shrinking area of agricultural land make it imperative to increase output of food per acre of land, and this necessitates both positive increases and better control of destructive pests and other disease-spreading agencies. Unfortunately some of the pests can change for the worse and start a more virulent attack.

Constant rapid movements of people and commodities have facilitated the transport of diseases of crops and animals: a disease appearing in America may be carried to West Africa and gradually work its way across the continent. Plant breeders have to be always ready to produce new strains capable of resisting new forms of a disease. But these are only modern forms of ancient difficulties. From their earliest beginnings farmers have never lacked troubles. Virgil knew this two thousand years ago when he wrote:

The Father of Agriculture
Gave us a hard calling: he first decreed it an art
To work the fields, sent worries to sharpen our mortal wits,
And would not allow his realm to grow listless from lethargy.[1]

[1] C. Day Lewis' translation.

INDEX

GEORGE ALLEN & UNWIN LTD

London: 40 Museum Street, W.C.1

Auckland: P.O. Box 36013, Northcote Central, N.4
Bombay: 15 Graham Road, Ballard Estate, Bombay 1
Barbados: P.O. Box 222, Bridgetown
Buenos Aires: Escritorio 454–459, Florida 165
Calcutta: 17 Chittaranjan Avenue, Calcutta 13
Cape Town: 68 Shortmarket Street
Hong Kong: 44 Mody Road, Kowloon
Ibadan: P.O. Box 62
Karachi: Karachi Chambers, McLeod Road
Madras: Mohan Mansions, 38c Mount Road, Madras 6
Mexico: Villalongin 32–10, Piso, Mexico 5, D.F.
Nairobi: P.O. Box 4536
New Delhi: 13–14 Asaf Ali Road, New Delhi 1
Ontario: 81 Curlew Drive, Don Mills
São Paulo: Caixa Postal 8675
Singapore: 36c Prinsep Street, Singapore 7
Sydney: N.S.W.: Bradbury House, 55 York Street
Tokyo: 10 Kanda-Ogawamachi, 3-Chome, Chiyoda-Ku

THE EVOLUTION OF THE ENGLISH FARM

M. E. Seebohm, F.R.Hist.S.

"This is a work of the first importance to all students of social and economic history. It is a veritable encyclopaedia of information. . . . The value is enormously increased by the eminently readable style in which the authoress has so admirably succeeded in expressing herself."—*Antiquity*.

This is another important book which we have been unable to reprint for all too long. It describes the gradual growth of the English farm, from its humble beginnings in the Stone Age to the fully equipped homesteads of today. The history of how the component parts of the farm, as we see it today, were acquired, modified, and developed during many centuries, presents an excellent picture of English country life.

"It is written with great care in a clear and interesting style, and no one who takes any interest in . . . country life can afford to miss it."

Demy 8vo   2nd edition   Illustrated   *30s. net*

COUNTRY LIFE THROUGH THE AGES

Elspeth Boog Watson, M.A., and J. Isobel Carruthers, M.A.

Making great use of illustrations and drawings the authors present a spirited and attractive outline of agriculture and country life from Celtic times until today. The Roman Villa, the Dark Ages, Anglo-Saxon advances, the Three-Field system, the Norman Conquest, the Manor, the Monastery, Tudor, Stuart and later development are all portrayed by two very experienced teachers. They supplement perfectly the excellent picture drawn by Dr. R. W. Morris in *Town Life Through the Ages*.

The Times Educational Supplement, describing the series, thought that "Pupils will gain a lively impression of the past in terms of their own age . . . exceptionally successful . . . There is a simplicity and concreteness about the text."

Cr. 4to   Illustrated 2nd Impression   *Library Edition 6s 6d net*
                                                    School Edition   4s 6d. non-net

GEORGE ALLEN AND UNWIN LTD